Catherine Rayner.

HANNAH THURSTON:

A

STORY OF AMERICAN LIFE.

BY BAYARD TAYLOR.

NEW YORK:

G. P. PUTNAM, 441 BROADWAY.

1864.

TO GEORGE P. PUTNAM.

My Dear Friend:

When I decided to write a brief letter of Dedication for this book, and thus evade a Preface—since all that need be said to the reader can be said just as well, if not better, to the friend—I began to cast about in my mind for the particular individual willing to stand by my side in this new literary venture, deserving of all the fleeting compliment which possible success may give, and too secure, in the shelter of his own integrity, to be damaged by whatever condemnation may fall upon the author. While various cherished names arose, one after the other, the cab in which I rode and meditated passed down Regent Street into Waterloo Place, and my eyes fell upon that door, where, seventeen years ago, I entered for the first time one dreary March afternoon—entered as a timid, desponding stranger, and issued thence with the cheer and encouragement which I owed to your unexpected kindness. The conditions which I sought are all fulfilled in you. From that day to this, in all our intercourse, I have found in you the faithful friend, the man of unblemished honor and unselfish ambition, to whom the author's interests were never secondary to his own. According to the poet Campbell, we should be "natural enemies," but I dedicate this book to you as my natural friend.

I am aware how much is required for the construction of a good work of fiction—how much I venture in entering upon a field so different from those over which I have hitherto been ranging. It is, however, the result of no sudden whim, no ambition casually provoked. The plan of the following story has long been familiar to my mind. I perceived peculiarities of development in American life which have escaped the notice of novelists, yet which are strikingly adapted to the purposes of fiction, both in the originality and occasional grotesqueness of their external manifestation, and the deeper questions which lie beneath the surface. I do not, therefore, rest the interest of the book on its slender plot, but on the fidelity with which it represents certain types of character and phases of society. That in it which most resembles caricature is oftenest the transcript of actual fact, and there are none of the opinions uttered by the various characters which may not now and then be heard in almost any country community of the

Northern and Western States. Whether those opinions are to be commended or condemned, the personages of the story are alone responsible for them. I beg leave, once more, to protest against the popular superstition that an author must necessarily represent himself in one form or another. I am neither Mr. Woodbury, Mr. Waldo, nor Seth Wattles.

This is all I have to say. The intelligent reader will require no further explanation, and you no further assurance of how steadily and faithfully I am your friend,

BAYARD TAYLOR.

WOOD'S HOTEL, LONDON,
August, 1863.

CONTENTS.

CHAPTER I.
        PAGE
In which we attend the Great Sewing-Union at Ptolemy....... 9

CHAPTER II.
Mr. Woodbury's Introduction to Lakeside...................... 26

CHAPTER III.
An Evening of Gossip, in which we learn something about the Persons already mentioned.................................... 37

CHAPTER IV.
An Interview on the Road, and a New Household............. 48

CHAPTER V.
In which Mr. Woodbury hears a Woman Speak................ 61

CHAPTER VI.
In which Lakeside becomes lively............................ 77

CHAPTER VII.
What Happened during the Evening 90

CHAPTER VIII.
In which Mr. Woodbury pays an Unexpected Visit............ 105

CHAPTER IX.
Spiritual and other Rappings 113

CHAPTER X.
In which we hear a Diverting Story........................... 129

CHAPTER XI.
Containing Two Declarations, and the Answers thereto........ 143

CHAPTER XII.
Mother and Daughter 155

CHAPTER XIII.
In which Spring Opens.. 167

CHAPTER XIV.
Containing Conversations more important than they seem to be 177

CHAPTER XV.
Which comes near being Tragic 189

CHAPTER XVI.
Concerning an Unexpected Journey to Tiberius................. 205

CHAPTER XVII.
Which Solves the preceding one 213

CHAPTER XVIII.   PAGE

ONE OF THE SUMMER DIVERSIONS OF PTOLEMY.................... 232

CHAPTER XIX.

IN WHICH THERE IS BOTH ATTRACTION AND REPULSION............ 246

CHAPTER XX.

IN WHICH SETH WATTLES IS AGAIN DISAPPOINTED 258

CHAPTER XXI.

WITH AN ENTIRE CHANGE OF SCENE............................. 269

CHAPTER XXII.

IN WHICH TROUBLE COMES TO LAKESIDE......................... 281

CHAPTER XXIII.

WHICH CONTAINS BOTH LOVE AND DEATH........................ 293

CHAPTER XXIV.

VARIOUS CHANGES, BUT LITTLE PROGRESS IN THE STORY.......... 308

CHAPTER XXV.

IN WHICH HANNAH THURSTON MAKES A NEW ACQUAINTANCE........ 319

CHAPTER XXVI.

IN WHICH A WEDDING TAKES PLACE............................. 333

CHAPTER XXVII.

DESCRIBING CERTAIN TROUBLES OF MR. WOODBURY................ 344

CHAPTER XXVIII.

IN WHICH HANNAH THURSTON ALSO HAS HER TROUBLES............ 356

CHAPTER XXIX.

IN WHICH A CRISIS APPROACHES............................... 368

CHAPTER XXX.

MR. WOODBURY'S CONFESSION.................................. 380

CHAPTER XXXI.

IN WHICH THE STRONG-MINDED WOMAN BECOMES WEAK............. 392

CHAPTER XXXII.

IN WHICH ALL RETREAT IS CUT OFF........................... 407

CHAPTER XXXIII.

CONCERNING MARRIAGE, DEATH, GOSSIP, AND GOING HOME.......... 419

CHAPTER XXXIV.

CONCERNING THE NEW HOUSEHOLD OF LAKESIDE.................. 430

CHAPTER XXXV.

IN WHICH WE ATTEND ANOTHER MEETING IN FAVOR OF "WOMEN'S RIGHTS"... 442

CHAPTER XXXVI.

IN WHICH THE MAN AND WOMAN COME TO AN UNDERSTANDING...... 455

HANNAH THURSTON.

CHAPTER I.

NEVER before had the little society of Ptolemy known so animated a season. For an inland town, the place could not at any time be called dull, and, indeed, impressed the stranger with a character of exuberant life, on being compared with other towns in the neighborhood. Mulligansville on the east, Anacreon on the north, and Atauga City on the west, all fierce rivals of nearly equal size, groaned over the ungodly cheerfulness of its population, and held up their hands whenever its name was mentioned. But, at the particular time whereof we write—November, 1852—the ordinarily mild flow of life in Ptolemy was unusually quickened by the formation of the great Sewing-Union. This was a new social phenomenon, which many persons looked upon as a long stride in the direction of the Millennium. If, however, you should desire an opposite view, you have but to mention the subject to any Mulligansvillain, any Anacreontic, or any Atauga citizen. The simple fact is, that the various sewing-circles of Ptolemy—three in number, and working for very different ends—had agreed to hold their meetings at the same time and place, and labor in company. It was a social arrangement which substituted one large gathering, all the more lively and interesting from its mixed constitution, in place of three small and somewhat monotonous circles. The plan was a very sensible one, and it must be said, to the credit of Ptolemy, that there are very few communities of equal size in the country where it could have been carried into effect.

First, the number of members being taken as the test of relative importance, there was the Ladies' Sewing-Circle, for raising a fund to assist in supporting a Mission at Jutnapore. It was drawn mainly from the congregation of the Rev. Lemuel Styles. Four spinsters connected with this circle had a direct interest in four children of the converted Telugu parents. There was a little brown Eliza Clancy, an Ann Parrott, and a Sophia Stevenson, in that distant Indian sheepfold ; while the remaining spinster, Miss Ruhaney Goodwin, boasted of a (spiritual) son, to whom she had given the name of her deceased brother, Elisha. These ladies were pleasantly occupied in making three mousseline-de-laine frocks, an embroidered jacket, and four half-dozens of pocket handkerchiefs for their little Telugu children, and their withered bosoms were penetrated with a secret thrill of the lost maternal instinct, which they only dared to indulge in connection with such pious and charitable labors.

The second Circle was composed of ladies belonging to the Cimmerian church, who proposed getting up a village fair, the profits of which should go towards the repair of the Parsonage, now sadly dilapidated. Mrs. Waldo, the clergyman's wife, was at the head of this enterprise. Her ambition was limited to a new roof and some repairs in the plastering, and there was a good prospect that the Circle would succeed in raising the necessary sum. This, however, was chiefly owing to Mrs. Waldo's personal popularity. Ptolemy was too small a place, and the Cimmerians too insignificant a sect, for the Church, out of its own resources, to accomplish much for its shepherd.

Lastly, there was the Sewing-Circle for the Anti-Slavery

Fair, which was limited to five or six families. For the previous ten years, this little community, strong in the faith, had prepared and forwarded their annual contribution, not discouraged by the fact that the circulation of their beloved special organ did not increase at the Ptolemy Post-Office, nor that their petitions to Congress were always referred, and never acted upon. They had outlived the early persecution, and could no longer consider themselves martyrs. The epithets "Infidel!" "Fanatic!" and "Amalgamationist!" had been hurled at them until their enemies had ceased, out of sheer weariness, and they were a little surprised at finding that their importance diminished in proportion as their neighbors became tolerant. The most earnest and enthusiastic of the little band were Gulielma Thurston, a Quaker widow, and her daughter Hannah; Mrs. Merryfield, the wife of a neighboring farmer, and Seth Wattles, a tailor in the village. Notwithstanding the smallness of this circle, its members, with one exception, were bright, clear-minded, cheerful women, and as the suspicions of their infidelity had gradually been allayed (mainly by their aptness in Biblical quotation), no serious objection was made to their admittance into the Union.

The proposition to unite the Circles came originally, we believe, from Mrs. Waldo, whose sectarian bias always gave way before the social instincts of her nature. The difficulty of carrying it into execution was much lessened by the fact that all the families were already acquainted, and that, fortunately, there was no important enmity existing between any two of them. Besides, there is a natural instinct in women which leads them to sew in flocks and enliven their labor by the discussion of patterns, stuffs, and prices. The Union, with from twenty-five to forty members in attendance, was found to be greatly more animated and attractive than either of the Circles, separately, had been. Whether more work was accomplished, is a doubtful question; but, if not, it made little difference in the end. The naked Telugus would not suffer from a scantier supply of clothing; the Cimmerians would charge outrageous prices for useless articles, in any case : nor would *The Slavery Annihilator* perish for want of support, if fewer pen-wipers, and book-marks, inscribed with appropriate texts, came from Ptolemy.

The Sewing-Union was therefore pronounced a great social success, and found especial favor in the eyes of the gentlemen, who were allowed to attend "after tea," with the understanding that they would contribute something to either of the three groups, according to their inclinations. Mrs. Waldo, by general acquiescence, exercised a matronly supervision over the company, putting down any rising controversy with a gentle pat of her full, soft hand, and preventing, with cheerful tyranny, the continual tendency of the gentlemen to interrupt the work of the unmarried ladies. She was the oleaginous solvent, in which the hard yelk of the Mission Fund, the vinegar of the Cimmerians, and the mustard of the Abolitionists lost their repellant qualities and blended into a smooth social compound. She had a very sweet, mellow, rounded voice, and a laugh as comforting to hear as the crackling of a wood-fire on the open hearth. Her greatest charm, however, was her complete unconsciousness of her true value. The people of Ptolemy, equally unconscious of this subduing and harmonizing quality which she possessed, and seeing their lionesses and lambs sewing peaceably together, congratulated themselves on their own millennial promise. Of course everybody was satisfied—even the clergymen in Mulligansville and Anacreon, who attacked the Union from their pulpits, secretly thankful for such a near example of falling from the stiff, narrow, and carefully-enclosed ways of grace.

It was the third meeting of the Union, and nearly all the members were present. Their session was held at the house of Mr. Hamilton Bue, Agent of the "Saratoga Mutual" for the town of Ptolemy, and one of the Directors of the Bank at Tiberius, the county-seat. Mrs. Hamilton Bue was interested in the contribution for the mission at Jutnapore, and the Rev. Lemuel Styles, pastor of the principal church in the village, had been specially invited to come "before tea," for the purpose of asking a blessing on the bountiful table of the hostess. The parlor, large as it was (for Ptolemy), had been somewhat overcrowded during the afternoon; therefore, anticipating a large arrival of gentlemen in the evening, Mrs. Bue had the tables transferred from the sitting-room to the kitchen, locked the hall door, and thus produced a suite of three apartments, counting the hall itself as one. The guests were admitted at the side-entrance, commonly used by the family. Two or three additional lamps had been borrowed, and the general aspect of things was so bright and cheerful that Mr. Styles whispered to Mrs. Hamilton Bue: "Really, I am afraid this looks a little like levity."

"But it's trying to the eyes to sew with a dim light," said she; "and we want to do a good deal for The Fund this evening."

"Ah! *that*, indeed!" he ejaculated, smiling blandly as he contemplated Miss Eliza Clancy and Miss Ann Parrott, who were comparing the dresses for their little brown namesakes.

"I think it looks better to be gored," said the former.

"Well—I don't know but what it does, with that figure," remarked Miss Parrott, "but my Ann's a slim, growing girl, and when you've tucks—and I'm making two of 'em—it seems better to *pleat*."

"How will this do, Miss Eliza?" asked Mrs. Waldo, coming up at the moment with a heavy knitted snood of crimson wool, which she carefully adjusted over her own abundant black hair. The effect was good, it cannot be denied. The contrast of colors was so pleasing that the pattern of the snood became quite a subordinate affair.

"Upon my word, very pretty!" said the lady appealed to.

"Pity you haven't knit it for yourself, it suits you so well," Miss Parrott observed.

"I'd rather take it to stop the leak in my best bed-room," Mrs. Waldo gayly rejoined, stealing a furtive glance at her

head in the mirror over the mantel-piece. "Oh, Miss Thurston, will you let us see your album-cover?"

Hannah Thurston had caught sight of a quiet nook in the
hall, behind the staircase, and was on her way to secure possession of it. She had found the warmth of the sitting-room
intolerable, and the noise of many tongues began to be dis-
tracting to her sensitive Quaker ear. She paused at once, and
in answer to Mrs. Waldo's request unfolded an oblong piece
of warm brown cloth, upon which a group of fern-leaves,
embroidered with green silk, was growing into shape. The
thready stems and frail, diminishing fronds were worked
with an exquisite truth to nature.

"It is not much more than the outline, as yet," she remarked, as she displayed the embroidery before the eager
eyes of Mrs. Waldo and the two spinsters.

The former, who possessed a natural though uncultivated
sense of beauty, was greatly delighted. "Why it's perfectly
lovely!" she exclaimed: "if I was younger, I'd get you to
teach me how you do it. You must be sure and let me see
the book when it's finished."

"I don't see why my Eliza couldn't make me one of the
flowers around Jutnapore," said Miss Clancy. "I'll mention
it in my next letter to Miss Bocrum—the missionary's wife,
you know. It would be such a nice thing for me to remember her by."

Meanwhile the gentlemen began to drop in. Mr. Merryfield
arrived, in company with the Hon. Zeno Harder, member of
the Legislature for Atauga county. Then followed the Rev.
Mr. Waldo, a small, brisk man, with gray eyes, a short nose,
set out from his face at a sharper angle than is usual with
noses, and a mouth in which the Lord had placed a set of
teeth belonging to a man of twice his size—for which reason his
lips could not entirely close over them. His face thus received
an expression of perpetual hunger. The air of isolation, common to clergymen of those small and insignificant sects which
seem to exist by sheer force of obstinacy, was not very per-

ceptible in him. It had been neutralized, if not suppressed, by the force of a strong animal temperament. On *that* side of his nature, there was no isolation.

A number of young fellows—bashful hobbledehoys, or over-assured men of two or three and twenty, with rigorously fashionable shirt-collars—now made their appearance and distributed themselves through Mrs. Hamilton Bue's rooms. In the rising noise of conversation the more timid ventured to use their tongues, and the company soon became so animated that all of Mrs. Waldo's authority was necessary, to prevent the younger ladies from neglecting their tasks. The Cimmerians, as a point of etiquette, were installed in the parlor, which also accommodated a number of the workers for the Mission Fund, the remainder being gathered in the sitting-room, where Mr. Styles and Mr. Waldo carried on an exceedingly guarded and decorous conversation. Hannah Thurston had secured her coveted nook behind the staircase in the hall, where she was joined by Mrs. Merryfield and Miss Sophia Stevenson. Mrs. Waldo, also, kept a chair at the same table, for the purpose of watching the expanding fern-leaves in the intervals of her commandership. Seth Wattles tilted his chair in a corner, eager for an opportunity to usurp the conversation.

Seth was an awkward, ungainly person, whose clothes were a continual satire on his professional skill. The first impression which the man made, was the want of compact form. His clay seemed to have been modelled by a bungling apprentice, and imperfectly baked afterwards. The face was long and lumpy in outline, without a proper coherence between the features—the forehead being sloping and contracted at the temples, the skull running backwards in a high, narrow ridge. Thick hair, of a faded brown color, parted a little on one side, was brushed behind his ears, where it hung in stiff half-curls upon a broad, falling shirt-collar, which revealed his neck down to the crest of the breast-bone. His eyes were opaque gray, prominent, and devoid of expression. His nose was long and coarsely constructed, with blunt end and thick nostrils, and his lips, though short, of that peculiar, shapeless formation, which prevents a clear line of division between them. Heavy, and of a pale purplish-red color, they seemed to run together at the inner edges. His hands were large and hanging, and all his joints apparently knobby and loose. His skin had that appearance of oily clamminess which belongs to such an organization. Men of this character seem to be made of sticks and putty. There is no nerve, no elasticity, no keen, alert, impressible life in any part of their bodies.

Leaving the ladies of the Fund to hear Mrs. Boerum's last letter describing the condition of her school at Jutnapore, and the Cimmerians to consult about the arrangements for their Fair, we will join this group in the hall. Mrs. Waldo had just taken her seat for the seventh time, saying: "Well, I never shall get any thing done, at this rate!"—when her attention was arrested by hearing Hannah Thurston say, in answer to some remark of Mrs. Merryfield:

"It is too cheerful a place, not to be the home of cheerful and agreeable people."

"Oh, you are speaking of Lakeside, are you not?" she asked.

"Yes, they say it's sold," said Mrs. Merryfield; "have you heard of it?"

"I believe Mr. Waldo mentioned it at dinner. It's a Mr. Woodbury, or some such name. And rich. He was related, in some way, to the Dennisons. He's expected immediately. I'm glad of it, for I want to put him under contribution. Oh, how beautiful! Did you first copy the pattern from the leaves, Hannah, or do you keep it in your head?"

"Woodbury? Related to the Dennisons?" mused Mrs. Merryfield. "Bless me! It can't be little Maxwell—Max. we always called him, that used to be there summers—well, nigh twenty years ago, at least. But you were not here then, Mrs. Waldo—nor you, neither, Hannah. I heard afterwards that he went to Calcutty. I remember him very well—a smart, curly-headed youngster, but knowed nothing about farming. Him and my poor Absalom"—here she smothered a rising sigh—" used to be a good deal with other."

An unusual stir in the sitting-room interrupted the conversation.

There were exclamations—noises of moving chairs—indistinct phrases—and presently the strong voice of the Hon. Zeno Harder was heard : "Very happy to make your acquaintance, Sir—*very* happy !" Mrs. Waldo slipped to the door and peeped in, telegraphing her observations in whispers to the little party behind the stairs. "There's Mr. Hammond—the lawyer, you know, from Tiberius, and another gentleman—a stranger. Tall and sunburnt, with a moustache —but I like his looks. Ah !" Here she darted back to her seat. "Would you believe it ?—the very man we were talking about—Mr. Woodbury !"

In accordance with the usages of Ptolemy society, the newcomers were taken in charge by the host, and formally introduced to every person present. In a few minutes the round of the sitting-room was completed and the party entered the hall. Miss Thurston, looking up with a natural curiosity, encountered a pair of earnest brown eyes, which happened, at the moment, to rest mechanically upon her. Mr. Hamilton Bue advanced and performed his office. The stranger bowed with easy self-possession and a genial air, which asserted his determination to enjoy the society. Mrs. Waldo, who was no respecter of persons—in fact, she often declared that she would not be afraid of Daniel Webster—cordially gave him her hand, exclaiming : "We were this minute talking of you, Mr. Woodbury ! And I wished you were here, that I might levy a contribution for our Sewing-Circle. But you're going to be a neighbor, and so I'll ask it in earnest, next time."

"Why not now ?" said the gentleman, taking out his purse. "First thoughts are often best, and you know the proverb about short settlements. Pray accept this, as a token that you do not consider me a stranger."

"Oh, thank you!" she cried, as she took the bank-note; "but" (hesitatingly) "is this a donation to *our* Society, or must I divide it with the others?" The peculiar tone in which the question was put rendered but one answer possible. No *man* could have uttered it with such artful emphasis.

The constitution of the Sewing-Union was explained, and Mr. Woodbury purchased a universal popularity by equal contributions to the three Circles. Had he been less impulsive—less kindly inclined to create, at once, a warm atmosphere around his future home—he would not have given so much. The consequences of his generosity were not long in exhibiting themselves. Two days afterwards, the Seventh-Day Baptists, at Atauga City, waited on him for a subscription towards the building of their new church; and even the ladies of Mulligansville so far conquered their antipathy to the Ptolemy district, as to apply for aid to the Mission at Pulo-Bizam, in the Ladrone Islands, which was a subject of their especial care.

The introduction of a new element into a society so purely local as that of Ptolemy, is generally felt as a constraint. Where the stranger is a man of evident cultivation, whose superiority, in various respects, is instinctively felt, but would be indignantly disclaimed if any one dared to assert it, there is, especially, a covert fear of his judgment. His eye and ear are supposed to be intensely alert and critical: conversation becomes subdued and formal at his approach: the romping youths and maidens subside into decorous and tedious common-places, until the first chill of his presence is overcome. Mr. Woodbury had tact enough to perceive and dissipate this impression. His habitual manners were slightly touched with reserve, but no man could unbend more easily and gracefully. To the few who remembered him as "Little Max."—among them Mrs. Merryfield—he manifested the cordial warmth of an old friend, and laughed with a delight which came from the

heart, at their mention of certain boyish mishaps which marked his summers at Lakeside.   The laborers for the Mission
Fund were rejoiced to learn that, though he had never been at
Jutnapore, yet he had once seen Mr. Boerum, on that gentleman's arrival at Calcutta.   ("What a pity he did'nt go to
Jutnapore!   He might have told me about my Eliza," remarked Miss Clancy, aside.)   In short, the ice between Mr.
Woodbury and the rest of the company was broken so quickly
that even the formation of the first thin crust was scarcely
perceived.   His introduction to Ptolemy society was—in the
social technology of Boston—"a success."

Again the clacking of tongues rose high and shrill, lessen-
ing only for a few minutes after the distribution of wedges of
molasses-cake, offered by Mrs. Hamilton Bue's black-mitted
hands.   Mr. Hamilton Bue followed in her wake with a jing-
ling tray, covered with glasses of lemonade, which the ladies
sipped delicately.   The four spinsters, observing that Mrs.
Lemuel Styles drank but the half of her glass, replaced theirs
also half-filled, though it went to their hearts to do so.   The
needles now stood at ease, no longer marching, with even
stitch, over their parade-grounds of silk, or cotton, or mousseline-de-laine.   One straggler after another fell out of the
ranks, until it was finally declared that "we have done enough
for this evening."   Then came singing, commencing with
"From Greenland's Icy Mountains," in which half the company joined.   Miss Sophia Stevenson, who had a good voice,
with—it must be admitted—an occasional tendency to sharps,
led the hymn; but the parts were unequally distributed,
which Mr. Woodbury perceiving, he struck in with a rich
baritone voice.   This acquisition was immediately noticed,
and, at the conclusion of the hymn, Mrs. Waldo requested
that he would favor them with a solo.

"I prefer to listen," he answered.   "I know none but the
old, old songs, which you all have heard.   But you are welcome to one of them, if you will first let me hear something
newer and fresher."   Unconsciously, he had hit the custom

of Ptolemy, never to sing until somebody else has first sung,
to encourage you. The difficulty is, to find the encourager.

Mrs. Waldo seized upon Seth Wattles, who, nothing loth,
commenced in a gritty bass voice:

> "Why-ee dooz the why-eet man follah mee pawth,
>   Like the ha-ound on the ty-eeger's tra-hack?
> Dooz the flu-hush on my da-hark cheek waken his wrawth—
>   Dooz he co-hovet the bow a-hat mee ba-hack?"

"What in the world is the song about?" whispered Mr.
Woodbury.

"It's the Lament of the Indian Hunter," said Mrs. Waldo:
"he always sings it. Now comes the chorus: it's queer:
listen!"

Thereupon, from the cavernous throat of the singer, issued
a series of howls in the minor key, something in this wise:

"Yo-HO—yo-ho! Yo-HO-O—yo-HO-ho-*ho*-ho!"

"After this," thought Woodbury, "they can bear to hear
an old song, though a thousand times repeated." And being
again pressed, he gave simply, without any attempt at brilliancy
of execution: "The Harp of Tara."

There was profound silence, as his voice, strung with true
masculine fibre, rang through the rooms. Generally, the least
intellectual persons sing with the truest and most touching expression, because voice and intellect are rarely combined: but
Maxwell Woodbury's fine organ had not been given to him at
the expense of his brain. It was a lucky chance of nature. His
hearers did not really know how admirably he interpreted that
sigh of the Irish heart, but they were pleased, and not nig-
gardly in their expressions of delight.

More songs were called for, and refused. There was the
usual coaxing, and a shocking prevalence of hoarseness, combined with sudden loss of memory. One young lady commenced with "Isle" (which she pronounced *eye-heel*) "of
Beauty," but broke down at the end of the first verse, and all
the cries of: "*Do* go on!" "It's *so* pretty!" could not encour-

age her to resume.   Finally some one, spying Hannah Thurston, who had folded up her embroidery and was sitting in a shaded corner, cried out:

"Oh, Miss Thurston!   Give us that song you sang the last time—that one about the mountains, you know."

Miss Thurston started, as if aroused out of a profound revery, while a flitting blush, delicate and transient as the shadow of a rose tossed upon marble, visited her face.   She had felt and followed, word by word and tone by tone, the glorious Irish lay.   The tragic pathos of the concluding lines—

> "For freedom now so seldom wakes,
>   The only throb she gives
> Is when some heart indignant breaks,
>   To show that still she lives!"

—thrilled and shook her with its despairing solemnity.   What a depth of betrayed trust, of baffled aspiration, it revealed! Some dormant sentiment in her own heart leapt up and answered it, with that quick inner pang, which would be a cry were it expressed in sound.   Yet was the despair which the melody suggested of a diviner texture than joy.   It was that sadness of the imaginative nature which is half triumph, because the same illumination which reveals the hopelessness of its desires reveals also their beauty and their divinity.

The request addressed to her was a shock which recalled her to herself.   It was so warmly seconded that refusal would have been ungracious, and a true social instinct told her that her revery, though involuntary, was out of place.   She profited by the little delay which ensued in order to secure silence —for in our country communities silence always *precedes* the song—to recover her full self-possession.   There was no tremor in her voice, which soared, with the words, into a still, clear ether, in which the pictures of the song stood out pure, distinct, and sublime.   It was one of those lyrics of Mrs. Hemans, which suggest the trumpet at woman's lips— shorn of its rough battle-snarl, its fierce notes tenderly muffled, but a trumpet still. She sang, with the bride of the Alpine hunter:

> "Thy heart is in the upper world,
>   And where the chamois bound;
> Thy heart is where the mountain-fir
>   Shakes with the torrent's sound:
> And where the snow-peaks gleam like stars
>   In the stillness of the air,
> And where the lawine's voice is heard,—
>   Hunter, thy heart is there!"

It was rather musical declamation, than singing. Her voice, pure, sweet, and strong, distinctly indicated the melody, instead of giving it positively, beyond the possibility of a mistaken semitone. It was a ringing chant of that "upper world" of the glaciers, where every cry or call is followed by a musical echo,—where every sound betrays the thin air and the boundless space. Hannah Thurston sang it with a vision of Alpine scenery in her brain. She saw, gleaming in the paler sunshine, beneath the black-blue heaven, the sharp horns of frosted silver, the hanging ledges of short summer grass, the tumbled masses of gray rock, and the dust of snow from falling avalanches. Hence, he who had once seen these things in their reality, saw them again while listening to her. She knew not, however, her own dramatic power: it was enough that she gave pleasure.

Maxwell Woodbury's eyes brightened, as the bleak and lofty landscapes of the Bernese Oberland rose before him. Over the dark fir-woods and the blue ice-caverns of the Rosenlaui glacier, he saw the jagged pyramid of the Wetterhorn, toppling in the morning sky; and involuntarily asked himself what was the magic which had started that half-forgotten picture from the chambers of his memory. How should this pale, quiet girl who, in a musical sense, was no singer, and who had assuredly never seen the Alps, have caught the voice which haunts their desolate glory? But these were questions which came afterwards. The concluding verse, expressing only the patience and humility of love in the valley, blurred the sharp crystal of the first impression and brought him back to the Sewing-Union without a rude shock of transition. He cordially thanked the singer—an act rather unusual in Ptolemy at that time, and hence a grateful surprise to Hannah Thurston, to whom his words conveyed a more earnest meaning than was demanded by mere formal courtesy.

By this time the assembled company had become very genial and unconstrained. The Rev. Lemuel Styles had entirely forgotten the levity of Mrs. Bue's illumination, and even indulged in good-humored badinage (of a perfectly mild and proper character) with Mrs. Waldo. The others were gathered into little groups, cheerfully chatting—the young gentlemen and ladies apart from the married people. Scandal was sugar-coated, in order to hide its true character: love put on a bitter and prickly outside, to avoid the observation of others: all the innocent disguises of Society were in as full operation as in the ripened atmosphere of great cities.

The nearest approach to a discord was in a somewhat heated discussion on the subject of Slavery, which grew up between Seth Wattles and the Hon. Zeno Harder. The latter was vehement in his denunciation of the Abolitionists, to which the former replied by quoting the Declaration of Independence. The two voices—either of them alike unpleasant to a sensitive ear—finally became loud enough to attract the attention of Mrs. Waldo, who had a keen scent for opportunities for the exercise of her authority.

"Come, come!" she cried, placing one hand on Seth's shoulder, while she threatened the Honorable Zeno with the other: "this is forbidden ground. The Sewing-Union would never hold together, if we allowed such things. Besides, what's the use? You two would talk together all night, I'll warrant, and be no nearer agreeing in the morning."

"No," cried Seth, "because your party politicians ignore the questions of humanity!"

"And your fanatical abstractionists never look at any thing
in a practical way!" rejoined the Honorable Zeno.

"And both are deficient in a sense of propriety—I shall
have to say, if you don't stop," was Mrs. Waldo's ready comment.

This little episode had attracted a few spectators, who
were so evidently on Mrs. Waldo's side, that "the Judge,"
as the Hon. Zeno was familiarly called, at once saw the politic
course, and rising magnificently, exclaimed: "Although we
don't *advocate* Women's Rights, we *yield* to woman's authority." Then, bowing with corpulent condescension, he passed
away. Seth Wattles, having no longer an opponent, was condemned to silence.

In the mean time, it had been whispered among the company
that the next meeting of the Union would be held at the
Merryfield farm-house, a mile and a half from Ptolemy. This
had been arranged by the prominent ladies, after a good deal
of consultation. Mr. Merryfield still belonged to the congregation of the Rev. Lemuel Styles, although not in very good
repute. His farm-house was large and spacious, and he was
an excellent "provider," especially for his guests. Moreover,
he was the only one of the small clan of Abolitionists, who
could conveniently entertain the Union,—so that in him were
discharged all the social obligations which the remaining members could fairly exact. The four spinsters, indeed, had ex
changed patient glances, as much as to say: "This is a cross
which we must needs bear." Mr. Merryfield, be it known,
had refused to contribute to Foreign Missions, on the ground
that we had already too many black heathen at home. The
younger persons, nevertheless, were very well satisfied, and
thus the millennial advance of Ptolemy was not interrupted.

The more staid guests had now taken leave, and there was
presently a general movement of departure. The ladies put
on their bonnets and shawls in the best bedroom up-stairs, and
the gentlemen picked out their respective hats and coats from
the miscellaneous heap on the kitchen settee. The hall-door

was unlocked to facilitate egress, and lively groups lingered on the stairs, in the doorway, and on the piazza. The gentlemen dodged about to secure their coveted privilege of escort: now and then a happy young pair slipped away in the belief that they were unnoticed: there were calls of "Do come and see us, now!"—last eager whispers of gossip, a great deal of superfluous female kissing, and the final remarks to Mr. and Mrs. Hamilton Bue: "Good-bye! we've had a *nice* time!"—as the company filtered away.

When the last guest had disappeared, Mr. Hamilton Bue carefully closed and locked the doors, and then remarked to his wife, who was engaged in putting out the extra lamps: "Well, Martha, I think we've done very well, though I say it that shouldn't. Mr. Styles liked your tea, and the cake must have been pretty good, judging from the way they stowed it out of sight."

"Yes," said Mrs. Bue; "I was afraid at one time, there wouldn't be enough to go round. It's well I made up my mind, at the last minute, to bake five instead of four. Molasses is so high."

"Oh, what's the odds of two shillings more or less," her husband consolingly remarked, "when you've got to make a regular spread? Besides, I guess I'll clear expenses, by persuading Woodbury to insure his house in our concern. Dennisons always took the Etna."

2

CHAPTER II.

MR. WOODBURY'S INTRODUCTION TO LAKESIDE.

ON the very day when the Sewing-Union met in Ptolemy, there was an unusual commotion at Lakeside. Only four or five days had elapsed since the secluded little household had been startled by the news that the old place was finally sold, and now a short note had arrived from Mr. Hammond, of Tiberius, who was the agent for the estate, stating that the new owner would probably make his appearance in the course of the day.

The first thing that suggested itself to the distracted mind of Mrs. Fortitude Babb, the housekeeper, was immediately to summon old Melinda, a negro woman, whose specialty was house-cleaning. Had there been sufficient time, Mrs. Babb would have scoured the entire dwelling, from garret to cellar. A stranger, indeed, would have remarked no appearance of disorder, or want of proper cleanliness, anywhere : but the tall housekeeper, propping her hands upon her hips, exclaimed, in despair : "Whatever shall I do? There's hardly time to have the rooms swep', let alone washin' the wood-work. Then, ag'in, I dunno which o' the two bed-rooms he'd like best. Why couldn't Mr. Hammond hold him back, till things was decent? And the libery's been shet up, this ever so long ; and there's bakin' to do—squinch tarts, and sich likes —and you must kill two chickens, Arbutus, right away!"

"Don't be worried, Mother Forty," replied Arbutus Wilson, the stout young man whom Mrs. Babb addressed, "things a'n't lookin' so bad, after all. Max.—well, Mr. Woodbury, I must say now, though it'll go rather queer, at first—was always easy satisfied, when he was here afore."

"I reckon you think people doesn't change in twenty year. There's no tellin' what sort of a man he's got to be. But here comes Melindy. I guess I'll open the libery and let it air, while she fixes the bedrooms."

Mrs. Babb's nervousness had a deeper cause than the condition of the Lakeside mansion. So many years had elapsed since she first came to the place as housekeeper, that it seemed to have become her own property as surely as that of the Dennison family. The death of Mrs. Dennison, eight months before, recalled her to the consciousness of her uncertain tenure. Now, since the estate was finally sold and the new owner about to arrive, a few days, in all probability, would determine whether her right was to be confirmed or herself turned adrift upon the world. Although her recollections of Maxwell Woodbury, whose last visit to Lakeside occurred during the first year of her reign, were as kindly as was consistent with her rigid nature, she awaited his arrival with a mixture of jealousy and dread. True, he was somewhat nearer to her than those relatives of Mrs. Dennison who had inherited the property at her death, for the latter Mrs. Babb had never seen, while him she had both gently scolded and severely petted : but she felt that the removal of Arbutus Wilson and herself from the place would be a shameful piece of injustice, and the fact that such removal was possible indicated something wrong in the world.

Arbutus, who was a hardy, healthy, strapping fellow, of eight-and-twenty, was her step-step-son, if there can be such a relation. His father, who died shortly after his birth, was one of those uneducated, ignorant men, whose ears are yet quick to catch and retain any word of grandiloquent sound. Nothing delighted him so much as to hear the Biblical genealogies read. He had somewhere picked up the word *arbutus*, the sound of which so pleased him that he at once conferred it upon his baby, utterly unconscious of its meaning. A year or two after his death, the widow Wilson married Jason Babb, an honest, meek-natured carpenter, who proved a good father

to the little Arbutus. She, however, was carried away by a
malignant fever, in the first year of her second marriage. The
widower, who both mourned and missed her, cherished her
child with a conscientious fidelity, and it was quite as much
from a sense of duty towards the boy, as from an inclination
of the heart, that he married Miss Fortitude Winterbottom, a
tall, staid, self-reliant creature, verging on spinsterhood.

The Fates, however, seemed determined to interfere with
Jason Babb's connubial plans; but the next time it was upon
himself, and not upon his wife, that the lot fell. Having no
children of his own, by either wife, he besought Fortitude,
with his latest breath, to be both father and mother to the
doubly-orphaned little Bute Wilson. It must be admitted
that Mrs. Babb faithfully performed her promise. The true
feeling of parental tenderness had never been granted to her,
and the sense of responsibility—*of ownership*—which came in
its stead—was a very mild substitute; but it impressed the
boy, at least, with a consciousness of care and protection,
which satisfied his simple nature. Mrs. Dennison, with her
kind voice, and gentle, resigned old face, seemed much more
the mother, while Mrs. Babb, with her peremptory ways and
strict idea of discipline, unconsciously assumed for him the
attitude of a father. The latter had come to Lakeside at a
time when Mr. Dennison's confirmed feebleness required his
wife to devote herself wholly to his care. Mrs. Babb, therefore, took charge of the house, and Arbutus, at first a younger
companion of Henry Dennison, afterwards an active farm-boy,
finally developed into an excellent farmer, and had almost the
exclusive management of the estate for some years before Mrs.
Dennison's death.

Thus these two persons, with an Irish field-hand, had been
the only occupants of Lakeside, during the summer and autumn. Arbutus, or Bute, as he was universally called in the
neighborhood, was well-pleased with the news of Mr. Woodbury's purchase. He remembered him, indistinctly, as the
" town-boy" who gave him his first top and taught him how

to spin it, though the big fellow couldn't tell a thrush's egg from a robin's, and always said " tortoise" instead of " tortle." Bute thought they'd get along together somehow—or, if they didn't, *he* could do as well somewheres else, he reckoned. Nevertheless, he felt anxious that the owner should receive a satisfactory impression on his arrival, and busied himself, with Patrick's assistance, in " setting every thing to rights" about the barn and out-houses.

After all, there was scarcely need of such hurried preparation. Mr. Hammond and Woodbury, detained by some necessary formalities of the law, did not leave Tiberius until the afternoon of that day. The town being situated at the outlet of Atauga Lake, they took the little steamer to Atauga City, near its head, in preference to the long road over the hills. The boat, with a heavy load of freight, made slow progress, and it was dusk before they passed the point on the eastern shore, beyond which Lakeside is visible from the water. On reaching Ptolemy by the evening stage from Atauga City, Maxwell Woodbury found the new "Ptolemy House" so bright and cheerful, that he immediately proposed their remaining for the night, although within four miles of their destination.

" I have a fancy for approaching the old place by daylight," said he to his companion. " Here begins my familiar ground, and I should be sorry to lose the smallest test of memory. Besides, I am not sure what kind of quarters I should be able to offer you, on such short notice."

"Let us stay, then, by all means," said the lawyer. " I can appreciate feelings, although I am occupied entirely with *deeds*." Here he quietly chuckled, and was answered by a roar from the landlord, who came up in time to hear the remark.

"Ha! ha! Good, Mr. Hammond!" exclaimed the latter. "Very happy to entertain you, gentlemen. Mr. Woodbury can have the Bridal Chamber, if he likes. But you should go to the Great Sewing-Union, gentlemen. You will find all

Ptolemy there to-night. It's at Hamilton Bue's: you know him, Mr. Hammond—Director of the Bank."

The results of this advice have already been described. After breakfast, on the following morning, the two gentlemen set out for Lakeside in a light open carriage. It was one of the last days of the Indian summer, soft and hazy, with a fore-boding of winter in the air. The hills, enclosing the head of the lake, and stretching away southwards, on opposite sides of the two valleys, which unite just behind Ptolemy, loomed through their blue veil with almost the majesty of mountain ranges. The green of the pine-forests on their crests, and of those ragged lines of the original woods which marked the courses of the descending ravines, was dimmed and robbed of its gloom. The meadows extending towards the lake were still fresh, and the great elms by the creek-side had not yet shed all of their tawny leaves. A moist, fragrant odor of decay per-vaded the atmosphere, and the soft southwestern wind, occasion-ally stealing down the further valley, seemed to blow the som-bre colors of the landscape into dying flickers of brightness.

As they crossed the stream to the eastward of the village, and drove along the base of the hills beyond, Woodbury ex-claimed :

"You cannot possibly understand, Mr. Hammond, how refreshing to me are these signs of the coming winter, after nearly fifteen years of unbroken summer. I shall enjoy the change doubly here, among the scenes of the only country-life which I ever knew in America,—where I was really happiest, as a boy. I suppose," he added, laughing, "now that the business is over, I may confess to you how much I congratu-late myself on having made the purchase."

"As if I did not notice how anxious you were to buy !" re-joined the lawyer. "You must be strongly attached to the old place, to take it on the strength of former associations. I wish it were nearer Tiberius, that we might have more of your society. Did you pass much of your youth here?"

"Only my summers, from the age of twelve to fifteen. My

constitution was rather delicate when I was young, and Mrs. Dennison, who was a distant relative of my father, and sometimes visited us in New York, persuaded him to let me try the air of Lakeside. Henry was about my own age, and we soon became great friends. The place was a second home to me, thenceforth, until my father's death. Even after I went to Calcutta, I continued to correspond with Henry, but my last letter from Lakeside was written by his mother, after his body was brought home from Mexico."

"Yes," said Mr. Hammond, "the old lady fairly broke down after that. Henry was a fine fellow and a promising officer, and I believe she would have borne his loss better, had he fallen in battle. But he lingered a long time in the hospital, and she was just beginning to hope for his recovery, when the news of his death came instead. But see! there is Roaring Brook. Do you hear the noise of the fall? How loud it is this morning!"

The hill, curving rapidly to the eastward, rose abruptly from the meadows in a succession of shelving terraces, the lowest of which was faced with a wall of dark rock, in horizontal strata, but almost concealed from view by the tall forest trees which grew at its base. The stream, issuing from a glen which descended from the lofty upland region to the eastward of the lake, poured itself headlong from the brink of the rocky steep, —a glittering silver thread in summer, a tawny banner of angry sound in the autumn rains. Seen through the hazy air, its narrow white column seemed to stand motionless between the pines, and its mellowed thunder to roll from some region beyond the hills.

Woodbury, who had been looking steadily across the meadows to the north, cried out: "It is the same—it has not yet run itself dry! Now we shall see Lakeside; but no—yet I certainly used to see the house from this point. Ah! twenty years! I had forgotten that trees cannot stand still; that ash, or whatever it is, has quite filled up the gap. I am afraid I shall find greater changes than this."

His eyes mechanically fell, as the wheels rumbled suddenly on the plank bridge over Roaring Brook. Mr. Hammond looked up, gave the horse a skilful dash of the whip and shot past the trees which lined the stream. "Look and see!" he presently said.

The old place, so familiar to Woodbury, and now his own property, lay before him. There was the heavy white house, with its broad verandah, looking southward from the last low shelf of the hills, which rose behind it on their westward sweep back to the lake. The high-road to Anacreon and thence to Tiberius, up the eastern shore, turned to the right and ascended to the upland, through a long winding glen. A small grove of evergreens still further protected the house on its northwestern side, so that its position was unusually sunny and sheltered. The head of the lake, the meadows around Ptolemy and the branching valleys beyond, were all visible from the southern windows; and though the hills to the east somewhat obscured the sunrise, the evenings wore a double splendor—in the lake and in the sky.

"Poor Henry!" whispered Woodbury to himself, as Mr. Hammond alighted to open the gate into the private lane. The house had again disappeared from view, behind the rise of the broad knoll upon which it stood, and their approach was not visible until they had reached the upper level, with its stately avenue of sugar-maples, extending to the garden wall.

The place was really unchanged, to all appearance. Perhaps the clumps of lilac and snowball, along the northern wall were somewhat higher, and the apple-trees in the orchard behind the house more gnarled and mossy; but the house itself, the turfed space before it, the flagged walk leading to the door, the pyramids of yew and juniper, were the same as ever, and the old oaks at each corner seemed, twig for twig, to have stood still for twenty years. A few bunches of chrysanthemum, somewhat nipped by the frost, gave their sober autumnal coloring and wholesome bitter-sweet odor to the garden-alleys. The late purple asters were shrivelled and drooping, and the hollyhocks stood like desolate floral towers, tottering over the summer's ruin.

For the first time in twenty years, Woodbury felt the almost forgotten sensation of *home* steal through his heart. Quickly and silently he recognized each familiar object, and the far-off days of the past swept into the nearness of yesterday. His ear took no note of Mr. Hammond's rattling remarks: the latter was not precisely the man whose atmosphere lures forth the hidden fragrance of one's nature.

As they drove along the garden-wall, a strong figure appeared, approaching with eager strides. He glanced first at the horse and carriage. "Fairlamb's livery—the bay," was his mental remark. The next moment he stood at the gate, waiting for them to alight.

"How do you do, Mr. Hammond?" he cried. "You're late a-comin': we expected ye las' night. And is this really Mr. Maxwell, I mean Mr. Woodbury—well, I'd never ha knowed him. I s'pose you don't know me, nuther, Mr. Max.?"

"God bless me! it must be little Bute!" exclaimed Woodbury, taking the honest fellow's hand. "Yes, I see it now—man instead of boy, but the same fellow still."

"Yes, indeed, that I *be!*" asserted the delighted Arbutus. He meant much more than the words indicated. Fully expressed, his thoughts would have run something in this wise: "I guess we can git on together, as well as when we was boys. If *you* ha'n't changed, *I* ha'n't. I'll do my dooty towards ye, and you won't be disapp'inted in me."

In the mean time, Mrs. Fortitude Babb had made her appearance, clad in the black bombazine which she had purchased for Jason's funeral, and was waiting, tall and rigid, but with considerable internal " flusteration " (as she would have expressed it), on the verandah. One mental eye was directed towards the new owner, and the other to the fowls in the kitchen, which she had cut up the evening before, for a fric-assee, and which were thus rendered unfit for roasting. "Why, he's a perfick stranger!" "If there's only time to make a pie of 'em!" were the two thoughts which crossed each other in her brain.

"Mrs. Babb! there's no mistaking who *you* are!" exclaimed Woodbury, as he hastened with outstretched hand up the flagged walk.

The old housekeeper gave him her long, bony hand in return, and made an attempt at a courtesy, a thing which she had not done for so long that one of her knee-joints cracked with the effort. "Welcome, Sir!" said she, with be-coming gravity. Woodbury thought she did not recognize him.

"Why, don't you remember Max.?" he asked.

"Yes, I recollex you as you was. And now I come to look, your eyes is jist the same. Dear, dear!" and in spite of herself two large tears slowly took their way down her lank cheeks. "If Miss Dennison and Henry could be here!" Then she wiped her eyes with her hand, rather than spoil the corner of her black silk apron. Stiffening her features the next moment, she turned away, exclaiming in a voice un-necessarily sharp: "Arbutus, why don't you put away the horse?"

The gentlemen entered the house. The hall-door had evi-dently not been recently used, for the lock grated with a sound of rust. The sitting-room on the left and the library beyond, were full of hazy sunshine and cheerful with the crackling of fires on the open hearth. Dust was nowhere to be seen, but the chairs stood as fixedly in their formal places as if screwed to the floor, and the old books seemed to be glued together in regular piles. None of the slight tokens of habit-ual occupation caught the eye—no pleasant irregularity of do-mestic life,—a newspaper tossed here, a glove there, a chair placed obliquely to a favorite window, or a work-stand or foot-stool drawn from its place. Mrs. Babb, it is true, with a

After dinner, Mr. Hammond paid them what was due from the estate. Bute turned the money over uneasily in his hand, grew red in the face, and avoided meeting the eye of the new owner. Mrs. Babb straightened her long spine, took out a buckskin purse, and, having put the money therein, began rubbing the steel clasp with the corner of her apron. Woodbury, then, with a few friendly words, expressed his pleasure at having found them in charge of Lakeside, and his desire that each should continue to serve him in the same capacity as before.

Mrs. Babb did not betray, by the twitch of a muscle, the relief she felt. On the contrary, she took credit to herself for accepting her good fortune. "There's them that would like to have me," said she. "Mrs. Dennison never havin' said nothin' ag'in my housekeepin', but the reverse; and I a'n't bound to stay, for want of a good home; but *somebody* must keep house for ye, and I'd hate to see things goin' to wrack, after keerin' for 'em, a matter o' twenty year. Well—I'll stay, I guess, and do my best, as I've always done it."

"*Et tu*, Bute?" said Mr. Hammond, whose small puns had gained him a reputation for wit, in Tiberius.

Bute understood the meaning, not the words. "I'm glad Mr. Max. wants me," he answered, eagerly. "I'd hate to leave the old place, though I'm able to get my livin' most anywheres. But it'd be like leavin' home—and jist now, with that two-year old colt to break, and a couple o' steers that I'm goin' to yoke in the spring—it wouldn't seem natural, like. Mr. Max. and me was boys together here, and I guess we can hitch teams without kickin' over the traces."

After arranging for an inventory and appraisal of the live stock, farming implements, and the greater part of the furniture, which Woodbury decided to retain, Mr. Hammond took his departure. Mrs. Babb prepared her tea at the usual early hour. After some little hesitation, she took her seat at the table, but evaded participation in the meal. Mr. Woodbury sat much longer than she was accustomed to see, in the people

of Ptolemy : he sipped his tea slowly, and actually accepted a
fourth cup. Mrs. Babb's gratification reached its height when
he began to praise her preserved quinces, but on his unthink-
ingly declaring them to be "better than ginger," her grimness
returned.

"Better than ginger! I should think so!" was her mental
exclamation.

Throwing himself into the old leather arm-chair before the
library fire, Woodbury enjoyed the perfect stillness of the November evening. The wind had fallen, and the light of a half-
moon lay upon the landscape. The vague illumination, the
shadowy outlines of the distant hills, and that sense of isolation from the world which now returned upon him, gratefully
brought back the half-obliterated moods of his Indian life. He
almost expected to hear the soft whish of the punka above his
head, and to find, suddenly, the "hookah-burdar" at his
elbow. A cheerful hickory-fed flame replaced the one, and a
ripe Havana cigar the other ; but his repose was not destined to be left undisturbed. "The world" is not so easy to
escape. Even there, in Ptolemy, it existed, and two of its
special agents (self-created) already knocked at the door of
Lakeside.

The housekeeper ushered Mr. Hamilton Bue and the Hon.
Zeno Harder into the library. The latter, as Member of the
Legislature, considered that this call was due, as, in some sort,
an official welcome to his district. Besides, his next aim was
the State Senate, and the favor of a new resident, whose
wealth would give him influence, could not be secured too
soon. Mr. Bue, as the host of the previous evening, enjoyed
an advantage over the agent of the "Etna," which he was not
slow to use. His politeness was composed of equal parts of
curiosity and the "Saratoga Mutual."

"We thought, Sir," said the Hon. Zeno, entering, "that
your first evening here might be a little lonesome, and you'd
be glad to have company for an hour or so."

The Member was a coarse, obese man, with heavy chaps,

thick, flat lips, small eyes, bald crown, and a voice which had been made harsh and aggressive in its tone by much vigorous oratory in the open air. The lines of his figure were rounded, it is true, but it was the lumpy roundness of a potato rather than the swelling, opulent curves of well-padded muscle Mr. Hamilton Bue, in contrast to him, seemed to be made of angles. His face and hands had that lean dryness which suggests a body similarly constructed, and makes us thankful for the invention of clothing. He was a prim, precise business man, as the long thin nose and narrow lips indicated, with a trace of weakness in the retreating chin. Neither of these gentlemen possessed a particle of that grapy bloom of ripe manhood, which tells of generous blood in either cell of the double heart. In one the juice was dried up; in the other it had become thick and slightly rancid.

They were not the visitors whom Woodbury would have chosen, but the ostensible purpose of their call demanded acknowledgment. He therefore gave them a cordial welcome, and drew additional chairs in front of the fire. The Hon. Zeno, taking a cigar, elevated his feet upon the lower moulding of the wooden mantel-piece, spat in the fire, and remarked:

"You find Ptolemy changed, I dare say. Let me see— when were you here last? In '32? I must have been studying law in Tiberius at that time. Oh, it's scarcely the same place. So many went West after the smash in '37, and new people have come in—new people and new idees, I may say."

"We have certainly shared in the general progression of the country, even during my residence here," said Mr. Hamilton Bue, carefully assuming his official style. "Ten years ago, there were but thirty-seven names on the books of the Saratoga Mutual. Now we count a hundred and thirteen. But there is a reason for it: the Company pays its loss punctually—most punctually."

Unconscious of this dexterous advertising, Woodbury

answered the Hon. Zeno: "Since I am to be, for a while, a member of your community, I am interested in learning something more about it. What are the new ideas you mentioned, Mr. Harder?"

"Well, Sir,—I can't exactly say that Hunkerism is a new thing in politics. I'm a Barnburner, you must know, and since the split it seems like new parties, though *we* hold on to the old principles. Then there's the Temperance Reform— swep' every thing before it, at first, but slacking off just now. The Abolitionists, it's hardly worth while to count—there's so few of them—but they make a mighty noise. Go for Non-Resistance, Women's Rights, and all other Isms. So, you see, compared to the old times, when 'twas only Whig and Democrat, the deestrict is pretty well stirred up."

Mr. Bue, uncertain as to the views of his host upon some of the subjects mentioned, and keeping a sharp eye to his own interests, here remarked in a mild, placable tone: "I don't know that it does any harm. People must have their own opinions, and there's no law to hinder it. In fact, frequent discussion is a means of intellectual improvement."

"But what's the use of discussing what's contrary to Scriptur' and Reason?" cried the Hon. Zeno, in his out-door voice. "*Our* party is for Free Soil, and you can't go further under the Constitution,—so, what's the use in talking? Non-Resistance might be Christian enough, if all men was saints; but we've got to take things as we find 'em. When you're hit, hit back, if you want to do any good in these times. As for Women's Rights, it's the biggest humbug of all. A pretty mess we should be in, if it could be carried out! Think of my wife taking the stump against Mrs. Blackford, and me and him doing the washing and cooking!"

"Who was the Abolitionist—for such I took him to be— with whom you were talking, last evening, at Mr. Bue's?" Woodbury asked.

"Wattles—a tailor in Ptolemy—one of the worst fanatics among 'em!" the irate Zeno replied. "Believes in all the

Isms, and thinks himself a great Reformer. It's disgusting to hear a man talk about Women's Rights, as he does. I don't mind it so much in Hannah Thurston; but the fact is, she's more of a man than the most of 'em."

"Hannah Thurston! Is not that the lady who sang—a pale, earnest-looking girl, in a gray dress?"

"I did'nt notice her dress," the Member answered. "She sings, though—not much voice, but what she has tells amazingly. Between ourselves, I'll admit that she's a first-rate speaker—that is, for a woman. I was tempted to have a round with her, at the last meeting they held; but then, you know, a woman always has you at a disadvantage. You daren't give it back to them as sharp as you get it."

"Do you really mean that she makes public harangues?" exclaimed Woodbury, who, in his long absence from home, had lost sight of many new developments in American society.

"Yes, and not bad ones, either, when you consider the subject. Her mother used to preach in Quaker Meetings, so it doesn't seem quite so strange as it might. Besides, she isn't married, and one can make some allowance. But when Sarah Merryfield gets up and talks of the tyranny of man, it's a little too much for me. I'd like to know, now, exactly what her meek lout of a husband thinks about it."

"Is Mrs. Waldo, also, an advocate of the new doctrine?"

"She? No indeed. She has her rights already: that is, all that a woman properly knows how to use. Though I don't like the Cimmerian doctrine—Mr. Waldo is pastor of the Cimmerians—yet I think she's a much better Christian than the Merryfields, who still hang on to our Church."

"What are the Cimmerians?" inquired Woodbury. "Are they so called from the darkness of their doctrines?"

The Hon. Zeno did not understand the classical allusion. "They're followers of the Rev. Beza Cimmer," he said. "He was first a Seceder, I believe, but differed with them on the doctrine of Grace. Besides, they think that Baptism, to be

saving, must be in exact imitation of that of the Saviour.
The preacher wears a hair garment, like John the Baptist,
when he performs the ceremony, and the converts long, white
robes. They pick out some creek for their Jordan, and do
not allow outsiders to be present. They don't grow in numbers, and have but a very small congregation in Ptolemy. In
fact, Mr. Waldo is considered rather shaky by some of the
older members, who were converted by Cimmer himself. He
don't hold very close communion."

A part of this explanation was incomprehensible to Woodbury, who was not yet familiar with the catch-words which
fall so glibly from the mouths of country theologians. He
detected the Member's disposition to harangue instead of
converse—a tendency which could only be prevented by a
frequent and dexterous change of subject. "Your church,"
he said:—"I take it for granted you refer to that of Mr.
Styles,—seems to be in a flourishing condition."

"Yes," replied Mr. Hamilton Bue, "we have prospered
under his ministry. Some have backslidden, it is true, but we
have had encouraging seasons of revival. Our ladies are now
very earnest in the work of assisting the Jutnapore Mission.
Mrs. Boerum is from Syracuse, and a particular friend of Miss
Eliza Clancy. I think Miss Eliza herself would have gone
if she had been called in time. You know it requires a
double call."

"A double call! Excuse me if I do not quite understand
you," said the host.

"Why, of course, they must first be called to the *work;*
and then, as they can't go alone among the heathen, they
must afterwards depend on a personal call from some unmarried missionary. Now Miss Clancy is rather too old
for that."

Woodbury could not repress a smile at this naïve statement,
although it was made with entire gravity. "I have seen something of your missions in India," he at last remarked, "and
believe that they are capable of accomplishing much good

Still, you must not expect immediate returns. It is only the lowest caste that is now reached, and the Christianizing of India must come, eventually, from the highest."

Rather than discuss a subject of which he was ignorant, the Hon. Zeno started a new topic. "By the way, the next meeting of the Sewing Union will be at Merryfield's. Shall you attend, Mr. Woodbury?"

"Yes. They are among the few persons who have kept me in good remembrance, though they, too, from what you have said, must be greatly changed since I used to play with their son Absalom. I am very sorry to hear of his death."

"It *is* a pity," replied the Member, biting off the end of a fresh cigar. "Absalom was really a fine, promising fellow, but they spoiled him with their Isms. They were Grahamites for a year or two—lived on bran bread and turnips, boiled wheat and dried apples. Absalom took up that and the water-cure, and wanted to become a patent first-class reformer. Now, Temperance is a good thing—though I can't quite go the Maine Law—but water inside of you and outside of you, summer and winter alike, isn't temperance, according to my idee. He had a spell of pleurisy, one winter, and doctored himself for it. His lungs were broken up, after that, and he went off the very next fall. They set a great deal of store by him."

"Is it possible that such delusions are held by intelligent persons?" exclaimed Woodbury, shocked as well as surprised. "I hope these theories are not included in the general progress of which Mr. Bue spoke. But I have almost forgotten my duty as a host. The nights are getting cold, gentlemen, and perhaps you will take a glass of wine."

The Hon. Zeno's small eyes twinkled, and his lips twitched liquorously. "Well—I don't care if I do," said he.

Mr. Hamilton Bue was silent, and slightly embarrassed. He had found it necessary to join the Temperance Society, because the reform was a popular one. He always went with the current as soon as it became too strong to stem con-

veniently. But the temptation to indulge still lurked in his
thin blood. It was evident that the Member, for his own
sake, would not mention the circumstance, and Mr. Woodbury, in all probability, would never think of it again.

Some of Mrs. Babb's "Madary" presently twinkled like
smoky topaz in the light of the wood-fire. Mr. Bue at first
sipped hesitatingly, like a bather dipping his toes, with a
shudder, into the waters of a cold river ; but having once
reached the bottom of the glass—so quickly, indeed, that it
excited his own surprise—he made the next plunge with the
boldness of a man accustomed to it.

"You will attend church, I presume, Mr. Woodbury?"
said he. "Of course you have convictions."

"Certainly," Woodbury answered, without a clear idea of
what was meant by the word—"very strong ones."

"Of course—it could not be otherwise. I shall be very
glad if you will now and then accept a seat in my pew. Mr.
Styles is a great authority on Galatians, and I am sure you
will derive spiritual refreshment from his sermons."

Here the Hon. Zeno rose and commenced buttoning his
coat, as a signal of departure. Growing confidential from his
inner warmth, he placed one hand affectionately on Woodbury's shoulder, somewhat to the latter's disgust, and said :
"Now you are one of us, Woodbury, you must take an active
part in our political concerns. Great principles are at stake,
Sir, and the country has need of men like you. Let me warn
you against the Hunkers—their game is nearly played out.
I'll be most happy, Sir, to explain to you the condition of
parties. You'll find me well posted up."

Mr. Bue took occasion to make a parting hint in the interest
of the Saratoga Mutual. "If you wish to have your house insured, Mr. Woodbury," said he, "I shall be glad to send you
our pamphlets. The Company is so well known, fortunately,
that its name is a sufficient recommendation."

The owner of Lakeside stood on the verandah, watching
his guests drive down the maple avenue. As the sound of

their wheels sank below the brow of the hill, the muffled voice of Roaring Brook came softly to him, across the dark meadows. A part of Atauga Lake threw back the light of the descending moon. "Here," thought he, "is the commencement of a new existence. It is not the old, boyish life of which I dreamed, but something very different. I foresee that I shall have to accustom myself to many features of this society, which are not attractive—some of them even repugnant—and perhaps the only counterbalancing delight left to me will be the enjoyment of this lovely scenery, the peace of this secluded life. Will that be sufficient? Or will these oaks and pines at last pall upon my eye, like the palms and banyans of the East? No: one cannot be satisfied with external resources. I must study, with a liberal human interest, the characteristics of this little community, however strange or repellant they may seem; and certainly, after making friends among the fossilized Brahmins, there must be a few among my fellow-Christians and fellow-countrymen, whom I can heartily respect and love. Those long Indian years must be placed in a closed Past, and I must adapt myself to habits and associations, which have become more foreign than familiar to me."

CHAPTER IV.

AN INTERVIEW ON THE ROAD, AND A NEW HOUSEHOLD.

THE Indian Summer still held its ground, keeping back the winter's vanguard of frost and keen nor'westers. Day by day the smoky air became more densely blue and still, and the leaves, long since dead, hung upon the trees for want of a loosening wind. The hickory-nuts fell by their own weight, pattering here and there in the woods, in single smart raps, and giving out a vigorous balsamic odor, as their cleft rinds burst open. Only at night a gathering chill and a low moaning in the air gave the presage of an approaching change in the season.

On one of those warm forenoons which almost reproduce the languor and physical yearning of the opening Spring, Bute Wilson, mounted on Dick, the old farm-horse, jogged slowly along the road to Ptolemy, whistling "The Rose that All are Praising," a melody which he had learned at the singing-school. Bute was bound for the village, on a variety of errands, and carried a basket on his arm. Dick's deliberate gait seemed to be in harmony with the current of his thoughts. The horse understood his rider, and knew very well when to take his ease, and when to summon up the little life left in his stiff old legs. Horses are better interpreters of one's moods than the most of one's human friends.

Bute was a very good specimen of the American country-man. A little over the average height, and compacted of coarse, hardy fibre, he possessed, in spite of the common stock from which he had sprung, the air of independent self-respect which a laboring man can only acquire in a community where caste is practically ignored.   His independence, however, had not degenerated into impudence : he knew his deficiencies of nature and education, and did not attempt to off-set them by a vulgar assertion of equality.   He could sit at Mr. Woodbury's table (using the knife a little too freely) without embarrassment, and could take his dinner in the kitchen without being conscious of degradation.   His horses, cattle, and crops occupied the first place in his mind—himself—no, another person had the second place—and his own personality gave him the least trouble.   He was a general favorite in the neighborhood, and his position was, perhaps, more fortunate than he knew, though the knowledge of it would not have made him happier than he was.   He was honestly respected by those below, and not looked down upon by those above him.   This consideration was won by his thorough frankness, simplicity, and kindness of heart.   His face was too broad and his nose too thick, to be called handsome; but there were fewer eyes into which men looked with more satisfaction than the pair of large blue-gray ones, divided by the nose aforesaid.   His forehead was rather low, but open and smooth, and his yellow hair, curling a little at the ends, grew back from the temples with a sturdy set, as if determined that they should not be hidden.   Add to these traits a voice mellow in spite of its volume—the cattle understood its every inflection—and it is easy to perceive that Bute was in especial favor with the opposite sex.   From head to foot, Nature had written upon him : This man is a male.

Bute had climbed the rise beyond Roaring Brook, when his reveries, whatever they might have been, were interrupted by the sight of a woman, walking towards Ptolemy, a short distance in advance of him.   Although no other person was near, to play the spy, he felt the blood creeping up to his ears, as he looked keenly and questioningly at the little figure, in its dark-blue merino dress, tripping forward with short, quick steps.   Dick noticed the change in his master, and broke into a trot down the gentle slope.   At the sound of hoofs, the figure

3

turned, disclosing a bunch of brown ringlets and a saucy little nose, then drew to one side of the road and stopped.

"Good-morning, Miss Carrie!" cried Bute, as he drew rein, on approaching: "I thought it was you. Goin' to Ptolemy? So am I. Git up on the bank, and I'll take ye on behind me. Dick'll carry double—he's as quiet as a lamb. Here, I'll jerk off my coat for you to set on." And he had his right arm out of the sleeve before he had finished speaking.

"Ah!" cried the lady, affecting a mild scream; "No, indeed, Mr. Wilson! I am so afraid of horses. Besides, I don't think it would look right."

It suddenly occurred to Bute's mind, that, in order to ride as he had proposed, she would be obliged to clasp him with both arms. Heaving a sigh of regret, he drew on his coat and jumped off the horse.

"Well, if you won't ride with me, I'll walk with you, any how. How's your health, Miss Carrie?" offering his hand.

"Very well, I thank you, Mr. Wilson. How's Mrs. Babb? And I hear that Mr. Woodbury has come to live with you."

Miss Caroline Dilworth was too well satisfied at meeting with Bute, to decline his proffered company. She was on her way from the house of a neighboring farmer, where she had been spending a fortnight as seamstress, to the cottage of the widow Thurston, who lived on the edge of the village. The old lady's health was declining, and Miss Dilworth occasionally rendered a friendly assistance to the daughter. They were both always glad to see the lively, chattering creature, in spite of her manifold weaknesses and affectations. She was twenty-five years of age, at least, but assumed all the timidity and inexperience of a girl of sixteen, always wearing her hair in a mesh of natural ringlets which hung about her neck, and talking with a soft childish drawl, unless—which rarely happened—she was so very much in earnest as to forget herself. Her nose was piquantly *retroussé*, her mouth small and cherry-red, and her complexion fair (for she took great care of it); but her eyes inclined to pale-green rather than blue, and she had an affected habit of dropping the lids. Perhaps this was to conceal the unpleasant redness of their edges, for they were oftentimes so inflamed as to oblige her to suspend her occupation. Her ambition was, to become a teacher—a post for which she was not at all qualified. Hannah Thurston, however, had kindly offered to assist her in preparing herself for the coveted career.

What it was that attracted Bute Wilson to Miss Dilworth, he was unable to tell. Had the case been reversed, we should not wonder at it. Only this much was certain; her society was a torment to him, her absence a pain. He would have cut off his little finger for the privilege of just once lifting her in his strong arms, and planting a kiss square upon the provoking mouth, which, as if conscious of its surplus of sweetness, could say so many bitter things to him. Bute had never spoken to her of the feeling which she inspired in him. Why should he? She knew just how he felt, and he knew that she knew it. She played with him as he had many a time played with a big trout at the end of his line. Over and over again he had been on the point of giving her up, out of sheer worriment and exhaustion of soul, when a sudden look from those downcast eyes, a soft word, half whispered in a voice whose deliberate sweetness tingled through him, from heart to finger-ends, bound him faster than ever. Miss Dilworth little suspected how many rocks she had sledged to pieces, how many extra swaths she had mowed in June, and shocks of corn she had husked in October, through Bute Wilson's arm. If Mr. Woodbury were a cunning employer, he would take measures to prolong this condition of suspense.

On the present occasion, the affected little minx was unusually gracious towards her victim. She had a keen curiosity to gratify. "Now, Bute," said she, as they started together towards Ptolemy, Bute leading Dick by the bridle; "I want you to tell me all about this Mr. Woodbury. What kind of a man is he?"

"He's only been with us three or four days. To be sure, I

knowed him as a boy, but that's long ago, and I *may* have to
learn him over ag'in. It won't be a hard thing to do, though:
he's a gentleman, if there ever was one. He's a man that'll
always do what's right, if he knows how."

"I mean, Bute, how he looks. Tall or short? Is he handsome? Isn't he burnt very black, or is it worn off?"

"Not so many questions at once, Miss Carrie. He a'n't
blacker 'n I'd be now, if I was complected like him. Tall, you
might call him—nigh two inches more'n I am, and a reg'lar
pictur' of a man, though a bit thinner than he'd ought to be.
But I dunno whether *you'd* call him handsome: women has
sich queer notions. Now, there's that Seth Wattles, that you
think sich a beauty—"

"Bute Wilson! You know I don't think any such thing!
It's Seth's *mind* that I admire. There's such a thing as moral
and intellectual beauty, but that you don't understand."

"No, hang it!—nor don't want to, if *he's* got it! I believe
in a man's doin' what he purtends to do—keepin' his mind on
his work, whatever it is. If Seth Wattles lays out to be a
tailor, let him *be* one: if he wants to be a moral and intellectual beauty, he may try *that*, for all I keer—but he can't do
both to once't. I wish he'd make better trowsus, or give up
his business."

Miss Dilworth knew her own weakness, and carefully avoided entering into a discussion. She was vexed that one of the
phrases she had caught from Hannah Thurston, and which she
had frequently used with much effect, had rattled harmlessly
against the hard mail of Bute's common sense. At another
time she would have taken—or have seemed to take—offence,
at his rough speech; but she had not yet heard enough of Mr.
Woodbury.

"Well, never mind Seth," she said, "you've not finished telling me about your new *master*."

If she had intended to prick Bute with this word, she utterly
failed. He quietly resumed the description: "Every man
that I like is handsome to me; but I think any woman would

admire to see Mr. Max. He's got big brown eyes, like them
o' the doe Master Harry used to have, and a straight nose, like
one o' the plaster heads in the libery. He wears a beard on
his upper lip, but no whiskers, and his hair is brown, and sort
o' curlin'. He's a man that knows what he's about, and can
make up his mind in five minutes, and looks you straight in
the face when he talks; and if he'd a hard thing to say (though
he's said nothin' o' the kind to me), he'd say it without flinchin',
a little worse to your face than what he'd say behind y'r back.
But what *I* like best in him, is, that he knows how to mind his
own business, without botherin' himself about other folks's.
You wouldn't ketch *him* a pitchin' into me because I chaw
tobacco, like Seth Wattles did, with all his moral and intellectual beauty."

"Oh, but, Bute, you know it's so unhealthy. I do wish
you'd give it up."

"Unhealthy! Stuff and nonsense—look at me!" And, indeed Bute, stopping, straightening himself, throwing out his
breast, and striking it with a hard fist until it rang like a muffled drum, presented a picture of lusty, virile strength, which
few men in the neighborhood of Ptolemy could have matched.
"Unhealthy!" he continued; "I s'pose you'd call *Seth*
healthy, with his tallow face, and breast-bone caved in. Why,
the woman that marries him can use his ribs for a wash-board,
when she's lost her'n. Then there was Absalom Merryfield,
you know, killed himself out and out, he was so keerful o' *his*
health. I'd ruther have no health at all, a darned sight, than
worry my life out, thinkin' on it. Not that I could'nt give
up chawin' tobacco, or any thing else, if there was a good
reason for it. What is it to you, Carrie, whether I chaw or
not?"

Miss Dilworth very well understood Bute's meaning, but
let it go without notice, as he knew she would. The truth is,
she was not insensible to his many good qualities, but she was
ambitious of higher game. She had not attended all the meetings held in Ptolemy, in favor of Temperance, Anti-Slavery

and Women's Rights, without imbibing as much conceit as the basis of her small mind could support. The expressions which, from frequent repetition, she had caught and retained, were put to such constant use, that she at last fancied them half original, and sighed for a more important sphere than that of a sempstress, or even a teacher. She knew she could never become a speaker—she was sure of that—but might she not be selected by some orator of Reform, as a kindred soul, to support him with her sympathy and appreciation? Thus far, however, her drooping lids had been lifted and her curls elaborately tangled, in vain. The eloquent disciples, not understanding these mute appeals, passed by on the other side.

She drew the conversation back to Mr. Woodbury, and kept it to that theme until she had ascertained all that Bute knew, or was willing to tell; for the latter had such a strong sense of propriety about matters of this kind, as might have inspired doubts of his being a native-born American. By this time they had reached the bridge over East Atauga Creek, whence it was but a short distance to the village.

"There is Friend Thurston's cottage, at last," said Miss Dilworth. "Have you seen Miss Hannah lately? But, of course, she can't visit Lakeside now."

"I'm sorry for it," Bute remarked. "She's a fine woman, in spite of her notions. But why can't she?"

"It would not be proper."

"Wouldn't it be proper for a man to visit us?"

"To be sure. How queer you talk, Bute!"

"Well—she says a woman should be allowed to do whatever a man does. If Women's Rights is worth talkin' about, it's worth carryin' out. But I guess Miss Hannah's more of a woman than she knows on. I like to hear her talk, mighty well, and she says a good many things that I can't answer, but they're ag'in nature, for all that. If she was married and had a family growin' up 'round her, she wouldn't want to be a lawyer or a preacher. Here we are, at the gate. Good-by, Miss Carrie!"

"Good-by, Bute!" said Miss Dilworth, mechanically, pausing at the gate to see him spring into the saddle and trot rapidly down the street. She was confounded, and a little angry, at the nonchalance with which he treated her oracle. "I wish it had been Hannah Thurston, instead of me," she said to herself, with a spiteful toss of her head—"she has an answer ready for everybody."

The plot of ground in front of the cottage already wore its winter livery. The roses were converted into little obelisks of straw, the flower-beds were warmly covered, and only the clumps of arbor-vitæ and the solitary balsam-fir were allowed to display their hardy green. Miss Dilworth passed around the house to the kitchen entrance, for she knew the fondness of the inmates for warmth and sunshine, and the sitting-room which they habitually occupied looked southward, over the vegetable garden, to the meadows of the eastern valley. Every thing was scrupulously neat and ordered. The tops of vegetables left for seed and the dead stalks of summer flowers had been carefully removed from the garden. The walks had been swept by a broom, and the wood-shed, elsewhere more or less chaotic in its appearance, was here visited by the same implement. Its scattered chips seemed to have arranged themselves into harmonious forms, like the atoms of sand under the influence of musical tones.

In the kitchen a girl of thirteen—the only servant the house afforded—was watching the kettles and pans on the cooking-stove. This operation might have been carried on in the parlor just as well, so little appearance was there of the usual "slops" and litter of a kitchen. This was Friend Thurston's specialty as a housekeeper—her maxim was, that there should be no part of a house where a visitor might not be received. Her neighbors always spoke of her kitchen with an admiration wherein there was a slight mixture of despair.

The sitting-room, beyond, was made cheerful by windows opening to the south and east; but more so by the homely simplicity and comfort of its arrangement. Every object spoke of limited means, but nothing of pinched self-denial. The motley-colored rag carpet was clean, thick, and warm; the chintz sofa was relieved by inviting cushions; the old-fashioned rocking-chair was so stuffed and padded as to remedy its stiffness; the windows were curtained, and a few brands were smouldering among white ashes in the grate. A shelf inside the southern window-held some tea-roses in pots, mignionette, heliotrope, and scarlet verbenas. There were but three pictures— a head of Milton, an old wood-engraving of the cottage where George Fox was born, and a tolerable copy of the Madonna della Seggiola. On a stand in the corner were the favorite volumes of the old lady, very plainly bound, as was meet, in calf of a drab color—Job Scott's Works, Woolman's Journal, and William Penn's "No Cross, No Crown." A swinging book-shelf, suspended on the wall, contained a different collection, which evidently belonged to the daughter. Several volumes of Carlyle, Margaret Fuller, Shelley, Bettina von Arnim, De Staël's "Corinne," the "Record of Woman," Milton, George Sands' "Consuelo," Mrs. Child's "Letters from New York," Hugh Miller, and bound numbers of the "Liberty Bell," were among them. Had a certain drawer been opened, one would have found files of *The Slavery Annihilator*, Mrs. Swisshelm's *Saturday Visitor*, and the weekly edition of the *New-York Tribune*. A rude vase of birch bark, on a bracket, was filled with a mass of flowering grasses, exquisitely arranged with regard to their forms and colors, from pale green and golden-gray to the loveliest browns and purples. This object was a work of art, in its way, and shed a gleam of beauty over the plainness of the apartment.

Friend Gulielma Thurston, leaning back in the rocking-chair, had suffered her hands, with the knitting they held, to sink into her lap, and looked out upon the hazy valley. Her thin face, framed in the close Quaker cap, which barely allowed her gray hair to appear at the temples, wore a sweet, placid expression, though the sunken eyes and set lips told of physical suffering. The spotless book-muslin handkerchief, many-folded, covered her neck and breast, and a worsted apron was tied over her drab gown, rather from habit than use. As she basked in the balmy warmth of the day, her wasted fingers unconsciously clasped themselves in a manner that expressed patience and trust. These were the prominent qualities of her nature— the secret of her cheerfulness and the source of her courage.

Late married, she had lost her first child, and shortly after the birth of her daughter Hannah, her husband also. The latter was a stern, silent man, rigid in creed and in discipline, but with a concealed capacity for passion which she had not understood while she possessed him. Her mind first matured in the sorrow of his loss, and she became, from that natural need which is content with no narrower comfort, a speaker in the meetings of her sect. The property she inherited at her husband's death was very small, and she was obliged to labor beyond her strength, until the bequest of an unmarried brother relieved her from pressing want. Hannah, to whom she had managed to give a tolerably thorough education, obtained a situation as teacher, for which she proved so competent that a liberal offer from the Trustees of the Young Ladies' Seminary at Ptolemy induced both mother and daughter to remove thither. Her earnings, added to the carefully husbanded property, finally became sufficient to insure them a modest support, so that, when her mother's failing health obliged Hannah to give up her place, there was no serious anxiety for the future to interfere with her filial duty.

The daughter was seated at the eastern window, beside a small table, which was covered with gorgeously tinted autumn leaves. She was occupied in arranging them in wreaths and groups, on sheets of card-board, which were designed to form an album, and to wear, as binding, the embroidery of fern-leaves, upon which we first found her engaged. Such an album, contributed by her to the Anti-Slavery Fair, the previous year, had enriched the treasury of the Society by the sum of ten dollars, and the managers had begged a second donation of the same kind.

3*

Catching a glimpse of Miss Dilworth through the window, she rose to receive her. In stature, she was somewhat above the average height of women, though not noticeably tall, and a little too slender for beauty. Her hands were thin, but finely formed, and she carried them as if they were a conscious portion of herself, not an awkward attachment. Her face would have been a perfect oval, except that the forehead, instead of being low and softly rounded, was rather squarely developed in the reflective region, and the cheeks, though not thin, lacked the proper fulness of outline. Her hair was of a rich, dark-brown, black in shadow, and the delicate arches of the eye-brows were drawn with a clear, even pencil, above the earnest gray eyes, dark and deep under the shadow of their long lashes. The nose was faultless, and the lips, although no longer wearing their maidenly ripeness and bloom, were so pure in outline, so sweetly firm in their closing junction, so lovely in their varying play of expression, that the life of her face seemed to dwell in them alone. Her smile had a rare benignity and beauty. The paleness of her face, being, to some extent, a feature of her physical temperament, did not convey the impression of impaired health: a ruddy tint would not have harmonized with the spiritual and sensitive character of her countenance. No one would have dreamed of calling Hannah Thurston a beauty. In society nine men would have passed her without a thought; but the tenth would have stood still, and said: "Here is a woman 'to sit at a king's right hand, in thunder-storms,'" and would have carried her face in his memory forever.

The severest test of a woman is to play an exceptional part in the world. Her respect, her dignity, her virtue itself, become doubtful, if not mythical, in the eyes of men. In the small circle of Ptolemy, Hannah Thurston had subjected herself to this test, and it was no slight triumph for her, had she known it, that, while her views were received with either horror or contempt, while the names of her fellow priestesses or prophetesses were bandied about in utter disrespect, she was never personally ridiculed. No tongue dared to whisper an insinuation against either her sincerity or her purity. This, however, was partly owing to the circumstances of her life in the place. She had first achieved popularity as a teacher, and honor as a daughter. Among other things, it was generally reported and believed that she had declined an offer of marriage, advantageous in a worldly point of view, and the act was set down to her credit as wholly one of duty towards her mother.

In her plain brown dress, with linen collar and cuffs, the only ornament being a knot of blue ribbon at the throat, she also, appeared to be a Quakeress; yet, she had long since perceived that the external forms of the sect had become obsolete, and no longer considered herself bound by them. Some concession in dress, however, was still due for her mother's sake, beyond whose rapidly shortening span of life she could see no aim in her own, unless it were devoted to righting the wrongs of her sex. She had had her girlish dreams; but the next birthday was her thirtieth, and she had already crossed, in resolve, that deep gulf in a woman's life.

Miss Caroline Dilworth, in her blue dress, came as if dipped in the Indian Summer, with a beryl gleam in her eyes, as she darted into the sitting-room. She caught Hannah Thurston around the waist, and kissed her twice: she was never known to greet her female friends with less. Then, leaning gently over the rocking-chair, she took the old woman's hand.

"Take off thy bonnet, child," said the latter, "and push thy hair back, so that I can see thy face. I'm glad thee's come."

"Oh, Friend Thurston, I was so afraid I couldn't get away from Parkman's. It's a lonely place, you know, over the hill, and she's hard of hearing. Ah! I'm out of breath, yet"—and therewith heaving a sigh of relief, the little creature threw off her shawl and untied the strings of her bonnet.

Their life had so much in it that was grave and earnest—their conversation naturally turning to the past rather than the future—that the Thurstons always felt themselves cheered by Miss Dilworth's visits. She dropped her affectations in their presence, and became, for the time, a light-hearted, amiable, silly woman. She never arrived without a fresh budget of gossip, generally of slight importance, but made piquant by her rattling way of telling it.

"How thee does run on!" Friend Thurston would sometimes say, whereupon the sempstress would only toss her curls and run on all the more inveterately.

"Oh, I must tell you all about Lakeside and the new owner!" she exclaimed, as she settled herself into a chair.

Hannah Thurston could probably have told her more about Mr. Woodbury than she already knew; but it would have been unkind to cut short the eager narrative, and so Bute's report, with many additions and variations, was served out to them in chapters, during the afternoon.

CHAPTER V.

IN WHICH MR. WOODBURY HEARS A WOMAN SPEAK.

In his intercourse with the society of his new home, Woodbury found fewer distasteful circumstances to be overlooked, than he had at first feared. The novelty of the experience had its charm, and, as his mind recovered something of that active interest in men which he had almost unlearned, he was surprised to find how vital and absorbing his relations with them became. From the very earnestness of his views, however, he was reticent in the expression of them, and could with difficulty accustom himself to the discussion, in mixed society, of subjects which are usually only broached in the confidential intimacy of friends. Not merely "Fate, free-will, foreknowledge absolute," but the privacy of individual faiths, doubts, and aspirations, became themes of discussion; even the shrinking sanctity of love was invaded, and the ability to converse fluently was taken by the community of Ptolemy as a sign of capacity to feel deeply on these subjects.

At the dinners and evening parties of the English, an intellectual as well as a social propriety is strictly observed, and the man who makes a habit of producing for general inspection, his religious convictions or his moral experiences, is speedily voted a bore. Maxwell Woodbury, whose long residence in Calcutta had fixed his habits, in this respect, was at first more amused than shocked, at the *abandon* with which spiritual intimacies were exchanged, in the society of Ptolemy. He soon learned, however, that much of this talk was merely a superficial sentimentalism, and that the true sanctities of the speakers'

hearts were violated more in appearance than in fact. Nevertheless, he felt no inclination to take part in conversation of
this character, and fell into the habit of assuming a mystical,
paradoxical tone, whenever he was forcibly drawn into the
discussion. Sometimes, indeed, he was tempted to take the
opposite side of the views advocated, simply in order to extort
more reckless and vehement utterances from their defenders.
It is not surprising, therefore, that his lack of earnestness,—as
it seemed to the others—was attributed by many to a stolid
indifference to humanity. Seth Wattles even went so far as
to say: "I should not wonder if he had made his money in
the accursed opium traffic."

The two topics which, for him, possessed an intrinsically repellant character, happened to be those which were at that
time most actively discussed: Spiritualism and Women's
Rights. He had seen the slight-of-hand of the Indian jugglers,
far more wonderful than any feats supernaturally performed
in the presence of mediums, and the professed communications
from the world of spirits struck him as being more inane
twaddle than that which fell from the lips of the living believers. He had not lived thirty-six years without as much
knowledge of woman as a single man may profitably acquire;
and the better he knew the sex, the more tender and profound
became his regard. To him, in his strength, however, the relation of protector was indispensable; the rudest blows of life
must first fall upon his shield. The idea of an independent
strength, existing side by side with his, yet without requiring
its support, was unnatural and repulsive. Aunt Dennison, in
her noble self-abnegation as wife and mother, was more queenly
in his eyes, than Mary Wollstonecraft or Madame de Staël.
It was difficult for him to believe how any truly refined and
feminine woman could claim for her sex a share in the special
occupations of man.

There is always a perverse fate which attracts one into the
very situations he wishes to avoid. On the evening when the
Sewing-Union met at Merryfield's, Woodbury happened to be

drawn into a group which contained Mrs. Waldo, Hannah Thurston, and the host. The latter was speaking of a plan for a Female Medical College.

"It is the first step," said he, "and its success will overthrow the dynasty of ideas, under which woman has been crushed, as it were." The phrase: "dynasty of ideas," he had borrowed from a recent lecturer.

"Well", said Mrs. Waldo, musingly, "if it went no further I should not have much to say against it, for we know that women are the best nurses, and they *may* make tolerable doctors. But I should prefer that somebody else than myself made the beginning."

"You are right," remarked Woodbury ; "it is not pleasant to think of a woman standing at a dissecting-table, with a scalpel in her hand, and a quarter of a subject before her."

Hannah Thurston shuddered inwardly, but at once took up the gauntlet. "Why not?" she asked. "Are not women capable of this, and more than this, for the sake of knowledge that will enable them to do good? Or is it because their minds are too weak to grapple with the mysteries of science?"

Woodbury, to avoid a discussion to which he was so strongly averse, assumed a gay, bantering tone. "In the presence of ladies," he said, smiling, and partly directing his words to Mrs. Waldo, "there is only one way of answering the latter question."

Hannah Thurston was of too earnest a nature to endure trifling—for such seemed his reply. Her gray eyes kindled with an emotion a very little milder than contempt. "So!" she exclaimed, "we must still endure the degradation of hollow compliment. We are still children, and our noise can be quieted with sugar-plums!"

"I beg your pardon, Miss Thurston!" Woodbury gravely answered. "My apparent disrespect was but a shift to avoid discussing a subject which I have never seriously considered, and which, I will only say, seems to me a matter of instinct rather than of argument. Besides," he added, "I believe

Mrs. Waldo, as our dictatress, prohibits debate on these occasions."

The lady referred to immediately came to his assistance. "I *do* prohibit it;" said she, with a magisterial wave of the hand; "and you cannot object to my authority, Hannah, since you have a chance to defend our sex, and cover with confusion all such incorrigible bachelors as Mr. Woodbury, on Thursday next. I'm sure he's a misanthrope, or—mis—whatever you call it."

"A misogynist?" Woodbury gayly suggested. "No, no, Mrs. Waldo. Do not you, as a clergyman's wife, know that there may be a devotional feeling so profound as to find the pale of any one sect too narrow?"

Hannah Thurston looked earnestly at the speaker. What did he mean?—was that also jest? she asked herself. She was unaccustomed to such mental self-possession. Most of the men she knew would have answered her with spirit, considering that to decline a challenge thrown down by a woman was equivalent to acknowledging the intellectual equality of the sexes—this being the assertion which they most strenuously resisted. Mr. Woodbury, however, had withdrawn as a matter of taste and courtesy. She had given him the opportunity of doing so, a little to her own discomfiture, and was conscious that her self-esteem was wounded by the result. She could not quite forgive him for this, though his manner, she felt, compelled respect. At the risk of having her silence misinterpreted, she made no reply.

Woodbury, who had not understood Mrs. Waldo's allusion, took an opportunity, later in the evening, to ask for an explanation.

"I thought you had heard," said she. "There is to be a meeting in favor of Women's Rights, on Thursday afternoon, at the Hall, in Ptolemy. Mr. Bemis, the great advocate of the reform, is to be there, and I believe they expect Bessie Stryker."

"Who is Bess'e Stryker?"

"Mr. Woodbury! It's well you did not ask Hannah Thurston that question. You've been out of the country—I had forgotten that; but I should think you must have heard of her in Calcutta. She has travelled all over the country, lecturing on the subject, and has made such a name as a speaker that everybody goes to hear her. She is quite pretty, and wears the new Bloomer dress."

"Really, you excite my curiosity. I must attend this meeting, if only to show Miss Thurston that I am above the vulgar prejudice which I presume she imputes to me."

"Oh, no, Mr. Woodbury. Hannah Thurston is not unjust, whatever faults she may have. But you should know that she has a dislike—morbid, it seems to me—of the compliments which you men generally pay to us women. For my part, I see no harm in them."

"Both of you, at least, are candid," replied Woodbury, laughing, "and that trait, with me, covers a multitude of weaknesses."

Woodbury went to the meeting on the following Thursday, much as he would have attended a Brahminical festival in honor of the Goddess Unna-Purna. He felt no particular interest in the subject to be treated, except a curiosity to know how it could be rendered plausible to a semi-intelligent auditory. Of Ptolemy, privately and socially, he had seen something, but he had not yet mingled with Ptolemy in public.

"The Hall," as it was called (being the only one in the place), was a brick building, situated on the principal street. Its true name was Tumblety Hall, from the builder and owner, Mr. Jabez Tumblety, who had generously bestowed his name upon it in consideration of receiving ten per cent. on his investment, from the lease of it to phrenologists, the dancing school, Ethiopian Minstrels, exhibitors of laughing gas, lecturers on anatomy (the last lecture exclusively for gentlemen), jugglers, temperance meetings, caucuses of the Hunkers and Barnburners, and, on Sundays, to the Bethesdeans in the

morning and the Spiritualists in the evening.   Its internal
aspect was rather shabby.   The roughly-plastered walls offered
too great a temptation for the pencils and charcoal of un-
fledged artists, when bored by a windy orator.   Various
grotesque heads, accompanied by names and dates, made up
for the absence of frescoes, but the talent thus displayed did
not seem to be appreciated, for under some of them was
written, in a later hand : " he is a fool."   The benches were
of unpainted pine, with long back-rails, which, where they
had not been split off by the weight of the leaning crowd,
were jagged with whittled notches.   Along the further end
of the hall ran a platform, raised three feet above the floor,
and containing a table, three arm-chairs, and two settees.   The
floor might have been swept, but had not recently been
washed, to judge from the stains of tobacco-juice by which it
was mottled.

When Woodbury entered, the seats were nearly all occupied, an audience of five hundred persons being in attendance.
Most of them were evidently from the country ; some, indeed,
who were favorably inclined to the cause, had come from Mulligansville and Atauga City.   All the loafers of Ptolemy were
there, of course, and occupied good seats.   The few members
of the respectable, conservative, moneyed class, whose curiosity
drew them in, lingered near the door, on the edges of the
crowd, in order that they might leave whenever so disposed,
without attracting attention to their presence.

Mr. Merryfield occupied the middle chair on the platform,
with a heavy-faced, bald-templed, belligerent looking gentleman
on his right, and a middle-aged lady in black silk, on his left.
The settees were also occupied by persons of both sexes who
were interested in the cause.   Among them was Hannah
Thurston.

A whispered consultation was carried on for some time
among the party on the platform, the belligerent gentleman
evidently having the most to say.   Finally Mr. Merryfield
arose, thumped upon the table, and after waiting a minute

for the "*shs!*" to subside, announced: "The meeting will now come to order!"

The meeting being already in order, no effect was produced by this announcement.

"As we have assembled together, as it were," he continued, "principally to listen to the noble advocates of the glorious cause who are to appear before us, my friends suggest that—that there should be no—that we should dispense, as it were, with a regular organization, and proceed to listen to their voices. The only—I would suggest, if the meeting is willing, that we should appoint—that is, that a committee should be named, as it were, to draw up resolutions expressing their—our sense on the subject of Women's Rights. Perhaps," he added, turning around, "some one will make the motion."

"I move that a committee of six be appointed!" "I second the motion!" were heard, almost simultaneously.

"Those in favor of that motion will signify their assent by saying 'Aye!'" said Mr. Merryfield.

"Aye!" rang through the house with startling unanimity, all the boys expressing their enthusiastic assent.

"Contrary—'No!'"

Dead silence.

"The Ayes have it. Who shall the Committee be composed of."

"Both sexes must be represented. Three men and three women," said the belligerent gentleman, suddenly, half rising from his seat.

In a short time the members of the Committee were appointed, and, there being no further business on hand, Mr. Merryfield said: "I have now the pleasure, as it were, of introducing to the audience the noble advocate of Women's Rights, Isaiah Bemis, who—whose name is—is well known to you all as the champion of his—I mean, her—persecuted sex." Mr. Merryfield was so disconcerted by the half-suppressed laughter which followed this blunder, that the termination of his eulogium became still more confused. "The name of Isaiah Bemis," he said, "does not need my condem—commendation. When Woman shall fill her true spere, it will shine—will be written among the martyrs of Reform, as it were, for Truth, crushed to Earth, rises up in spite of—of—though the heavens fall!"

Mr. Bemis, who was no other than the gentleman of belligerent aspect, already mentioned, at once arose, bowing gravely in answer to a slight, hesitating, uncertain sound of applause. The Ptolemy public had not listened for years to speakers of all kinds, and on all subjects, without acquiring some degree of critical perception. They both enjoyed and prided themselves on their acumen, and a new man, whatever his doctrines might be, was sure that he would find a full house to receive him. If he possessed either eloquence or humor, in any appreciable degree, he had no reason to complain of his reception. The class of hearers to which we refer did not consider themselves committed to the speaker's views by their manifestations of applause. Off the platform, there were not twenty advocates of Women's Rights in the whole audience, yet all were ready to hear Mr. Bemis, and to approve a good thing, if he should happen to say it.

A few minutes, however, satisfied them that he was not the kind of speaker they coveted. He took for his text that maxim of the Declaration of Independence, that "all governments derive their just powers from the consent of the governed," first proved the absolute justice of the theory, and then exhibited the flagrant violation of it in the case of woman. She is equally obliged, with man, to submit to the laws, he said, but has no voice in making them; even those laws which control her property, her earnings, her children, her person itself, are enacted without consultation with her. She not only loses her name, but her individual privileges are curtailed, as if she belonged to an inferior order of beings. The character of his harangue was aggressive throughout. He referred as little as possible, to any inherent difference in the destinies of sex; men and women were simply human beings, and in Society, and Law, and Government, there should be no distinction made between them. There was a certain specious display of logic in his address; the faulty links were glozed over, so that his chain of argument appeared sound and strong, from end to end. Granting his premises, indeed, which he assumed with an air, as if they were beyond dispute—all the rest readily followed. Those who believed with him, not perceiving the defect in his basis, were charmed with the force and clearness of his views.

A crowd feels, not reasons, and the auditors, after an hour of this talk, began to manifest signs of weariness. Even Woodbury, to whom the whole scene was a study—or, rather, a *show*—only kept his place from a desire to hear the famous Bessie Stryker.

Mr. Bemis at last sat down, and some further whispering ensued. There was a slight hitch in the proceedings, it was evident. In a few minutes, Mr. Merryfield again arose. "My friends," said he; "I regret to be able to state that we are disappointed, as it were, in listening—in the arrival of Bessie Stryker. We expected her in the afternoon stage coming from Cephalonia, and was to have lectured there last night, but has arrived without her. But I hope, nevertheless, that you will— that it will be agreeable to you, as it were, to hear a few words from our friend, Hannah Thurston, who requires—whom you know already."

Hearty signs of approbation greeted this announcement. Thus appealed to, Hannah Thurston, who at first made a movement of hesitation, rose, quietly removed her bonnet, and walked forward to the table. Her face seemed a little paler than usual, but her step was firm, and the hand which she placed upon the table did not tremble. After a pause, as if to collect and isolate her mind from external impressions, she commenced speaking, in a voice so low that only its silver purity of tone enabled her to be heard. Yet the slight tremulousness it betrayed indicated no faltering of courage; it was simply a vibration of nerves rather tensely strung.

"I will not repeat," she began, "the arguments by which

the eloquent speaker has illustrated the wrongs endured by
woman, under all governments and all systems of law, whether
despotic or republican. These are considerations which lie
further from us; we are most concerned for those injuries
which require an immediate remedy. When we have removed
the social prejudices which keep our sex in a false position—
when we have destroyed the faith of the people in the tyrannical traditions by which we are ruled—the chains of the law
will break of themselves. As a beginning to that end, woman
must claim an equal right to education, to employment, and reward. These are the first steps in our reform, to reach the
sources of those evils which cause our greatest suffering. We
can endure a little longer, to be deprived of the permission to
vote and to rule, because the denial is chiefly an assault upon
our intelligence; but we need now—at once—and, my friends,
I am pleading for millions who cannot speak for themselves—
we need an equal privilege with man, to work and to be justly
paid. The distinction which is made, to our prejudice, renders
us weak and helpless, compared with our brethren, to whom
all fields are open, and who may claim the compensation which
is justified by their labor, without incurring ridicule or contempt. They are even allowed to usurp branches which, if
the popular ideas of woman's weakness, and man's chivalry
towards her be true, should be left for us. Even admitting
that our sphere is limited—that there are only a few things
which we may properly do—is it generous, is it even just, that
man, who has the whole range of life to choose from, should
crowd us out from these few chances of earning our bread?
Or to force us to perform the same labor for a smaller remu-
neration, because we are women? Could we not measure a
yard of calico as rapidly, or choose a shade of zephyr as correctly as the elegant young men who stand behind the coun-
ter? With our more sensitive physical organization, might
not all tasks requiring quickness, nicety of touch, and careful
arrangement, be safely confided to our hands?"

At this point the audience, which had quite lost its air of

weariness, broke into subdued but cordial applause. Hannah Thurston's voice, as she acquired possession of her subject, increased in strength, but at no time appeared to rise above a conversational tone. Her manner also, was simply conversational. The left hand slightly touched the table, as if she only wished to feel a support at hand, not use it; while she now and then, involuntarily, made a simple movement with the right. The impression she produced was that of a woman compelled by some powerful necessity or duty to appear before a public assembly, not of one who coveted and enjoyed the position. Woodbury was profoundly interested in the speaker, and in her words. Both were equally new to him.

"What we *now* ask, therefore, my friends," she continued, "is that the simple justice be meted out to us, which we feel that man—without adopting any of our views concerning the true position of woman—is bound to give. We ask that his boasted chivalry be put into practice, not merely in escorting us to concerts, or giving us his seat in a railroad-car, or serving us first at the table—or in all other ways by which the reputation of chivalry and gallantry towards our sex is earned at little cost; but in leaving open to us those places which he confesses we are fitted to fill—in paying us, as teachers, clerks, tailors, or operatives, the same wages for the same work which men do!"

This was so simply and fairly stated, that the audience again heartily approved. There was nothing, in fact, of the peculiar doctrines of Women's Rights in what she said—nothing to which they could not have individually assented, without compromising their position in regard to the main point. Mr. Bemis, however, drew down his heavy brows, and whispered to the chairman: "Very good, so far as it goes, but timidly stated. We must strike the evil at its root."

After dwelling for some time on this aspect of the question, and illustrating it by a number of examples, Hannah Thurston went a step further.

"But we deny," she said, "that Man has any natural right

to prescribe the bounds within which Woman may labor and live. God alone has that right, and His laws govern both sexes with the same authority. Man has indeed assumed it, because he disbelieves in the intellectual equality of women. He has treated her as an older child, to whom a certain amount of freedom might be allowed, but whom it was not safe to release entirely from his guardianship. He has educated her in this belief, through all the ages that have gone by since the creation of the world. Now and then, women have arisen, it is true, to vindicate the equal authority of their sex, and have nobly won their places in history; but the growth of the truth has been slow—so slow, that to-day, in this enlightened maturity of the world, we must plead and prove all that which you should grant without our asking. It is humiliating that a woman is obliged to collect evidence to convince men of her equal intelligence. She, who is also included in the one word, Man! Placed side by side with him in Paradise—Mother of the Saviour who came to redeem his fallen race—first and holiests among the martyrs and saints! Young men! Think of your own mothers, and spare us this humiliation!"

These words, uttered with startling earnestness, produced a marked sensation in the audience. Perhaps it was a peculiarity springing from her Quaker descent, that the speaker's voice gradually assumed the character of a musical recitative, becoming a clear, tremulous chant, almost in monotone. This gave it a sad, appealing expression, which touched the emotional nature of the hearer, and clouded his judgment for the time being. After a pause, she continued in her ordinary tone:

"The pages of history do not prove the superiority of man. When we consider the position which he has forced woman to occupy, we should rather wonder that she has so often resisted his authority, and won possession of the empire which he had appropriated to himself. In the earliest ages he admitted her capacity to govern, a power so high and important in its nature, that we should be justified in claiming that it embraces

all other capacities, and in resting our defence on that alone.
Such women as Semiramis and Zenobia, Margaret of Denmark,
and Elizabeth of England, Maria Theresa, and Catharine of
Russia, are not the least—not second, even—among great
rulers. Jael and Judith, and the Maid of Orleans stand no
less high among the deliverers of nations, than Leonidas and
William Tell. The first poet who sang may have been Homer,
but the second was Sappho.* Even in the schools of Philosophy, the ancients had their Hypatia, and the scholars of the
Middle Ages honored the learning of Olympia Morata. Men
claim the field of scientific research as being exclusively their
own; but the names of Caroline Herschel in England, and
Maria Mitchell in America, prove that even here women cannot justly be excluded. Ah, my friends! when God calls a
human being to be the discoverer of His eternal laws, or the
illustrator of His eternal beauty, He does not stop to consider
the question of sex! If you grant human intellect at all to
Woman, you must grant the possibility of inspiration, of genius, of a life divinely selected as the instrument of some great
and glorious work. Admitting this, you may safely throw
open to us all avenues to knowledge. Hampered as Woman
still is—circumscribed in her spheres of action and thought
(for her false education permanently distorts her habits of
mind)—she is yet, at present, far above the Saxon bondmen
from whom the most of you are descended. You know that
she has risen thus far, not only without injury to herself, but
to *your* advantage: why check her progress, here? Nay, why
check it any where? If Man's dominion be thereby limited,
would his head be less uneasy, if the crown he claims were
shared with another? Is not a friend better than a servant?
If Marriage were a *partnership* for Woman, instead of a *clerkship*, the Head of the House would feel his burthen so much
the lighter. If the physician's wife were competent to prepare
his medicines, or the merchant's to keep his books, or the law-

---

* Miss Thurston makes these statements on her own responsibility.

4

yer's to draw up a bond, the gain would be mutual. For Woman, to be a true helpmeet to Man, must know all that Man knows; and, even as she is co-heir with him of Heaven—receiving, not the legal 'Third part,' but *all* of its infinite blessedness,—so she should be co-proprietor of the Earth, equally armed to subdue its iniquities, and prepare it for a better future!"

With these words, Hannah Thurston closed her address. As she quietly walked back to her seat and resumed her bonnet, there was a stir of satisfaction among the audience, terminating in a round of applause, which, however, she did not acknowledge in any way. Although, in no part of the discourse, had she touched the profounder aspects of the subject, especially the moral distinctions of sex, she had given utterance to many absolute truths, which were too intimately connected, in her mind, with the doctrine she had adopted, for her to perceive their real independence of it. Thus, most of her hearers, while compelled to agree with her in many respects, still felt themselves unconvinced in the main particular. She was not aware of her own inability to discuss the question freely, and ascribed to indifference or prejudice that reluctance among men, which really sprang from their generous consideration for her sex.

As for Woodbury, he had listened with an awakened interest in her views, which, for the time, drew his attention from the speaker's personality. Her first appearance had excited a singular feeling of compassion—partly for the trial which, he fancied, she must undergo, and partly for the mental delusion which was its cause. It was some time before he was reassured by her calmness and self-possession. At the close, he was surprised to discover in himself a lurking sensation of regret that she had not spoken at greater length. "I was wrong the other night," he thought. "This woman is in severe earnest, and would have been less offended if I had plumply declined her challenge, instead of evading it. I have yet something to learn from these people."

The Committee of Six now made their report. Seth Wattles, who was one of the number, and had assumed to himself the office of Chairman, read a string of Resolutions, setting forth, That : Whereas, this is an Age of Progress, and no reform should be overlooked in the Great Battle for the Right : Therefore, Resolved—That we recognize in this movement for the Equal Rights of Woman a cause without the support of which no other cause can be permanently successful : and, Resolved, That we will in every way help forward the good work, by the Dissemination of Light and Information, tending to set forth the claims of Woman before the Community : also, Resolved, That we will circulate petitions to the State Legislature, for the investment of Woman with all civil and political rights : and, lastly, Resolved, That, we will use our best endeavors to increase the circulation of *The Monthly Hollyhock*, a journal devoted to the cause of Women's Rights.

Mr. Merryfield arose and inquired : "Shall the Report of the Committee be adopted ?" He fortunately checked himself in time not to add : "as it were."

"I move its adoption !" "I second the motion !" were immediately heard from the platform.

"All who are in favor of adopting the Resolutions we have just heard read, will signify their assent by saying 'Aye !'"

A scattering, irregular fire of "Ayes" arose in reply. The boys felt that their sanction would be out of place on this occasion, with the exception of two or three, who hazarded their voices, in the belief that they would not be remarked, in the general vote. To their dismay, they launched themselves into an interval of silence, and their shrill pipes drew all eyes to their quarter of the house.

"Contrary,—'No !'"

The opponents of the movement, considering that this was not *their* meeting, refrained from voting.

"Before the meeting adjourns," said Mr. Merryfield, again rising, "I must—I take the liberty to hope, as it were, that the truths we have heard this day may spread—may sink deeply into our hearts. We expect to be able to announce, before long, a visit from Bessie Stryker, whose failure—whom we have missed from among our eleg—eloquent champions. But we trust she is elsewhere, and our loss is their gain. I thank the audience for your attendance—attention, I should say, and approbation of our glorious reform. As there is no further business before the meeting, and our friends from Mulligansville and Atauga City have some distance to return home, we will now adjourn in time to reach their destination."

At this hint the audience rose, and began to crowd out the narrow door-way and down the steep staircase. Woodbury, pushed and hustled along with the rest, was amused at the remarks of the crowd: "He?—oh, he's a gassy old fellow!" "Well, there's a good deal of truth in it!" "Bessie Stryker? I'd rather hear Hannah Thurston any day!" "He didn't half like it!" "She has a better right to say such things than he has!"—and various other exclamations, the aggregate of which led him to infer that the audience felt no particular interest in the subject of Women's Rights, but had a kindly personal feeling towards Hannah Thurston.

CHAPTER VI.

IN WHICH LAKESIDE BECOMES LIVELY.

WINTER at last set in—the steady winter of Central New York, where the snow which falls at the beginning of December usually covers the ground until March. Ptolemy, at least, which lies upon the northern side of the watershed between the Susquehanna and the rivers which flow into Lake Ontario, has a much less variable winter temperature than the great valley, lying some thirty miles to the southward. Atauga Lake, in common with Cayuga and Seneca, never freezes, except across the shallows at its southern end; but its waters, so piercingly cold that they seem to cut the skin like the blade of a knife, have no power to soften the northern winds. The bottoms between Ptolemy and the lake, and also, in fact, the Eastern and Western Valleys, for some miles behind the village, are open to the North; and those sunny winter days which, in more sheltered localities, breathe away the snow, here barely succeed in softening it a little. On the hills it is even too deep for pleasure. As soon as a highway has been broken through the drifts, the heavy wood-sleds commence running, and very soon wear it into a succession of abrupt hollows, over which the light cutters go pitching like their nautical namesakes in a chopping sea.

Woodbury, in obedience to a promise exacted by his sister, went to New York for the holidays, and, as might have been anticipated, became entangled in a succession of social engagements, which detained him until the middle of January. He soon grew tired of acting as escort to his two pretty, but (it

must be confessed, in strict confidence), shallow nieces, whose
sole æsthetic taste was opera—and in opera, especially Verdi.
After a dozen nights of "darling Bosio," and "delightful Be-
neventano," and "all the rest of them," he would have been
glad to hear, as a change, even the "*Taza be-taza*" of the Hindoo nautch-girls. A season of eastern rains and muddy streets
made the city insupportable, and—greatly to the wonder of
his sister's family—he declined an invitation to the grand
Fifth Avenue ball of Mrs. Luther Leathers, in order to return
to the wilderness of Ptolemy.

Taking the New York and Erie express-train to the town
of Miranda, he there chartered a two-horse cutter, with an
Irish attachment, and set out early the next morning. He
had never before approached Ptolemy from this side, and the
journey had all the charm of a new region. It was a crisp,
clear day, the blood of the horses was quickened by the frosty
air, and the cutter slid rapidly and noiselessly over the well-
beaten track. With a wolf-skin robe on his knees, Woodbury
sat in luxurious warmth, and experienced a rare delight in
breathing the keen, electric crystal of the atmosphere. It was
many years since he had felt such an exquisite vigor of life
within him—such a nimble play of the aroused blood—such
lightness of heart, and hope, and courage ! The snow-crystals
sparkled in the sunshine, and the pure shoulders of the hills
before him shone like silver against the naked blue of the sky.
He sang aloud, one after another, the long-forgotten songs,
until his moustache turned to ice and hung upon his mouth
like the hasp of a padlock.

Rising out of the Southern valleys, he sped along, over the
cold, rolling uplands of the watershed, and reached Mulligansville towards noon. Here the road turned westward, and a
further drive of three miles brought him to the brink of the
long descent to East Atauga Creek. At this point, a superb
winter landscape was unfolded before him. Ptolemy, with its
spires, its one compactly-built, ambitious street, its scattered
houses and gardens, lay in the centre of the picture. On the

white floor of the valley were drawn, with almost painful sharpness and distinctness, the outlines of farm-houses, and barns, fences, isolated trees, and the winding lines of elm and alder which marked the courses of the streams. Beyond the mouth of the further valley rose the long, cultivated sweep of the western hill, flecked with dull-purple patches of pine forest. Northward, across the white meadows and the fringe of trees along Roaring Brook, rose the sunny knoll of Lakeside, sheltered by the dark woods behind, while further, stretching far away between the steep shores, gleamed the hard, steel-blue sheet of the lake. The air was so intensely clear that the distance was indicated only by a difference in the hue of objects, not by their diminished distinctness.

"By Jove! this is glorious!" exclaimed Woodbury, scarcely conscious that he spoke.

"Shure, an' it's a fine place, Surr!" said the Irish driver, appropriating the exclamation.

Shortly after commencing the descent, a wreck was descried ahead. A remnant of aristocracy—or, at least, a fondness for aristocratic privilege—still lingers among our republican people, and is manifested in its most offensive form, by the drivers of heavy teams. No one ever knew a lime-wagon or a wood-sled to give an inch of the road to a lighter vehicle. In this case, a sled, on its way down, had forced an ascending cutter to turn out into a deep drift, and in attempting to regain the track both shafts of the latter had been snapped off. The sled pursued its way, regardless of the ruin, and the occupants of the cutter, a gentleman and lady, were holding a consultation over their misfortune, when Woodbury came in sight of them. As the gentleman leading his horse back into the drift to give room, turned his face towards the approaching cutter, Woodbury recognized, projecting between ear-lappets of fur, the curiously-planted nose, the insufficient lips, and the prominent teeth, which belonged to the Rev. Mr. Waldo. The recognition was mutual.

"My dear, it is Mr. Woodbury!" the latter joyfully cried,

turning to the muffled lady. She instantly stood up in the
cutter, threw back her veil, and hailed the approaching deliverer:
" Help me, good Samaritan ! The Levite has wrecked me, and
the Priest has enough to do, to take care of himself !"

Woodbury stopped his team, sprang out, and took a survey
of the case. " It is not to be mended," said he ; " you must
crowd yourselves in with me, and we will drive on slowly, leading the horse."

" But I have to attend a funeral at Mulligansville—the child
of one of our members," said Mr. Waldo, " and there is no
time to lose. My dear, you must go back with Mr. Woodbury. Perhaps he can take the harness and robes. I will
ride on to Van Horn's, where I can borrow a saddle."

This arrangement was soon carried into effect. Mr. Waldo
mounted the bare-backed steed, and went off up the hill, thump-
ing his heels against the animal's sides. The broken shafts
were placed in the cutter, which was left " to be called for,"
and Mrs. Waldo took her seat beside Woodbury. She had
set out to attend the funeral, as a duty enjoined by her husband's office, and was not displeased to escape without damage
to her conscience.

" I'm glad you've got back, Mr. Woodbury," she said, as
they descended the hill. " We like to have our friends about
us, in the winter, and I assure you, you've been missed."

" It is pleasant to feel that I have already a place among
you," he answered. " What is the last piece of gossip ? Is
the Great Sewing-Union still in existence ?"

" Not quite on the old foundation. *Our* fair has been held
—by the bye, there I missed you. I fully depended on selling
you a quantity of articles. The Anti-Slavery Fair is over, too ;
but they are still working for the Jutnapore Mission, as there
is a chance of sending the articles direct to Madras, before
long ; and so the most of us still attend, and either assist them
or take our own private sewing with us."

" Where do you next meet ?"

" Ah, that's our principal trouble. We have exhausted all

the available houses, besides going twice to Bue's and Wilkinson's. Our parsonage is so small—a mere pigeon-house—that it's out of the question. I wish I had some of your empty rooms at Lakeside. Now, there's an idea! Capital! Confess that my weak feminine brain is good at resorts!"

"What is it?" Woodbury asked.

"Can't you guess? *You* shall entertain the Sewing-Union one evening. We will meet at Lakeside: it is just the thing!"

"Are you serious, Mrs. Waldo? I could not, of course, be so ungracious as to refuse, provided there is no impropriety in compliance. What would Ptolemy say to the plan?"

"I'll take charge of that!" she cried. "Impropriety! Are you not a steady, respectable Member of Society, I should like to know? If there's any thing set down against you, we must go to Calcutta to find it. And we are sure there are no trapdoors at Lakeside, or walled-up skeletons, or Blue Beard chambers. Besides, this isn't Mulligansville or Anacreon, and it is not necessary to be so very straight-laced. Oh yes, it is the very thing. As for the domestic preparations, count on my help, if it is needed."

"I am afraid," he replied, "that Mrs. Babb would resent any interference with her authority. In fact," he added, laughing, "I am not certain that it is safe to decide, without first consulting her."

"There, now!" rejoined Mrs. Waldo. "Do you remember what I once told you? Yes, you bachelors, who boast of your independence of woman, are the only real slaves to the sex. No wife is such a tyrant as a housekeeper. Not but what Mrs. Babb is a very honest, conscientious, proper sort of a person,—but she don't make a home, Mr. Woodbury. You should get married."

"That is easily said, Mrs. Waldo," he replied, with a laugh which covered, like a luxuriant summer vine, the entrance to a sighing cavern,—"easily said, and might be easily done, if one were allowed to choose a wife for her domestic qualities valued at so much per month."

4*

"Pshaw!" said she, with assumed contempt. "You are not a natural cynic, and have no right to be single, at your age, without a good reason."

"Perhaps there *is* a good reason, Mrs. Waldo. Few persons, I imagine, remain single from choice. I have lost the susceptibility of my younger days, but not the ideal of a true wedded life. I should not dare to take the only perfect woman in the world, unless I could be lover as well as husband. I sincerely wish my chances were better: but would you have me choose one of the shallow, showy creatures I have just been visiting, or one of your strong-minded orators, here in Ptolemy?"

Mrs. Waldo understood both the earnest tone of the speaker, and the veiled bitterness of his concluding words. She read his heart at a glance, thorough woman as she was, and honored him then, and forever thenceforth.

"You must not take my nonsense for more than it is worth, Mr. Woodbury," she answered softly. "Women at my age, when God denies them children, take to match-making, in the hope of fulfilling their mission by proxy. It is unselfish in us, at least. But, bless me! here we are, at the village. Remember, the Sewing-Union meets at Lakeside."

"As soon as the Autocrat Babb has spoken," said he, as he handed her out at the Cimmerian Parsonage, "I will send word, and then the matter will rest entirely in your hands."

"Mine? Oh, I am a female General Jackson—I take the responsibility!" she cried, gayly, as the cutter drove away.

Woodbury, welcomed at the gate of Lakeside by the cheery face of Bute Wilson, determined to broach the subject at once to the housekeeper. Mrs. Fortitude Babb was glad to see him again, but no expression thereof manifested itself in her countenance and words. Wiping her bony right-hand on her apron—she had been dusting the rooms, after sweeping—she took the one he offered, saying: "How's your health, Sir?" and then added: "I s'pose you've had a mighty fine time, while you was away?"

"Not so fine but that I'm glad to get home again," he answered. The word "home" satisfied Mrs. Babb's sense of justice. His sister, she was sure, was not the housekeeper she herself was, and it was only right that he should see and acknowledge the fact.

"I want your advice, Mrs. Babb," Woodbury continued. "The Sewing-Union propose to meet here, one evening. They have gone the round of all the large houses in Ptolemy, and there seems to be no other place left. Since I have settled in Lakeside, I must be neighborly, you know. Could we manage to entertain them?"

"Well—comin' so suddent, like, I don't hardly know what to think. Things has been quiet here for a long time:" the housekeeper grimly remarked, with a wheezy sigh.

"That is true," said Woodbury; "and of course you must have help."

"No!" she exclaimed, with energy, "I don't want no help—leastways only Melindy. The rooms must be put to rights—not but what they're as good as Mrs. Bue's any day; and there'll be supper for a matter o' twenty; and cakes and things. When is it to be?"

"Next Friday, I presume; but can you get along without more assistance?"

"'Taint every one that would do it," replied Mrs. Babb, "There's sich a settin' to rights, afterwards. But I can't have strange help mixin' in, and things goin' wrong, and me to have the credit of it. Melindy's used to my ways, and there's not many others that knows what housekeepin' is. *Sich* a mess as *some* people makes of it!"

Secretly, Mrs. Babb was well pleased at the opportunity of publicly displaying her abilities, but it was not in her nature to do any thing out of the regular course of her housekeeping, without having it understood that she was making a great sacrifice. She was not so unreasonable as to set herself up for an independent power, but she stoutly demanded and maintained the rights of a belligerent. This point having once been conceded, however, she exhibited a wonderful energy in making the necessary preparations.

Thanks to Mrs. Waldo, all Ptolemy soon knew of the arrangement, and, as the invitation was general, nearly everybody decided to accept it. Few persons had visited Lakeside since Mrs. Dennison's funeral, and there was some curiosity to know what changes had been made by the new owner. Besides, the sleighing was superb, and the moon nearly full. The ladies connected with the Sewing-Union were delighted with the prospect, and even Hannah Thurston, finding that her absence would be the only exception and might thus seem intentional, was constrained to accompany them. She had seen Woodbury but once since their rencontre at Merryfield's, and his presence was both unpleasant and embarrassing to her. But the Merryfields, who took a special pride in her abilities, cherished the hope that she would yet convert him to the true faith, and went to the trouble of driving to Ptolemy in order to furnish her with a conveyance.

Early in the afternoon the guests began to arrive. Bute, aided by his man Patrick, met them at the gate, and, after a hearty greeting (for he knew everybody), took the horses and cutters in charge. Woodbury, assuming the character of host according to Ptolemaic ideas, appeared at the door, with Mrs. Babb, rigid in black bombazine, three paces in his rear. The latter received the ladies with frigid courtesy, conducted them up-stairs to the best bedroom, and issued the command to each of them, in turn: "lay off your Things!" Their curiosity failed to detect any thing incomplete or unusual in the appointments of the chamber. The furniture was of the Dennison period, and Mrs. Fortitude had taken care that no fault should be found with the toilet arrangements. Miss Eliza Clancy had indeed whispered to Miss Ruhaney Goodwin: "Well, I think they might have some lavender, or bay-water, for us,"—but the latter immediately responded with a warning "*sh!*" and drew from her work-bag a small oiled-silk package, which she unfolded, producing therefrom a diminutive bit of sponge, saturated with a mild extract of lemon verbena. "Here," she said, offering it to the other spinster, "I always take care to be pervided."

The spacious parlor at Lakeside gradually filled with workers for the Mission Fund. Mrs. Waldo was among the earliest arrivals, and took command, by right of her undisputed social talent. She became absolute mistress for the time, having, by skilful management, propitiated Mrs. Babb, and fastened her in her true place, at the outset, by adamantine chains of courtesy and assumed respect. She felt herself, therefore, in her true element, and distributed her subjects with such tact, picking up and giving into the right hands the threads of conversation, perceiving and suppressing petty jealousies in advance, and laughing away the awkwardness or timidity of others, that Woodbury could not help saying to himself: "What a queen of the *salons* this woman would have made!" It was a matter of conscience with her, as he perhaps did not know, that the occasion should be agreeable, not only to the company, but also to the host. She was responsible for its occurrence, and she felt that its success would open Lakeside to the use of Ptolemy society.

There was also little in the principal parlor to attract the attention of the guests. The floor was still covered by the old Brussels carpet, with its colossal bunches of flowers of impossible color and form,—the wonder of Ptolemy, when it was new. There were the same old-fashioned chairs, and deep sofas with chintz covers: and the portraits of Mrs. Dennison, and her son Henry, as a boy of twelve, with his hand upon the head of a Newfoundland dog, looked down from the walls. Woodbury had only added engravings of the Madonna di San Sisto and the Transfiguration, neither of which was greatly admired by the visitors. Mrs. Hamilton Bue, pausing a moment to inspect the former, said of the Holy Child : "Why, it looks just like my little Addy, when she's got her clothes off!"

In the sitting-room were Landseer's "Challenge" and Ary Scheffer's "Francesca da Rimini." Miss Ruhaney Goodwin turned suddenly away from the latter, with difficulty suppressing an exclamation. "Did you ever?" said she to Miss Eliza Clancy; "it isn't right to have such pictures hung up."

"Hush!" answered Miss Eliza, "it may be from Scripture."

Miss Ruhaney now contemplated the picture without hesitation. It was a proof before lettering. "What can it be, then?" she asked.

"Well—I shouldn't wonder if 'twas Jephthah and his daughter. They both look so sorrowful."

The Rev. Lemuel Styles and his wife presently arrived. They were both amiable, honest persons, who enjoyed their importance in the community, without seeming to assume it. The former was, perhaps, a little over-cautious lest he should forget the strict line of conduct which had been prescribed for him as a theological student. He felt that his duty properly required him to investigate Mr. Woodbury's religious views, before thus appearing to endorse them by his presence at Lakeside; but he had not courage to break the dignified reserve which the latter maintained, and was obliged to satisfy his conscience with the fact that Woodbury had twice attended his church. Between Mr. Waldo and himself there was now a very cordial relation. They had even cautiously discussed the differences between them, and had in this way learned, at least, to respect each other's sincerity.

The last of all the arrivals before tea was Mr. and Mrs. Merryfield, with Hannah Thurston. The latter came, as already mentioned, with great reluctance. She would rather have faced an unfriendly audience than the courteous and self-possessed host who came to the door to receive her. He oppressed her, not only with a sense of power, but of power controlled and directed by some cool faculty in the brain, which she felt she did not possess. In herself, whatever of intellectual force she recognized, was developed through the excitement of her feelings and sympathies. His personality, it seemed to her, was antagonistic to her own, and the knowledge gave her a singular sense of pain. She was woman enough not to tolerate a difference of this kind without a struggle.

"Thank you for coming, Miss Thurston," said Woodbury, as he frankly offered his hand. "I should not like any member of the Union to slight my first attempt to entertain it. I am glad to welcome you to Lakeside."

Hannah Thurston lifted her eyes to his with an effort that brought a fleeting flush to her face. But she met his gaze steadily. "We owe thanks to you, Mr. Woodbury," said she, "that Lakeside still belongs to our Ptolemy community. I confess I should not like to see so pleasant a spot isolated, or --what the people of Ptolemy would consider much worse," she added, smiling—"attached to Anacreon."

"Oh, no !" he answered, as he transferred her to the charge of Mrs. Babb. "I have become a thorough Ptolemaic, or a Ptolemystic, or whatever the proper term may be. I hurl defiance across the hill to Anacreon, and I turn my back on the south-east wind, when it blows from Mulligansville."

"Come, come ! We won't be satirized ;" said Mrs. Waldo, who was passing through the hall. "Hannah, you are just in time. There are five of the Mission Fund sitting together, and I want their ranks broken. Mr. Woodbury, there will be no more arrivals before tea; give me your assistance."

"Who is the tyrant now ?" he asked.

"Woman, always, in one shape or other," she answered, leading the way into the parlor.

After the very substantial tea which Mrs. Babb had prepared, and to which, it must be whispered, the guests did ample justice, there was a pause in the labors of the Union. The articles intended for the Jutnapore Mission were nearly completed, in fact, and Mrs. Waldo's exertions had promoted a genial flow of conversation, which did not require the aid of the suggestive needle. The guests gathered in groups, chatting at the windows, looking out on the gray, twilight landscape, or watching the approach of cutters from Ptolemy, as they emerged from the trees along Roaring Brook. Mr.

Hamilton Bue and the Hon. Zeno Harder were the first to make their appearance, not much in advance, however, of the crowd of ambitious young gentlemen. Many of the latter were personally unknown to Woodbury, but this was not the least embarrassment to them. They gave him a rapid salutation, since it was not to be avoided, and hurried in to secure advantageous positions among the ladies. Seth Wattles not only came, to enjoy a hospitality based, as he had hinted, on the "accursed opium traffic," but brought with him a stranger from Ptolemy, a Mr. Grindle, somewhat known as a lecturer on Temperance.

The rooms were soon filled and Woodbury was also obliged to throw open his library, into which the elderly gentlemen withdrew, with the exception of the Rev. Mr. Styles. Mr. Waldo relished a good story, even if the point was somewhat coarse, and the Hon. Zeno had an inexhaustible fund of such. Mr. Bue, notwithstanding he felt bound to utter an occasional mild protest, always managed to be on hand, and often, in his great innocence, suggested the very thing which he so evidently wished to avoid. If the conversation had been for some time rather serious and heavy, he would say: "Well, Mr. Harder, I am glad we shall have none of your wicked stories to-night"—a provocation to which the Hon. Zeno always responded by giving one.

Bute Wilson, after seeing that the horses were properly attended to, washed his hands, brushed his hair carefully, and put on his Sunday frock-coat. Miss Caroline Dilworth was one of the company, but he had been contented with an occasional glimpse of her through the window, until the arrival of Seth Wattles. The care of the fires in the grates, the lamps, and other arrangements of the evening, gave him sufficient opportunity to mix with the company, and watch both his sweetheart and his presumed rival, without appearing to do so. "Darn that blue-gilled baboon!" he muttered to himself; "I believe his liver's whiter than the milt of a herrin', an' if you'd cut his yaller skin, he'd bleed whey 'stid o' blood."

Seth Wattles, nevertheless, was really guiltless of any designs on the heart of the little seamstress. Like herself, he was ambitious of high game, and, in the dreams of his colossal conceit, looked forward with much confidence to the hour when Hannah Thurston should take his name, or he hers : he was prepared for either contingency. To this end he assumed a tender, languishing air, and talked of Love, and A Mission, and The Duality of The Soul, in a manner which, in a more cultivated society, would have rendered him intolerable. He had a habit of placing his hand on the arm or shoulder of the person with whom he was conversing, and there were in Ptolemy women silly enough to be pleased by these tokens of familiarity. Hannah Thurston, though entirely harmonizing with him as a reformer, and therefore friendly and forbearing in her intercourse, felt a natural repugnance towards him which she could not understand. Indeed, the fact gave her some uneasiness. "He is ugly," she thought; "and I am so weak as to dislike ugliness—it must be that :" which conclusion, acting on her sensitive principle of justice, led her to treat him sometimes with more than necessary kindness. Many persons, the Merryfields included, actually fancied that there was a growing attachment between them.

"Miss Carrie," whispered Bute, as he passed her in the hall, "Do you like your lemonade sweet? We're goin' to bring it in directly, and I'll git Mother Forty to make a nice glass of it, o' purpose for you."

"Thank you, Mr. Wilson : yes, if you please," answered the soft, childish drawl and the beryl-tinted eyes, that sent a thousand cork-screw tingles boring through and through him.

Bute privately put six lumps of sugar into one glass, which he marked for recognition; and then squeezed the last bitter drops of a dozen lemons into another.

The latter was for Seth Wattles.

CHAPTER VII.

WHAT HAPPENED DURING THE EVENING.

WOODBURY had prudently left the preparations for the refreshment of his numerous guests in the hands of Mrs. Babb,
who, aided by the sable Melinda, had produced an immense
supply of her most admired pastry. By borrowing freezers
from the confectioner in Ptolemy, and employing Patrick to do
the heavy churning, she had also succeeded in furnishing very
tolerable ices. The entertainment was considered to be—and,
for country means, really was—sumptuous. Nevertheless, the
housekeeper was profuse in her apologies, receiving the abundant praises of her guests with outward grimness and secret
satisfaction.

"Try these crullers," she would say: "p'r'aps you'll find
'em better 'n the jumbles, though I'm afeard they a'n't hardly
done enough. But you'll have to put up with sich as there
is."

"Oh, Mrs. Babb!" exclaimed Mrs. Hamilton Bue, "don't
say that! Nobody bakes as nice as you do. I wish you'd
give me the receipt for the jumbles."

"You're welcome to it, if you like 'em, I'm sure. But it
depends on the seasonin', and I don't never know if they're
goin' to come out right."

"Mrs. Babb," said Woodbury, coming up at this moment,
"will you please get a bottle of Sherry. The gentlemen, I see,
have nothing but lemonade."

"I told Bute to git some for them as likes it."

"A-hm!" Mrs. Bue ejaculated, as the housekeeper departed to look after the wine; "I think, Mr. Woodbury, they
don't take any thing more."

"Let me give them a chance, Mrs. Bue. Ah, here comes Bute, with the glasses. Shall I have the pleasure?" offering her one of the two which he had taken.

"Oh, dear me, no—not for any thing!" she exclaimed, looking a little frightened.

"Mr. Bue," said Woodbury, turning around to that gentleman, "as Mrs. Bue refuses to take a glass of wine with me, you must be her substitute."

"Thank you, I'd—I'd rather not, *this* evening," said Mr. Bue, growing red in the face.

There was an embarrassing pause. Woodbury, looking around, perceived that Bute had already offered his tray to the other gentlemen, and that none of the glasses upon it had been taken. He was about to replace his own without drinking, when the Hon. Zeno Harder said: "Allow me the pleasure, Sir!" and helped himself. At the same moment the Rev. Mr. Waldo, in obedience to a glance from his wife, followed his example.

"I have not tasted wine for some years," said the latter, "but I have no objection to its rational use. I have always considered it sanctioned," he added, turning to Mr. Styles, "by the Miracle of Cana."

Mr. Styles slightly nodded, but said nothing.

"Your good health, Sir!" said the Hon. Zeno, as he emptied his glass.

"*Health?*" somebody echoed, in a loud, contemptuous whisper.

Woodbury bowed and drank. As he was replacing his glass, Mr. Grindle, who had been waiting for the consummation of the iniquity, suddenly stepped forward. Mr. Grindle was a thin, brown individual, with a long, twisted nose, and a voice which acquired additional shrillness from the fact of its appearing to proceed entirely from the said nose. He had occasionally lectured in Ptolemy, and was known,—by sight, at least,—to all the company. Woodbury, however, was quite ignorant of the man and every thing concerning him.

"I am surprised," exclaimed Mr. Grindle, with his eyes fixed on vacancy, "that a man who has any regard for his reputation will set such a pernicious example."

"To what do you refer?" asked Woodbury, uncertain whether it was he who was addressed.

"To *that!*" replied the warning prophet, pointing to the empty wine-glass—"the source of nine-tenths of all the sin and suffering in the world!"

"I think you would have some difficulty in finding Sherry enough to produce such a result," Woodbury answered, beginning to understand the man.

"Sherry, or Champagne, or Heidsick!" retorted Mr. Grindle, raising his voice: "it's all the same—all different forms of Rum, and different degrees of intemperance!"

Woodbury's brown eyes flashed a little, but he answered coolly and sternly: "As you say, Sir, there are various forms of intemperance, and I have too much respect for my guests to allow that any of them should be exhibited here. Mrs. Waldo," he continued, turning his back on the lecturer, and suddenly changing his tone, " did you not propose that we should have some music?"

"I have both persuaded and commanded," she replied, "but singers, I have found, are like a flock of sheep. They huddle together and hesitate, until some one takes the lead, and then they all follow, even if it's over your head. You must be bell-wether, after all."

"Any thing for harmony," he answered, gayly. "Ah! I have it—a good old song, with which none of our friends can find fault."

And he sang, in his mellow voice, with an amused air, which Mrs. Waldo understood and heartily enjoyed: " *Drink to me only with thine eyes.*"

Mr. Grindle, however, turned to Seth Wattles and said, sneeringly: "It's easy enough to shirk an argument you can't answer." A fortnight afterwards he exploited the incident in a lecture which he gave before the Sons of Temperance, at

Ptolemy. Commencing with the cheap groggeries, he gradually rose in his attacks until he reached the men of wealth and education. "There are some of these in our neighborhood," he said : "it is not necessary for me to mention names—men whom perhaps we might excuse for learning the habit of rum-drinking on foreign shores, where our blessed reform has not yet penetrated, if they did not bring it here with them, to corrupt and destroy our own citizens. Woe unto those men, say I! Better that an ocean of fire had rolled between those distant shores of delusion and debauchery and this redeemed land, so that they could not have returned! Better that they had perished under the maddening influence of the bowl that stingeth like an adder, before coming here to add fresh hecatombs to the Jaws of the Monster!" Of course, everybody in Ptolemy knew who was meant, and sympathizing friends soon carried the report to Lakeside.

The unpleasant episode was soon forgotten, or, from a natural sense of propriety, no longer commented upon. Even the strongest advocates of Temperance present felt mortified by Mr. Grindle's vulgarity. Hannah Thurston, among others, was greatly pained, yet, for the first time, admired Woodbury's coolness and self-possession, in the relief which it gave her. She wished for an opportunity to show him, by her manner, a respect which might in some degree counterbalance the recent rudeness, and such an opportunity soon occurred.

She was standing before the picture of Francesca da Rimini, lost in the contemplation of the wonderful grace and pathos of the floating figures, when Woodbury, approaching her, said :

"I am glad that you admire it, Miss Thurston. The picture is a great favorite with me."

"The subject is from Dante, is it not?" she asked ; " that figure is he, I think."

Woodbury was agreeably surprised at her perception, especially as she did not say "*Dant,*" which he might possibly have expected. He explained the engraving, and found that she recollected the story, having read Cary's translation.

"Since you are so fond of pictures, Miss Thurston," said he, "let me show you another favorite of mine. Here, in the library."

Taking a large portfolio from its rack, he opened it on the table, under a swinging lamp. There were views of Indian scenery—strange temples, rising amid plumy tufts of palm; elephants and tigers grappling in jungles of gigantic grass; pillared banians, with gray-bearded fakirs sitting in the shade, and long ghauts descending to the Ganges. The glimpses she caught, as he turned the leaves, took away her breath with sudden delight.

At last he found the plate he was seeking, and laid it before her. It was a tropical brake, a tangle of mimosa-trees, with their feathery fronds and balls of golden down, among which grew passion-flowers and other strange, luxuriant vines. In the midst of the cool, odorous darkness, stood a young Indian girl of wonderful beauty, with languishing, almond-shaped eyes, and some gorgeous unknown blossom drooping from her night-black hair. Her only garment, of plaited grass or rushes, was bound across the hips, leaving the lovely form bare in its unconscious purity. One hand, listlessly hanging among the mimosa leaves, which gradually folded up and bent away where she touched them, seemed to seek the head of a doe, thrust out from the foliage to meet it. At the bottom of the picture a fawn forced its way through the tangled greenery. The girl, in her dusky beauty, seemed a dryad of the sumptuous forest—the child of summer, and perfume, and rank, magnificent bloom.

"Oh, how beautiful!" exclaimed Hannah Thurston, at once impressed by the sentiment of the picture: "It is like the scent of the tube rose."

"Ah, you comprehend it!" exclaimed Woodbury, surprised and pleased: "do you know the subject?"

"Not at all, but it scarcely needs an explanation."

"Have you ever heard of Kalidasa, the Hindoo poet?"

"I have not, I am sorry to say," she answered; "I have

sometimes found references to the old Sanscrit literature in modern authors, but that is all I know about it."

"My own knowledge has been derived entirely from translations," said he, "and I confess that this picture was the cause of my acquaintance with Kalidasa. I never had patience to read their interminable epics. Shall I tell you the story of Sakontala, this lovely creature ?"

"Certainly, if you will be so kind : it must be beautiful."

Woodbury then gave her a brief outline of the drama, to which she listened with the greatest eagerness and delight. At the close, he said :

"I am sorry I have not a copy of the translation to offer you. But, if you would like to read another work by the same poet, I think I have the '*Megha-Duta*,' or 'Cloud-Messenger,' somewhere in my library. It is quite as beautiful a poem, though not in the dramatic form. There are many characteristic allusions to Indian life, but none, I think, that you could not understand."

"Thank you, Mr. Woodbury. It is not often that I am able to make the acquaintance of a new author, and the pleasure is all the greater. I know very little of literature outside of the English language, and this seems like the discovery of a new world in the Past. India is so far-off and unreal."

"Not to me," he answered, with a smile. "We are creatures of habit to a greater extent than the most of us guess. If you could now be transplanted to India, in less than five years you would begin to imagine that you were born under the lotus-leaf, and that this life in Ptolemy had occurred only in the dreams of a tropical noonday."

"Oh, no, no !" said she, with earnestness. "We cannot so forget the duties imposed upon us—we cannot lose sight of our share in the great work intrusted to our hands. Right, and Justice, and Conscience, are everywhere the same !"

"Certainly, as absolute principles. But our individual duties vary with every change in our lives, and our individual action is affected, in spite of ourselves, by the influences of the external world. Are you not—to take the simplest evidence of this fact—cheerful and hopeful on some days, desponding and irresolute on others, without conscious reason? And can you not imagine moods of Nature which would permanently color your own?"

Hannah Thurston felt that there was a germ of harsh, material truth in his words, beside which her aspirations lost somewhat of their glow. Again she was conscious of a painful, unwelcome sense of repulsion. "Is there no faith?" she asked herself; "are there no lofty human impulses, under this ripe intelligence?" The soft, liquid lustre faded out of her eyes, and the eager, animated expression of her face passed away like the sunshine from a cloud, leaving it cold and gray.

Woodbury, seeing Miss Eliza Clancy, in company with other ladies, entering the library, tied up the portfolio and replaced it in its rack. Mrs. Waldo, pressing forward at the same time, noticed upon the table a Chinese joss-stick, in its lackered boat. She was not a woman to disguise or restrain an ordinary curiosity.

"What in the world is this?" she asked, taking the boat in her hands. The other ladies clustered around, inspecting it from all sides, but unable to guess its use.

"Now," said Woodbury, laughing, "I have half a mind to torment you a little. You have all read the Arabian Nights? Well, this is an instrument of enchantment."

"Enchantment! Do the Indian jugglers use it?" asked Mrs. Waldo.

"*I* use it," said he. "This rod, as it appears to be, is made of a mysterious compound. It has been burned at one end, you see. When lighted, it is employed to communicate fire to another magical substance, through which the Past is recalled and the Future made clear."

Miss Clancy and the other spinsters opened their eyes wide, in wonderment. "Provoking! Tell us now!" cried Mrs. Waldo.

"It is just as I say," he answered. "See, when I light the

end—thus—it burns with a very slow fire. This single piece would burn for nearly a whole day."

"But what is the other magical substance?" she asked.

"Here is a specimen," said he, taking the lid from a circular box of carved bamboo, and disclosing to their view some cigars.

The spinsters uttered a simultaneous exclamation. "Dreadful!" cried Mrs. Waldo, in affected horror. "Hannah, can you imagine such depravity?"

"I confess, it seems to me an unnatural taste," Hannah Thurston gravely answered; "but I presume Mr. Woodbury has some defence ready."

"Only this," said he, with an air between jest and earnest, "that the habit is very agreeable, and, since it produces a placid, equable tone of mind, highly favorable to reflection, might almost be included in the list of moral agencies."

"Would it not be more satisfactory," she asked, "if you could summon up the same condition of mind, from an earnest desire to attain the Truth, without the help of narcotic drugs?"

"Perhaps so," he replied; "but we are all weak vessels, as you know, Mrs. Waldo. I have never yet encountered such a thing as perfect harmony in the relations between body and mind. I doubt, even, if such harmony is possible, except at transient intervals. For my part, my temper is so violent and uncontrollable that the natural sedative qualities of my mind are insufficient."

Mrs. Waldo laughed heartily at this assertion, and the serious tone in which it was uttered. Hannah Thurston, to whom every fancied violation of the laws of nature was more or less an enormity, scarcely knew whether to be shocked or amused. She had determined to carefully guard herself against committing such an indiscretion as Mr. Grindle, but it was hard to be silent, when Duty demanded that she should bear a stern testimony against evil habits.

"You should be charitable, ladies," Woodbury continued, "towards some of our masculine habits, seeing that we do not interfere with yours."

"Bless me! what habits have we, I should like to know!" exclaimed Mrs. Waldo.

"A multitude: I don't know the half of them. Crochet-work, and embroidery, and patterns, for instance. Tea is milder than tobacco, I grant, but your systems are more sensitive. Then, there are powders and perfumes; eau de Cologne, lavender, verbena, heliotrope, and what not—against all of which I have nothing to say, because their odors are nearly equal to that of a fine Havana cigar."

Miss Eliza Clancy and Miss Ruhaney Goodwin exchanged glances of horror. They were both too much embarrassed to reply.

"You understand our weaknesses," said Hannah Thurston, with a smile in which there was some bitterness.

"I do not call them weaknesses," he answered. "I should be glad if this feminine love of color and odor were more common among men. But there are curious differences of taste, in this respect. I have rarely experienced a more exquisite delight than in riding through the rose-fields of Ghazeepore, at the season for making attar: yet some persons cannot endure the smell of a rose. Musk, which is a favorite perfume with many, is to me disagreeable. There is, however, a physical explanation for this habit of mine, which, perhaps, you do not know."

"No," said she, still gravely, "I know nothing but that it seems to me unnecessary, and—if you will pardon me the word—pernicious."

"Certainly. It is so, in many cases. But some constitutions possess an overplus of active nervous life, which suggests the use of a slight artificial sedative. The peculiar fascination of smoking is not in the taste of the weed, but the sight of the smoke. It is the ear of corn which we hold out to entice into harness the skittish thoughts that are running loose. In the Orient, men accomplish the same result by a rosary, the beads of which they run through their fingers."

"Yes!" interrupted Mrs. Waldo: "My brother George,

who was always at the head of his class, had a habit of twisting a lock of his hair while he was getting his lessons. It stuck out from the side of his head, like a horn. When mother had his hair cut, he went down to the foot, and he never got fairly up to head till the horn grew out again."

"A case in point," said Woodbury. "Now, you, ladies, have an exactly similar habit. Sewing, I have heard, is oftentimes this soothing agent, but knitting is the great feminine narcotic. In fact, women are more dependent on these slight helps to thought—these accompaniments to conversation—than men. There are few who can sit still and talk a whole evening, without having their hands employed. Can you not see some connecting link between our habits?"

The spinsters were silent. The speaker had, in fact, rather gone beyond their depth, with the exception of Mrs. Waldo, whose sympathy with him was so hearty and genial that she would have unhesitatingly accepted whatever sentiments he might have chosen to declare. Hannah Thurston was not a little perplexed. She scarcely knew whether he was entirely sincere, yet his views were so novel and unexpected that she did not feel prepared to answer them. Before this man's appearance in Ptolemy, her course had been chosen. She had taken up, weighed, and decided for herself the questions of life: a period of unpleasant doubt and hesitation had been solved by the acceptance of (to her) great and important theories of reform. Was a new and more difficult field of doubt to be opened now?—more difficult, because the distinctions of the sexes, which had been almost bridged over in her intercourse with reformers of kindred views, were suddenly separated by a new gulf, wider than the old.

Woodbury, noticing something of this perplexity in her countenance, continued in a lighter tone: "At least, Miss Thurston, I think you will agree with me that a physical habit, if you prefer to call it so, is not very important in comparison with those vices of character which are equally common and not so easy to eradicate. Is not the use of a 'narcotic drug' less objectionable than the systematic habit of avarice, or envy, or hypocrisy ?"

"Yes, indeed !" said Mrs. Waldo, recollecting his generous donation to the Cimmerians, "and I, for one, will not prohibit the use of your magical ingredients."

"I cannot judge for you, Mr. Woodbury," said Hannah Thurston, feeling that some response was expected ; "but have you no duty towards those who may be encouraged in the same habit, to their certain injury, by your example ?"

"There, Miss Thurston, you touch a question rather too vague to enter practically into one's life. After accepting, in its fullest sense, the Christian obligation of duty towards our fellow-men, there must be a certain latitude allowed for indi- vidual tastes and likings. Else we should all be slaves to each other's idiosyncrasies, and one perverted or abnormal trait might suppress the healthy intellectual needs of an entire com- munity. Must we cease to talk, for example, because there is scarcely a wholesome truth which, offered in a certain way, might not operate as poison to some peculiarly constituted mind ? Would you cease to assert an earnest conviction from the knowledge that there were persons unfitted to receive it ?"

"I do not think the analogy is quite correct," she answered, after a moment's pause, "because you cannot escape the re- cognition of a truth, when it has once found access to your mind. A habit, which you can take up or leave off at will, is a very different thing."

"Perhaps, then," said Woodbury, who perceived by the rising shade on Mrs. Waldo's smooth brow that it was time to end the discussion, "I had best plead guilty, at once, to being something of an Epicurean in my philosophy. I am still too much of an Oriental to be indifferent to slight material com- forts."

"In consideration of your hospitality," interposed Mrs. Waldo, brightening up, "the Sewing Union will not judge you very severely. Is it not so, Miss Clancy ?"

"Well—really—oh no, we are under obligations to Mr. Woodbury;" said the spinster, thus unexpectedly appealed to, and scarcely knowing how to reply.

"Our community have reason to congratulate themselves, Sir," here broke in the Hon. Zeno Harder, who had entered the library in time to hear the last words.

Woodbury bowed dryly and turned away.

Soon afterwards, the sound of sleigh-bells in front of the house announced the first departures. The company became thinner by slow degrees, however, for the young gentlemen and ladies had found the large parlor of Lakeside full of convenient nooks, which facilitated their habit of breaking into little groups, and were having such agreeable conversation that they would probably have remained until the small hours, but for the admonitions of the older folks. Among the earliest to leave were the Merryfields, taking with them Hannah Thurston and Miss Dilworth, greatly to Bute's regret. The latter, unable to detect any signs of peculiar intimacy between Seth Wattles and the little seamstress, became so undisguised in his fondness for her society as to attract, at last, Mrs. Babb's attention. The grim housekeeper had a vulture's beak for scenting prey of this kind. While she assisted Mrs. Styles to find her "Things," in the bedroom up-stairs, she steadfastly kept one eye on the snowy front yard, down which the Merryfield party were moving. Bute, as she anticipated, was hovering around the last and smallest of the hooded and cloaked females. He put out his arm two or three times, as if to steady her steps. They had nearly reached the cutter, where Patrick was holding the impatient horses, when she saw another male figure hurry down the walk. There was a sudden tangle among the dim forms, and one of them, she noticed, plunged full length into a bank of snow.

Mrs. Babb was so agitated by this tableau, that she suddenly threw up her hands, exclaiming: "Well, if that don't beat all!"

Mrs. Styles, carefully muffled for the journey home, had just

turned to say good-night to the housekeeper, and stood petrified, unable to guess whether the exclamation was one of admiration or reproach. She slightly started back before the
energy with which it was uttered.

"Well, to be sure, how I do forget things!" said Mrs. Babb,
coming to her senses. "But you know, Ma'am, when you're
not used to havin' company for a while, y'r head gits bothered.
'Pears to me I haven't been so flustered for years. You're
sure, Ma'am, you're right warm. I hope you won't take no
cold, goin' home."

The scene that transpired in front of the house was sufficiently amusing. Bute Wilson, as deputy-host, escorted Miss
Dilworth to the cutter, and was delighted that the slippery
path gave him at least one opportunity to catch her around the
waist. Hearing rapid footsteps behind him, he recognized
Seth Wattles hard upon his track, and, as the ungainly tailor
approached, jostled him so dexterously that he was tumbled
headlong into a pile of newly-shovelled snow.

"Ah! Who is it? Is he hurt?" exclaimed Miss Dilworth.

A smothered sound, very much resembling "Damn!" came
from the fallen individual.

"Let me help you up," said Bute; "you pitched ag'in me
like an ox. Why, Seth, is it you? You ha'n't tore your
trowsus, nor nothin', have you?"

Seth, overwhelmed before the very eyes of Hannah Thurston, whom he was hastening to assist into the cutter, grum-
bled: "No, I'm not hurt." Meantime, Bute had said good-
night to the party, and the cutter dashed away.

"Well, it's one comfort that you can always mend your own
rips," the latter remarked, consolingly.

Finally, the last team departed, and the sound of the bells
diminished into a faint, fairy sweetness, as if struck by the
frosty arrows of the starlight from the crystals of the snow.
Lakeside returned to more than its wonted silence and seclusion. Woodbury closed the door, walked into his library,
lighted a cigar at the still burning piece of joss-stick, and

threw himself into a chair before the fire. Now and then puffing a delicate, expanding ring of smoke from his lips, he watched it gradually break and dissolve, while reviewing, in his thoughts, the occurrences of the evening. They were not wholly agreeable, yet the least so—Mr. Grindle's rude attack,— was not to be dismissed from the mind like an ordinary piece of vulgarity. It was a type, he thought, of the manners which self-constituted teachers of morality must necessarily assume in a community where intellect is characterized by activity rather than development. Society, in its broader sense, is un- known to these people,—was his reflection. In the absence of cultivation, they are ruled by popular ideas: Reforms are marshalled in, as reserve corps, behind the ranks of Religion, and not even the white flag of a neutral is recognized in the grand crusade. "Join us and establish your respectability, or resist us and be cut down!" is the cry.

"Yet"—he mused further—"is it not something that, in a remote place like this, Ideas have vitality and power? Ad- mitting that the channels in which they move are contracted, and often lead in false directions, must they not rest on a basis of honest, unselfish aspiration? The vices which spring from intolerance and vulgar egotism are not to be lightly pardoned, but, on the other hand, they do not corrupt and demoralize like those of the body. One must respect the source, while resist- ing the manifestation. How much in earnest that Quaker girl seemed! It was quite a serious lecture she gave me, about such a trifle as this" (puffing an immense blue ring into the air). "But it was worth taking it, to see how she enjoyed the Sakontala. She certainly possesses taste, and no doubt thinks better than she talks. By the by, I quite forgot to give her the translation of the *Megha-Duta*."

Springing up, Woodbury found the volume, after some search, and soon became absorbed, for the second time, in its pages.

"Bute," said Mrs. Babb, as she wiped the dishes, and care- fully put away the odds and ends of the refreshments; " 'Pears to me you was gallivantin' round that Carrline Dilwuth, more than's proper."

Bute, standing with legs spread out and back to the fire, answered, as he turned around to face it, whereby, if he blushed, the evidence was covered by the glow of the flame: "Well, she's a gay little creetur, and 'taint no harm."

"I dunno about that," sharply rejoined the housekeeper. "She's a cunnin', conceited chit, and 'll lead you by the nose. You're just fool enough to be captivated by a piece o' wax-work and curls. It makes me sick to look at 'em. Gals used to comb their hair when I was young. I don't want no sich a thing as *she* is, to dance at my buryin'."

"Oh, Mother Forty, don't you go off about it!" said Bute, deprecatingly. "I ain't married to her, nor likely to be."

"Married! I guess not! Time enough for that when *I*'m dead and gone. Me that brought you up, and to have some-body put over my head, and spendin' all your earnins on fine clothes, and then hankerin' after *my* money. But it's locked up, safe and tight, I can tell you that."

"I'm man-grown, I reckon," said Bute, stung into resistance by this attack, "and if I choose to git married, some day or other, I don't see who can hinder me. It's what everybody else does, and what you've done, yourself."

Bute strode off to bed, and the housekeeper, sitting down before the fire, indulged in the rare luxury of shedding seve-ral tears.

CHAPTER VIII.

IN WHICH MR. WOODBURY PAYS AN UNEXPECTED VISIT.

On the following Monday, Woodbury having occasion to visit Ptolemy, took with him the volume of Kalidasa, intending to leave it at the cottage of the widow Thurston. The day was mild and sunny, and the appearance of the plank sidewalk so inviting to the feet, that he sent Bute forward to the Ptolemy House with the cutter, on alighting at the cottage gate.

The door of the dwelling, opening to the north, was protected by a small outer vestibule, into which he stepped, designing simply to leave the book, with his compliments, and perhaps a visiting-card—though the latter was not *de rigueur* in Ptolemy. There was no bell-pull; he knocked, gently at first, and then loudly, but no one answered. Turning the knob of the door he found it open, and entered a narrow little hall, in which there was a staircase leading to the upper story, and two doors on the left. Knocking again at the first of these, an answer presently came from the further room, and the summons, "Come in !" was repeated, in a clear though weak voice.

He no longer hesitated, but advanced into the sitting-room. Friend Thurston, sunning herself in her comfortable chair, looked around. A fleeting expression of surprise passed over her face, but the next moment she stretched out her hand, saying: "How does thee do ?"

"My name is Woodbury," said he, as he took it respectfully, "I——"

5*

"I thought it must be thee," she interrupted. "Hannah described thy looks to me. Won't thee sit down?"

"I have only called to leave a book for your daughter, and will not disturb you."

"Thee won't disturb me. I feel all the better for a little talk now and then, and would be glad if thee could sit and chat awhile. Thee's just about the age my little Richard would have been if he had lived."

Thus kindly invited, Woodbury took a seat. His eye appreciated, at a glance, the plainness, the taste, and the cozy comfort of the apartment, betraying in every detail, the touches of a woman's hand. Friend Thurston's face attracted and interested him. In spite of her years, it still bore the traces of former beauty, and its settled calm of resignation recalled to his mind the expression he remembered on that of Mrs. Dennison. Her voice was unusually clear and sweet, and the deliberate evenness of her enunciation,—so different from the sharp, irregular tones of the Ptolemy ladies,—was most agreeable to his ear.

"Hannah's gone out," she resumed ; "but I expect her back presently. It's kind of thee to bring the book for her. Thee bears no malice, I see, that she lectured thee a little. Thee must get used to that, if thee sees much of our people. We are called upon to bear testimony, in season and out of season, and especially towards men of influence, like thee, whose responsibilities are the greater."

"I am afraid you over-estimate my influence," Woodbury replied; "but I am glad you do not suppose that I could bear malice on account of a frank expression of opinion Every man has his responsibilities, I am aware, but our ideas of duty sometimes differ."

"Thee's right there," said the old lady ; "and perhaps we ought not to ask more than that the truth be sought for, in a sincere spirit. I don't think, from thy face, that there is much of stubborn worldly pride in thy nature, though thee belongs to the world, as we Friends say."

"I have found that a knowledge of the world cures one of unreasonable pride. The more I mingle with men, the more I find reflections of myself, which better enable me to estimate my own character."

"If thee but keeps the heart pure, the Holy Spirit may come to thee in the crowded places, even as The Saviour was caught up from the midst of His Disciples!" she exclaimed with fervor. Gazing on her steady, earnest eyes, Woodbury could not help thinking to himself: "The daughter comes legitimately by her traits."

"Can thee accustom thyself to such a quiet life as thee leads now?" she asked; and then gazing at him, continued, as if speaking to herself: "It is not a restless face. Ah, but that is not always a sign of a quiet heart. There are mysteries in man, past finding out, or only discovered when it is too late!"

"This life is not at all quiet," he answered, "compared with that which I have led for the past ten or twelve years. In a foreign country, and especially within the tropics, the novelty of the surroundings soon wears off, and one day is so exactly the repetition of another, that we almost lose our count of time. It seems to me, now, as if I were just awaking out of a long sleep. I have certainly thought more, and felt more, in these three months than in as many years abroad; for I had come to believe that the world was standing still, while now I see that it really moves, and I must move with it."

"I like to hear thee say that!" exclaimed the widow, turning suddenly towards him, with a bright, friendly interest in her face. "Men are so apt to be satisfied with their own opinions—at least, when they've reached thy age. Thee's over thirty, I should think?"

"Thirty-six," Woodbury respectfully answered, "but I hope I shall never be so old as to suppose, like the counsellors of Job, that wisdom will die with me."

The widow understood his allusion, in the literal sense which he intended: not so another auditor. Hannah Thurston, who heard the last words as she entered the room, at once suspected a hidden sarcasm, aimed principally at herself. The indirect attacks to which she had been subjected,—especially from persons of her own sex,—had made her sensitive and suspicious. Her surprise at Woodbury's presence vanished in the spirit of angry antagonism which suddenly arose within her. She took the hand he frankly offered, with a mechanical coldness strangely at variance with her flushed cheeks and earnest eyes.

"I'm glad thee's come, Hannah," said the old lady. "Friend Woodbury has been kind enough to bring thee a book, and I've been using an old woman's privilege, to make his acquaintance. He'll not take it amiss, I'm sure!"

Woodbury replied with a frank smile, which he knew she would understand. His manner towards the daughter, however, had a shade of formal deference. Something told him that his visit was not altogether welcome to her. "I found the translation of the *Megha-Duta*, Miss Thurston," he said, "and have called to leave it, on my way to the village. If it interests you, I shall make search for whatever other fragments of Indian literature I may have."

"I am very much obliged to you," she forced herself to say, inwardly resolving, that, whether interesting or not, this was the first and last book she would receive from the library of Lakeside.

"It is really kind of thee," interposed the widow; "Hannah finds few books here in Ptolemy that she cares to read, and we cannot afford to buy many. What was the work, Hannah, thee spoke of the other night?"

Thus appealed to, the daughter, after a moment's reluctance, answered: "I was reading to mother Carlyle's Essay on Goethe, and his reference to 'Wilhelm Meister' excited my curiosity. I believe Carlyle himself translated it, and therefore the translation must be nearly equal to the original."

"I read it some years ago, in Calcutta," said Woodbury, "but I only retain the general impression which it left upon my mind. It seemed to me, then, a singular medley of wisdom and weakness, of the tenderest imagination and the coarsest reality. But I have no copy, at present, by which to test the correctness of that impression. I am not a very critical reader, as you will soon discover, Miss Thurston. Do you like Carlyle ?"

"I like his knowledge, his earnestness, and his clear insight into characters and events, though I cannot always adopt his conclusions. His thought, however, is strong and vital, and it refreshes and stimulates at the same time. I am afraid he spoils me for other authors."

"Is not that, in itself, an evidence of something false in his manner ? That which is absolutely greatest or truest should not weaken our delight in the lower forms of excellence. Peculiarities of style, when not growing naturally out of the subject, seem to me like condiments, which disguise the natural flavor of the dish and unfit the palate to enjoy it. Have you ever put the thought, which Carlyle dresses in one of his solemn, involved, oracular sentences, into the Quaker garb of plain English ?"

"No," said Hannah Thurston, somewhat startled. "I confess," she added, after a pause, "the idea of such an experiment is not agreeable to me. I cannot coldly dissect an author whom I so heartily admire."

Woodbury smiled very, very slightly, but her quick eye caught and retained his meaning. "Then I will not dissect him for you," he said ; "though I think you would find a pleasure in the exercise of the critical faculty, to counterbalance the loss of an indiscriminate admiration. I speak for myself, however. I cannot be content until I ascertain the real value of a man and his works, though a hundred pleasant illusions are wrecked in the process. I am slow to acknowledge or worship greatness, since I have seen the stuff of which many idols are composed. The nearer an author seems to reflect my own views, the more suspicious I am, at first, of his influence upon me. A man who knows how to see, to think, and to judge, though he may possess but an average intellect, is able to get at all important truths himself, without taking them at second-hand."

There was no assumption of superiority—not the slightest trace of intellectual arrogance in Woodbury's manner. He spoke with the simple frankness of a man who was utterly unconscious that he was dealing crushing blows on the mental habits of his listener—not seeming to recognize, even, that they were different from his own. This calmness, so unlike the heat and zeal with which other men were accustomed to discuss questions with her, disconcerted and silenced Hannah Thurston. He never singled out any single assertion of hers as a subject of dispute, but left it to be quietly overwhelmed in the general drift of his words. It was a species of mental antagonism for which she was not prepared. To her mother, who judged men more or less by that compound of snow and fire who had been her husband, Woodbury's manner was exceedingly grateful. She perceived, as her daughter did not, the different mental complexion of the sexes ; and moreover, she now recognized, in him, a man with courage enough to know the world without bitterness of heart.

"I thank thee," said she, as he rose to leave with an apology for the length of his stay ; " I have enjoyed thy visit. Come again, some time, if thee finds it pleasant to do so. I see thee can take a friendly word in a friendly way, and thee may be sure that I won't judge thy intentions wrongly, where I am led to think differently."

"Thank you, Friend Thurston: it is only in differing, that we learn. I hope to see you again." He took the widow's offered hand, bowed to Hannah, and left the room.

"Mother!" exclaimed the latter, as she heard the outer door close behind him, "why did thee ask him to come again?"

"Why, Hannah! Thee surprises me. It is right to bear testimony, but we are not required to carry it so far as that. Has thee heard any thing against his character?"

"No, mother: he is said to be upright and honorable, but I

do not like to be obliged to him for kindnesses, when he, no doubt, thinks my condemnation of his habits impertinent,—when, I know, he despises and sneers at my views!"

"Hannah," said the mother, gravely, "I think thee does him injustice. He is not the man to despise thee, or any one who thinks earnestly and labors faithfully, even in a cause he cannot appreciate. We two women, living alone here, or only seeing the men who are with us in sympathy, must not be too hasty to judge. Is thee not, in this way, committing the very fault of which thee accuses him?"

"Perhaps so," said Hannah: "I doubt whether I know what *is* true." She sank wearily into a chair. The volume Woodbury left behind, caught her eye. Taking it up, she turned over the leaves listlessly, but soon succumbed to the temptation and read—read until the fairy pictures of the Indian moonlight grew around her, as the Cloud sailed on, over jungle and pagoda, and the dance of maidens on the marble terraces.

Meanwhile, Woodbury having transacted his business and Bute Wilson his, the two were making preparations to return to Lakeside, when a plump figure, crossing the beaten snow-track in front of the Ptolemy House, approached them. Even before the thick green veil was thrown back, Woodbury recognized the fat hand which withdrew itself from a worn chinchilla muff, as the hand of Mrs. Waldo. Presently her round dark eyes shone full upon him, and he heard—what everybody in Ptolemy liked to hear—the subdued trumpet of her voice.

"Just in time to catch you!" she laughed. "How do you do, Bute? Will you call at the parsonage, Mr. Woodbury? No? Then I must give you my message in the open street. Is anybody near? You must know it's a secret." After having said this in a loud tone, she lowered her voice: "Well, I don't mind Bute knowing it: Bute is not a leaky pitcher, I'm sure."

"I reckon Mr. Max knows that," said Arbutus, with a broad laugh dancing in his blue eyes.

"What is it? Another fair for the Cimmerians? Or is Miss Eliza Clancy engaged to a missionary?" asked Woodbury.

"Be silent, that you may hear. If it were not for my feet getting cold, I would be a quarter of an hour telling you. But I must hurry—there's Mrs. Bue coming out of her yard, and she scents a secret a mile off. Well—it's to be at Merryfield's on Saturday evening. You must be sure to come."

"What—the Sewing Union?"

"Bless me! I forgot. No—Dyce is to be there."

"Dyce?"

"Yes. They don't want it to be generally known, as so many would go out of mere curiosity. I must say, between us, that is *my* only reason. Neither you nor I have any faith in it; but Mrs. Merryfield says she will be glad if you can come."

"First tell me who Dyce is, and what is to be done," said Woodbury, not a little surprised. The expression thereof was instantly transferred to Mrs. Waldo's face.

"Well—to be sure, you're as ignorant as a foreigner. Bute knows, I'll be bound. Tell him, Bute, on the way home. Good-by! How do you do, Mrs. Bue? I was just telling Mr. Woodbury that the vessel for Madras"—and the remainder of the sentence was lost in the noise of the departing bells.

"Dyce is what they call a Mejum," explained Bute, as they dashed out on the Anacreon road: "Merryfields believe in it. I was there once't when they made the dinner-table jump like a wild colt Then there's sperut-raps, as they call 'em, but it's not o' much account what they say. One of 'em spoke to me, lettin' on to be my father. 'Arbutus,' says he (they spelt it out), 'I'm in the third spere, along with Jane.' Ha! ha! and my mother's name was Margaretta! But you'd better see it for yourself, Mr. Max. Seein' 's believin', they say, but you won't believe more'n you've a mind to, after all."

CHAPTER IX.

SPIRITUAL AND OTHER RAPPINGS.

HAD the invitation to a spiritual *séance* been given by any one but Mrs. Waldo, Woodbury would probably have felt little inclination to attend. The Merryfields alone, with their ambitious sentiment and negative intellect, were beginning to be tiresome acquaintances, now that the revival of old memories was exhausted; but the warm heart and sound brain of that one woman made any society tolerable. His thoughts reverted to Hannah Thurston: would she be there? Of course: was his mental reply—yet she certainly could not share in the abominable delusion. Why not, after all? Her quick, eager intelligence, too proud and self-reliant to be restrained by traditional theories,—too unbalanced, from the want of contact with equal minds,—too easily moved by the mere utterance of attractive sentiment,—was it not, rather, the soil in which these delusions grew strong and dangerous? He would go and see.

Nevertheless, he was conscious of a feeling of reluctance, almost of shame at his own curiosity, as he left Lakeside. The night was overcast, with a raw, moaning wind in the tree-tops, and Bute was forced to drive slowly, feeling rather than seeing the beaten tracks. This employment, with the necessary remarks to the old horse Dick, fully occupied his attention. Finally, however, he broke silence with:

"I s'pose they'll have Absalom up to-night?"

"What! Do they go so far as that? Can they really believe it?" Woodbury asked.

"They jest *do*. They *want* to b'lieve it, and it comes easy.

If brains was to be ground, between you and me, neither of 'em would bring much grist to the mill. I don't wonder at *her* so much, for she set a good deal of store by Absalom, and 't seems natural, you know, for women to have notions o' that kind."

"Are there many persons in Ptolemy who believe in such things?"

"Well—I don't hardly think there be. Leastways, they don't let on. There's Seth Wattles, o' course: he's fool enough for any thing; and I guess Lawyer Tanner. Ever sence Mr. Styles preached ag'in 'em, it a'n't considered jist respectable. Infidel-like, you know."

Woodbury laughed. "Well, Bute," said he, "we shall hardly find Mr. Waldo there to-night, if that is the case."

"He'll be there, Mr. Max, if *she* is. She'll bring him clear, no matter what folks says. Miss Waldo's a wife worth havin'—not but what he's got considerable grit, too. He's not strong at revivals, but he's a good hand at holdin' together all he gits."

As they drove up the lane to Merryfield's farm-house, all was dark and silent. The shutters were closed, and there was no appearance of other visitors having arrived. At the noise of the bells, however, the door opened, and the owner, after summoning his hired man from the kitchen, to assist Bute in taking charge of the horse, waited until Woodbury approached, in order to help him off with his overcoat. "They are all here that are likely to come," he announced in a whisper.

James Merryfield was a man of fifty, or a little more, in whom the desire to be a reformer had been excited long after he had reached his maturity as a simple, unpretending farmer. The fictitious character but imperfectly overlaid the natural one, giving him an uncertain, hesitating air. Indeed, with all his assertion and self-gratulation, he never could overcome a secret doubt of his ability to play the new part. But he was honest and sincerely conscientious, and a more prominent position than he would have assumed, of his own choice, was forced upon him by his friends. He possessed a comfortable property, and they were well aware of the advantage of being represented by men with bases.

His frame had been soundly developed, not over-worn, by labor in his own fields, yet he was awkward, almost shambling, in his movements. His head was usually held on the left side, and a straight line dropped from the centre of his brow would not nearly have coincided with the axis of his nose. The large, irregular mouth expressed both the honesty and the weakness of the man. His voice, always nasal, rose into a shrill, declamatory monotone when he became excited—a key which he continually let drop, and again resumed, in disagreeable fluctuations. Thus Woodbury, while heartily respecting his character, found much of his society tiresome.

His wife, Sarah, who was six or seven years younger, was one of those women, who, without the power of thinking for themselves, have, nevertheless, a singular faculty for accepting the thoughts and conclusions of others. She was entirely dependent on two or three chosen leaders in the various "Reforms," without the slightest suspicion of her mental serfdom. Every new phase of their opinions she appropriated, and reproduced as triumphantly as if it had been an original discovery. She had, in fact, no intellectual quality except a tolerable fluency of speech. This, alone, gave her some consideration in her special circle, and kept her hesitating husband in the background. Both had been touched by the Hand of Progress, rather too late for their equilibrium. They had reached the transition state, it is true, but were doomed never to pass through it, and attain that repose which is as possible to shallow as to deep waters.

In person she was thin, but not tall, with a face expressive of passive amiability, slightly relieved by dyspepsia. The pale, unhealthy color of her skin, the dulness of her eyes, and the lustreless hue of her thin, reddish-brown hair, hinted at a system hopelessly disordered by dietetic experiments. Her children had all died young, with the exception of Absalom, who had barely reached manhood, when the care of his health, as Bute said, proved too great a burden to him.

Woodbury was ushered, not into the parlor, but into the room ordinarily occupied by the family. A single candle was burning on the table, dimly lighting the apartment. Mrs. Merryfield came forward to receive her guest, followed by Mrs. Waldo, who said, with unusual gravity: "You are in time— we were just about to commence."

Seated around the table were Hannah Thurston, Mr. Waldo, Seth Wattles, Tanner, the lawyer, and a cadaverous stranger, who could be no other than Mr. Dyce. A motion of his hand dissuaded the company from rising, and they gravely bowed to Woodbury without speaking. Mr. Dyce, after a rapid glance at the new-comer, fixed his eyes upon the table. He was a middle-aged man, broad-shouldered but spare, with long, dark hair, sunken cheeks, and eyes in which smouldered some powerful, uncanny magnetic force.

After Woodbury had taken his seat at the table, and Mr. Merryfield had closed the door, the medium spoke, in a low but strong voice:

"Take away the candle."

It was placed upon a small stand, in a corner of the room. "Shall I put it out?" asked the host.

Mr. Dyce shook his head.

Presently a succession of sharp, crackling raps was heard, as if made on the under surface of the table. They wandered about, now fainter, now stronger, for a few moments, and then approached Mrs. Merryfield.

"It's Absalom!" she cried, the yearning of a mother's heart overleaping the course of experiment. "What has he to say to-night?"

"Will the spirit communicate through the alphabet?" asked the medium.

Three raps—"Yes."

Lettered cards were laid upon the table, and the medium, commencing at A, touched them in succession until a rap announced the correct letter. This was written, and the process repeated until the entire communication was obtained.

"*I have been teaching my sisters. They are waiting for me on the steps of the temple. Good-night, mother!*"—was Absalom's message.

"How beautiful!" exclaimed Seth Wattles. "The temple must mean the future life, and the steps are the successive spheres. Will any spirit communicate with me?"

The raps ceased. Mr. Dyce raised his head, looked around with his glow-worm eyes, and asked: "Does any one desire to speak with a relative or friend? Does any one feel impressed with the presence of a spirit?" His glance rested on Hannah Thurston.

"I would like to ask," said she, as the others remained silent, "whether the person whose name is in my mind, has any message for me."

After a pause, the medium shuddered, stretched out his hands upon the table, with the fingers rigidly crooked, lifted his head, and fixed his eyes on vacancy. His lips scarcely seemed to move, but a faint, feminine voice came from his throat.

"*I am in a distant sphere,*" it said, "*engaged in the labors I began while on earth. I bear a new name, for the promise of that which I once had is fulfilled.*"

Hannah Thurston said nothing. She seemed to be pondering the meaning of what she had heard. Mrs. Waldo turned to Woodbury, with a face which so distinctly said to him, without words: "It's awful!" that he answered her, in a similar way: "Don't be afraid!"

"Will you ask a question, Mr. Woodbury?" said the host.

"I have no objection," he said, in a serious tone, "to select a name, as Miss Thurston has done, and let the answer test from what spirit it comes."

After a rapid glance at the speaker, the medium pushed pencil and paper across the table, saying: "Write the name, fold the paper so that no one can see it, and hold it in your hand." He then placed one elbow on the table, and covered his face with his hand, the fingers slightly separated.

Woodbury wrote—a long name, it seemed to be—and folded the paper as directed. Some wandering, uncertain raps followed. Communication by means of the alphabet was proposed to the spirit, without a response. After a sufficient pause to denote refusal, the raps commenced again.

Mr. Dyce shuddered several times, but no sound proceeded from his mouth. Suddenly turning towards Woodbury with set eyes, and pointing his finger, he exclaimed: "He is stand ing behind you!"

The others, startled, looked towards the point indicated, and even Woodbury involuntarily turned his head.

"I see him," continued the medium—"a dark man, not of our race. He wears a splendid head-dress, and ornaments of gold. His eyes are sad and his lips are closed: he is permitted to show his presence, but not to speak to you. Now he raises both hands to his forehead, and disappears."

"Who was it?" asked Mrs. Waldo, eagerly.

Woodbury silently unfolded the paper, and handed it to her. Even Mr. Dyce could not entirely conceal his curiosity to hear the name.

"What is this!" said she. "I can scarcely read it: Bab— Baboo Rugbutty Churn Chuckerbutty! It is certainly nobody's name!"

"It is the actual name of an acquaintance of mine, in Calcutta," Woodbury answered.

"A Hindoo!" exclaimed Mr. Dyce, with a triumphant air: "that accounts for his inability to use the alphabet."

"I do not see why it should," rejoined Woodbury, "unless he has forgotten his English since I left India."

"He *did* speak English, then?" several asked.

"Did, and still does, I presume. At least, he was not dead, three months ago," he answered, so quietly and gravely that none of the company (except, perhaps, the medium) supposed that a trick had been intended.

"Not dead!" some one exclaimed, in great amazement. "Why did you summon him?"

"Because I did not wish to evoke any friend or relative whom I have lost, and I had a curiosity to ascertain whether the spirits of the living could be summoned, as well as those of the dead."

There was a blank silence for a few moments. Only Bute, who had stolen into the room and taken a quiet seat in one corner, with his eyes wide open, gave an audible chuckle.

Mr. Dyce, who had concealed a malignant expression under his hand, now lifted a serene face, and said, in a solemn voice: "The *living*, as we call them, cannot usurp the powers and privileges of those who have entered on the spiritual life. The spirit, whose name was written, has either left the earth, or that of another, unconsciously present in the gentleman's mind, has presented itself."

The believers brightened up. How simple was the explanation! The mere act of writing the name of one Hindoo had recalled others to Mr. Woodbury's memory, and his thoughts must have dwelt, *en passant*,—probably without his being in the least aware of it, so rapid is mental action,—on some other Hindoo friend, long since engaged in climbing the successive spheres. In vain did he protest against having received even a flying visit from the recollection of any such person. Seth Wattles triumphantly asked: "Are you always aware of every thing that passes through your mind?"

Mrs. Merryfield repeated a question she had heard the week before: "Can you always pick up the links by which you pass from one thought to another?"

Her husband modestly thrust in a suggestion: "Perhaps your friend Chuckerchurn is now among the spirits, as it were."

Mr. Dyce, who had been leaning forward, with his arms under the table, during these remarks, suddenly lifted his head, exclaiming: "He has come back!"—which produced a momentary silence. "Yes—I cannot refuse you!" he added, as if addressing the spirit, and then started violently from his seat, twisting his left arm as if it had received a severe blow. He drew up his coat-sleeve, which was broad and loose, then the sleeve of his shirt, and displayed a sallow arm, upon the skin of which were some red marks, somewhat resembling the letters "R. R." In a few moments, however, the marks faded away.

"His initials! Who can it be?" said Seth.

"Rammohun Roy!" said Hannah Thurston, betrayed, as it almost seemed, into a temporary belief in the reality of the visitation.

"I assure you," Woodbury answered, "that nothing was further from my thoughts than the name of Rammohun Roy, a person whom I never saw. If I wished to be convinced that these phenomena proceed from spirits, I should select some one who could give me satisfactory evidence of his identity."

"The skeptical will not believe, though one came from heaven to convince them," remarked the medium, in a hollow tone.

There was an awkward silence.

"My friends, do not disturb the atmosphere!" cried Mr. Merryfield; "I hope we shall have further manifestations."

A loud rap on the table near him seemed to be intended as a reply.

Mr. Dyce's hand, after a few nervous jerks, seized the pencil, and wrote rapidly on a sheet of paper. After completing the message and appending the signature to the bottom, he heaved a deep sigh and fell back in his chair.

Mr. Merryfield eagerly grasped the paper. "Ah!" said he, "it is my friend!" and read the following:

"*Be ye not weak of vision to perceive the coming triumph of Truth. Even though she creep like a tortoise in the race, while Error leaps like a hare, yet shall she first reach the goal.*

The light from the spirit-world is only beginning to dawn up-on the night of Earth.   When the sun shall rise, only the owls and bats among men will be blind to its rays.   Then the per-fect day of Liberty shall fill the sky, and even the spheres of spirits be gladdened by reflections from the realm of mortals !
"BENJAMIN LUNDY."

In spite of certain inaccuracies in the spelling of this mes-sage, the reader's face brightened with satisfaction. "There !" he exclaimed—"there is a genuine test! No one but the spirit of Lundy, as it were, could have written those words."

"Why not ?" asked Woodbury.

"Why—why—the foot of Hercules sticks out!" said Mr. Merryfield, falling, in his confusion, from the lofty strain. "You never knowed the sainted Lundy, the purest and most beautiful spirit of this age. Those are his very—yes, he would make the same expressions, as it were, if his voice could,—if he were still in the flesh."

Woodbury's eyes, mechanically, wandered to Mrs. Waldo and Hannah Thurston. The former preserved a grave face, but a smile, perceptible to him alone, lurked at the bottom of her eyes. The latter, too earnest in all things to disguise the expression of her most fleeting emotions, looked annoyed and uneasy. Woodbury determined to take no further part in the proceedings—a mental conclusion which Mr. Dyce was suffi-ciently clairvoyant to feel, and which relieved while it discon-certed him.

Various other spirits announced their presence, but their communications became somewhat incoherent, and the semi-believers present were not strengthened by the evening's ex-periments. Mr. Waldo, in answer to a mental question, re-ceived the following message:

"I will not say that my mind dwelt too strongly on the symbols by which Faith is expressed, for through symbols the Truth was made clear to me.   There are many paths, but they all have the same ending."

6'

"There can be no doubt of that. Are you not satisfied?" asked Seth Wattles.

"Not quite. I had expected a different message from the spirit I selected," said Mr. Waldo.

"Was it not Beza Cimmer?"

"No!" was the astonished reply: "I was thinking of a school-mate and friend, who took passage for the West Indies in a vessel that was never heard of afterwards."

"We must not forget," said Mr. Dyce, "that our friends in the spirit-world still retain their independence. You may send for a neighbor to come and see you, and while you are waiting for him, another may unexpectedly step in. It is just so in our intercourse with spirits: we cannot control them. We cannot say to one: 'come!' and to another: 'go!' We must abide their pleasure, in faith and humility."

Mr. Waldo said nothing, and made no further attempt at conversation with his lost school-mate. Seth Wattles summoned, in succession, the spirits of Socrates, Touissant L'Ouverture, and Mrs. Hemans, but neither of them was inclined to communicate with him.

After a while, some one remarked: "Will they not more palpably manifest themselves?"

"We can try," said Mr. Dyce.

Mr. Merryfield thereupon took the solitary candle into an adjoining room. As the shutters were closed, the apartment was thus left in complete darkness. The guests kept their seats around the table, and it was specially enjoined upon them not to move. At the end of a few minutes rustling noises were heard, loud raps resounded on the table, which was several times violently lifted and let down, and blows were dealt at random by invisible hands. Those who were so fortunate as to be struck, communicated the news in a whisper to their neighbors. Presently, also, the little old-fashioned piano, standing on one side of the room, began to stir its rusty keys. After a few discordant attempts at chords, a sin-le hand appeared to be endeavoring to play "*Days of*

Absence," the untuned keys making the melody still more dismal.

It was enough to set one's teeth on edge, but Mrs. Merryfie'd burst into tears. "Oh!" she cried, "it's Angelina herself! She was taking lessons, and had just got that far when she died."

The sounds ceased, and light was restored to the room. Mr. Dyce was leaning on the table, with his face in his hands. As he lifted his head, a large dark stain appeared under his right eye.

"Why, what has happened to you?" cried Merryfield. "Your eye is quite black!"

The medium, whose glance happened to fall upon his right hand, closed it so suddenly that the gesture would have attracted notice, if he had not skilfully merged it into one of his convulsive shudders. A rapid flush came to his face, and passed away, leaving it yellower than before.

"The unfriendly spirits are unusually active to-night," he finally answered: "They are perhaps encouraged by the presence of doubters or scoffers. I name no names. I received several severe blows while the light was removed, and feel exhausted by the struggles I have undergone. But it is nothing. The spirit of Paracelsus will visit me to-night, and remove the traces of this attack. Had the atmosphere been pure, it could not have occurred. But some who are here present are yet incapable of receiving the Truth, and their presence clouds the divine light through which the highest manifestations are made."

Woodbury was too much disgusted to answer. His eye fell upon Bute, who sat in the corner, with his large hand covering his mouth, and his face scarlet.

"I confess," said Mr. Waldo, turning to the medium, "that I am not convinced of the spiritual character of these phenomena. I do not profess to explain them, but neither can I explain much that I see in Nature, daily; and I do not perceive the necessity of referring them at once to supernatural causes.

By such an assumption, the spiritual world is degraded in our eyes, without, in my opinion, any increase of positive truth, even if the assumption were correct. A man who is really so blind as to disbelieve in the future life, would not be converted by any thing we have seen here to-night; while for us, who believe, the phenomena are unnecessary."

"What!" exclaimed Mr. Dyce. "You do not appreciate the divine utterances from the world of spirits! You do not recognize the new and glorious Truths, the germs of a more perfect Creed!"

"I would prefer," the parson mildly answered, "not to hear the word 'divine' so applied. No: to be entirely frank, I see nothing new, or even true, in comparison with the old, Eternal Truth."

"But," interrupted Merryfield, desperately, seeing the bright assent on Hannah Thurston's face; "do you not believe in Progress? Have we, as it were, exhausted—are we at the end of truth?"

"Most certainly I believe in the forward march of our race. We are still children in wisdom, and have much to learn. But let me ask, my friend, do *you* not believe that the future life is an immeasurable advance upon this?"

"Yes," said Merryfield.

"Then," Mr. Waldo continued, "why is it that the professed communications from great minds, such as Socrates, Luther, or the Apostles themselves, are below the expressions of even average human intellect?"

The believers stared at each other in dumb amazement. The coolness with which the parson took hold of and trampled upon their gems of superhuman wisdom, was like that of St. Boniface, when he laid the axe to the sacred Hessian oak. His hearers, like the Druids on that occasion, were passive, from the sheer impossibility of comprehending the sacrilege. Mr. Dyce shook his head and heaved a sigh of commiseration. Seth Wattles clasped his hands, lifted his eyes, and muttered in a hoarse voice: "The time will come." Mrs. Merryfield was unable to recall any phrase that applied to the case, but wiped her eyes for the third time since the mysterious performance on the piano.

Mrs. Waldo, however, looked at her husband with a smile which said to him: "I knew you could silence them whenever you choose to show your strength." Then, rising, she added, aloud: "Now the atmosphere is certainly disturbed. Let us come back to our present existence, which, after all, is very good, when one has health, friends, and a contented spirit."

Mr. Merryfield whispered to his wife, who disappeared in the kitchen. "Don't go yet," he said to his guests, who had risen from the table; "we must warm you, before you start."

"Is it possible? whiskey-punch?" asked Woodbury, aside, of Mrs. Waldo.

"Hush! The very suggestion of such a thing would ruin you, if it were known," she replied.

At the end of a few minutes, Mrs. Merryfield reappeared, followed by a negro girl, who bore several steaming plates on a japanned tray. They proved to contain slices of mince-pie, *réchauffée*, and rather palatable, although heavy, in the absence of brandy. Mrs. Merryfield, during the day, had seriously thought of entertaining her guests with coffee; but as she was thoroughly convinced of the deleterious nature of the beverage, she decided that it would be no less criminal to furnish it to others than if she drank it herself. Consequently they received, instead, glasses of hot lemonade, which, by an association of ideas, almost convinced Woodbury, in spite of himself, that he was suffering under an attack of influenza.

Mr. Dyce, who adroitly managed to keep the left side of his face towards the candle, ate his portion with great relish. His spiritual office being ended for the day, he returned with avidity to the things of this world, and entered into a defence of animal food, addressed to Seth Wattles, who was inclined to be a Vegetarian. Indeed, the medium dropped hints unfavorable to the Temperance reform, which would have shocked some of his hearers, if he had not based them, like the most of his opinions, on spiritual communications.

As the guests were putting on their coats and cloaks in the hall, Woodbury overheard Mrs. Waldo, furtively saying to her spouse: "I am *so* glad you spoke your mind."

"I must thank you, also, Mr. Waldo," said Hannah Thurston. "One should not too willingly accept any thing so new and strange. For the sake of the truth we already possess, it is right to be cautious"

"And now it is my turn to thank *you*, Miss Thurston," rejoined Woodbury, gayly, as they went out into the cool night-air.

She understood him. For one instant her habitual antagonism asserted itself, but she conquered it by a strong effort. The night hid her face, and her voice was even-toned and sweet as ever, as she answered: "I am glad there is one point on which we can agree."

"Oh, there are a great many, I assure you," he exclaimed, with a lightness which, she knew not why, struck her unpleasantly: "If we could take away from your surplus of earnestness, to complete my lack of it, we should get on very well together."

"Can one be too much in earnest?" she asked.

"Decidedly. There are relative values in ethics, as in every thing else. You would not pull a pink with the same serious application of strength which you would use, to wind a bucket out of a well. But Mrs. Waldo waits: good-night!"

He lifted her into the cutter, the horses started, and she was off before she had fairly time to consider what he meant. But the words were too singular to be forgotten.

Bute now made his appearance, and Woodbury took his seat in the cutter beside him. Dick was another horse when his head was pointed towards home, and the bells danced to a lively measure as they passed up the valley in the face of the wind. The rising moon struggled through clouds, and but two or three stars were visible overhead. The night was weird and sad, and in its presence the trials and the indulgencies of daylight became indistinct dreams. Woodbury recalled, with a feeling of intense repugnance, the occurrences of the evening. "Better," he said to himself, " a home for the soul within the volcanic rings of yonder barren moon, with no more than the privacy it may command in this life, than to be placed on the fairest star of the universe, and be held at the beck and call of every mean mind that dares to juggle with sanctities."

Plunged in these meditations, he did not at first notice the short, half-suppressed spirts of laughter into which Bute occasionally broke. The latter, at last, unable to enjoy his fun alone, said :

"When you looked at me, Mr. Max., I thought I'd ha' bust. I never was so nigh givin' way in my life."

"What was it ?" asked Woodbury.

"Well, you musn't say nothin'. *I* done it."

"You !"

"Yes, ha ! ha ! But he's no idee who it was."

"Did you strike him in the face, Bute ?"

"Lord, no ! *He* done all the strikin' there was done to-night. I fixed it better 'n that. You see I suspicioned they'd git Angeliny's spirut to playin' on the pyanna, like th' other time I was there. Thinks I, I've a notion how it's done, and if I'm right, it's easy to show it. So, afore comin' into the settin'-room, I jist went through the kitchen, and stood awhile on the hearth, to warm my feet, like. I run one arm up the chimbley, when nobody was lookin', and rubbed my hand full o' soft sut. Then I set in the corner, and held my arm behind me over the back o' the cheer, till the candle was took out. Now's the time, thinks I, and quick as wink I slips up to the pyanna—I knowed if they'd heerd me they'd think it was a spirut—and rubbed my sutty hand very quietly over the black keys. I didn't dare to bear on, but, thinks I, *some* 'll come off, and he 'll be sure to git it on *his* hands. Do you see it, Mr. Max. ? When the light come back, there he was, solemn enough, with a black eye, ha! ha! I couldn't git a sight of his hand, though; he shet his fist and kep' it under the table."

Woodbury at first laughed heartily, but his amusement soon gave place to indignation at the swindle. "Why did you not expose the fellow?" he asked Bute.

"Oh, what's the use! Them that believes wouldn't believe any the less, if they'd seen him play the pyanna with their own eyes. I've no notion o' runnin' my head into a hornet's nest, and gittin' well stung, and no honey to show for my pains."

With which sage observation Bute drove up to the door of Lakeside.

CHAPTER X.

IN WHICH WE HEAR A DIVERTING STORY.

THE winter wore away, slowly to the inhabitants of Ptolemy, rapidly and agreeably to the owner of Lakeside, who drank life, activity, and cheerfulness from the steady cold. Every day, while the snow lasted, his cutter was to be seen on the roads. Dick proved entirely inadequate to his needs and was turned over to Bute's use, while the fastest horse out of Fairlamb's livery-stable in Ptolemy took his place. Woodbury's drives extended not only to Anacreon and the neighboring village of Nero Corners—a queer little place, stuck out of sight in a hollow of the upland,—but frequently as far as Tiberius, which, being situated on a branch of the New York Central, considered itself quite metropolitan. The inhabitants took especial delight in its two principal streets, wherein the houses were jammed together as compactly as possible, and huge brick blocks, with cornices and window-caps of cast-iron, started up pompously between one-story buildings of wood, saying to the country people, on market days: " Behold, a city !"

The farmers around Ptolemy, who believe that every man born in a large town, and ignorant of either farming or some mechanical employment, must necessarily be soft, weak, and effeminate in his nature—" spoiled," so far as true masculine grit is concerned—were not a little astonished at Woodbury's activity and powers of endurance. More than once some of them had met him, sheeted with snow and driving in the teeth of a furious north-eastern storm, yet singing merrily to himself as if he liked it all ! It was noticed, too, that a vigorous red was driving away the tan of Indian summers from his cheeks,

6*

that a listless, indifferent expression, which at first made them
say " he has sleepy eyes," had vanished from those organs, as
if a veil had been withdrawn, leaving them clear and keen,
with a cheerful, wide-awake nature looking out. Thus,
although his habitual repose of manner remained, it no longer
impressed the people as something foreign and uncomfortable ;
and the general feeling towards him, in spite of the attacks of
Mr. Grindle and the insinuations of Seth Wattles, was respectful and friendly.   Bute, who was a confirmed favorite among
the people, would suffer no word to be said against his master,
and went so far as to take a respectable man by the throat, in
the oyster-cellar under the Ptolemy House, for speaking of
him as a " stuck-up aristocrat."

That part of a man's life which springs from his physical
temperament seemed, in Woodbury's case, to have stood still
during his sojourn abroad.   After the tropical torpidity of his
system had been shaken off, he went back ten years in the
sudden refreshment of his sensations.   The delicate cuticle of
youth, penetrated with the finer nerves which acknowledge
every touch of maturing existence as a pleasure, was partially
restored.   The sadness engendered by hard experience, the
scorn which the encounter with human meanness and selfishness left behind, the half-contemptuous pity which the pride
of shallow brains provoked—these were features of his nature,
which, impressed while it was yet plastic, were now too firmly
set to be erased ; but they were overlaid for the time by the
joyous rush of physical sensation.   His manner lost that first
gravity which suggested itself even in his most relaxed and
playful moods ; he became gay, brilliant, and bantering, and
was the life of the circles in which he moved.   As the owner
of Lakeside, *all* circles, of course, were open to him ; but he
soon discovered the most congenial society and selected it,
without regard to the distinctions which prevailed in Ptolemy.
As no standard of merely social value was recognized, the
little community was divided according to the wealth, or the
religious views of its members ; whence arose those jealousies

and rivalries which the Great Sewing-Union had for a time suppressed. Woodbury soon perceived this fact, and determined, at the start, to preserve his social independence. Neither of the circles could complain of being neglected, yet neither could claim exclusive possession of him. He took tea twice in one week with the Rev. Lemuel Styles, and the heart of Miss Legrand, the clergyman's sister-in-law, began to be agitated by a vague hope; but, in a few days afterwards, he accompanied the Misses Smith (Seventh-day Baptists) on a sleighing party to Atauga City, and was seen, on the following Sunday, to enter the Cimmerian church.

Between the Waldos and himself, a sincere friendship had grown up. The parson and his wife possessed, in common with Woodbury, a basis of healthy common sense, which, in spite of the stubborn isolation of their sect, made them tolerant. They had no idea of turning life into a debating-school, and could hear adverse opinions incidentally dropped, in the course of conversation, without considering that each word was thrown down as a gage of combat. Hence, Woodbury found no pleasanter house than theirs, in all his rounds, and the frank way in which he occasionally claimed their scanty hospitality was so much like that of a brother, that the parson declared to his wife, it expressed his idea of Christian society. I am afraid I shall injure Mr. Waldo's reputation, but I am bound to state that Woodbury was the last man whom he would have attempted to secure, as a proselyte.

One evening in March, after the winter had begun to melt away on the long hill sweeping from the eastern valley around to Lakeside, a little party accidentally assembled in Mrs. Waldo's parlor. Since the proceeds of the Fair had enabled her to cover its walls with a cheap green paper, and to substitute a coarse carpet of the same color for the tattered thing which she had transferred to her bed-room, the apartment was vastly improved. The horse-hair sofa and chairs, it is true, had performed a great deal of service, but they were able to do it; the sheet-iron stove gave out a comfortable warmth; and the one treasure of the parsonage, a melodeon, which did the duty of an organ on Sundays, was in tolerable tune. Hannah Thurston contributed a vase of grasses, exquisitely arranged, which obliged Mrs. Waldo to buy a plaster bracket from an itinerant Italian. She could ill afford to spare the half-dollar which it cost—and, indeed, most of the women in her husband's congregation shook their heads and murmured: "Vanity, vanity!" when they saw it—but a little self-denial in her housekeeping, which no one else than herself ever knew, reconciled the deed to her conscience. Woodbury brought to her from New York an engraving of Ary Scheffer's "Christus Consolator," which not only gave her great delight, but was of service in a way she did not suspect. It hung opposite to the grasses, and thus thoroughly counterbalanced their presumed "vanity," in the eyes of Cimmerian visitors. Indeed, they were not sure but a moral effect was intended, and this uncertainty stopped the remarks which might otherwise have spread far and wide.

The party in Mrs. Waldo's parlor was assembled by accident, we have said; but not entirely so. Hannah Thurston had been invited to tea by the hostess, and Woodbury by Mr. Waldo, who had met him in the streets of Ptolemy. This coincidence was unintentional, although not unwelcome to the hosts, who, liking both their guests heartily, could not account for the evident prejudice of the one and the indifference of the other. Mrs. Waldo had long since given up, as insane, her first hope of seeing the two drawn together by mutual magnetism; all she now desired was to establish an *entente cordiale*, since the *entente d'amour* could never be. On this occasion, the parties behaved towards each other with such thorough courtesy and propriety, that, had Hannah Thurston been any other woman, Mrs. Waldo would have suspected the existence of an undying enmity.

After tea Mr. and Mrs. Merryfield made their appearance. They had come to Ptolemy to attend a lecture on Temperance by Abiram Stokes, a noted orator of the cause, who, however, failed to arrive. Seth Wattles presently followed, apparently by accident, but really by design. He had ascertained where Hannah intended to pass the evening, from the widow Thurston's little servant-maid, whom he waylaid as she was coming out of the grocery-store, and did not scruple to thrust himself upon the company. His self-complacency was a little disturbed by the sight of Woodbury, whose discomfiture, during the evening, he mentally resolved to accomplish.

His victim, however, was in an unusually cheerful mood, and every arrow which the indignant Seth shot, though feathered to the barb with insinuation, flew wide of the mark. Woodbury joined in denunciation of the opium traffic ; he trampled on the vices of pride, hypocrisy, and selfishness ; he abhorred intemperance, hated oppression, and glorified liberty. But he continually brought the conversation back to its key-note of playful humor, cordially seconded by Mrs. Waldo, whose only fault, in the eyes of her reforming friends, was that she had no taste for serious discussion. Seth, finally, having exhausted his quiver, began to declaim against the corrupting influence of cities.

"It is time that hackneyed superstition were given up," said Woodbury. "Everybody repeats, after poor old Cowper, 'God made the country and man made the town ;' therefore, one is divine, and the other—the opposite. As if God had no part in that human brain and those human affections, out of which spring Art, and Discovery, and the varied fabric of Society ! As if man had no part in making Nature attractive and enjoyable to us !"

"Cities are created by the selfishness of man," cried Seth, a little pompously.

"And farms, I suppose, are created entirely by benevolence !" retorted Woodbury, laughing. "You Reformers have the least cause to complain of cities. You got your Temperance from Baltimore, and your Abolition from Boston."

"That proves nothing: there was one just man even in

Sodom!" exclaimed Seth, determined not to be put down "But, of course, people who think *fashion* more important than *principle*, will always admire a city life."

"Yes, it is Fashion," added Mrs. Merryfield, who was unusually dyspeptic that evening—"it is Fashion that has impeded the cause of woman. Fashion is the fetters which chains her down as the slave of man. How can she know her rights, when she is educated, as a child, to believe that Dress is her Doom?"

"If you were familiar with cities, Mrs. Merryfield," said Woodbury, "you would find that they admit of the nearest approach to social independence. Fashion is just as rigid in Ptolemy as it is in New York; among the Hottentots or Digger Indians, far more so. Not only that, but Fashion is actually necessary to keep us from falling into chaos. Suppose there were no such thing, and you and Mr. Merryfield lived in tents, dressed in oriental costume, while Mr. Waldo preached in feathers and war-paint, to Miss Thurston, in a complete suit of steel armor, Mr. Wattles with Chinese pig-tail and fan, and myself in bag-wig, powder, and ruffles!"

The hearty laughter which followed this suggestion did not silence Seth. "It is not a subject for frivolity," he exclaimed; "you cannot deny that Fashion corrupts the heart and destroys all the better impulses of human nature."

"I do deny it," replied Woodbury, whose unusual patience was nearly exhausted. "All sweeping, undiscriminating assertions contain much that is both false and absurd, and yours is no exception. The foundation of character lies deeper than external customs. The honor of man, the virtue of woman, the pure humanity of both, is not affected by the cut or colors of their dress. If the race is so easily corrupted as one might infer from your assertions, how can you ever expect to succeed with your plans of reform?"

"I should not expect it," interposed Mrs. Merryfield, "if I had to depend on the women that worships the Moloch of fashion. Why, if I was the noblest and wisest of my sex, they'd turn up their noses at me, unless I lived in Fifth Avenue."

A sweet, serious smile, betraying that breath of dried roses which greets us as we open some forgotten volume of the past, stole over Woodbury's face. His voice, also, when he spoke, betrayed the change. Some memory, suddenly awakened, had banished the present controversy from his mind.

"It is strange," said he, slowly, addressing Mrs. Waldo, rather than the speaker, "how a new life, like mine in India, can make one forget what has gone before it. In this moment, a curious episode of my youth suddenly comes back to me, distinct as life, and I wonder how it could ever have been forgotten. Shall I give you a story in place of an argument, Mrs. Merryfield? Perhaps it may answer for both. But if you can't accept it in that light, you may have the last word."

"Pray tell us, by all means!" exclaimed Mrs. Waldo.

Woodbury looked around. Hannah Thurston, meeting his questioning glance, silently nodded. Seth was sullen and gave no sign. Mrs. Merryfield answered, "I'd like to hear it, well enough, I'm sure," whereto her husband added: "So would I, as—as it were." Thus encouraged, Woodbury began:

"It happened after my father's death, and before I left New York for Calcutta. I was not quite twenty when he died, and his bankruptcy left me penniless, just at the time of life when such a condition is most painfully felt. In my case it was worse than usual, because so utterly unexpected, and my education had in no way prepared me to meet it. Every thing went: house, furniture, library, and even those domestic trifles which are hardest to part with. A few souvenirs of my mother were saved, and a friend of the family purchased and gave to me my father's watch. My brother-in-law was unable to help me, because he was greatly involved in the ruin. He sent my sister and their children to live in a cheap New Jersey village, while he undertook a journey to New Orleans, in the hope of retrieving his position by a lucky stroke of

business. Thus, within a month after the funeral of my
father, I found myself alone, poor, and homeless. It was in
1837, and the great financial crash was just beginning to
thunder in men's ears. My father's friends were too much
concerned about their own interests to care especially for
mine. It was no single case of misfortune : there were examples equally hard, on all sides, very soon.

"Nevertheless, I was not suffered to become a vagabond.
A subordinate clerkship was procured for me, at a salary of
two hundred and fifty dollars a year I was ignorant of
business, for my father had intended that I should study Law,
after completing my collegiate course, and the character of
my mind was not well adapted for commercial life. The
salary, small as it was, fully equalled the value of my services,
and I should have made it suffice to meet my wants, if I had
received it punctually. But my employer so narrowly escaped
ruin during the crisis that he was often unable to pay me, or
my fellow-clerks, our monthly wages, and I, who had no little
hoard to draw upon, like the others, sometimes suffered the
most painful embarrassment. I have frequently, this winter,
heard the praises of a vegetable diet. I have some right to
give my opinion on the subject, as I tried the experiment for
two months at a time, and must say that it totally failed.

"I was too proud to borrow money, at such times, and was,
moreover, exceedingly sensitive lest my situation should become
known. The boarding-house, where I first made my home, became uncomfortable, because I was not always ready with my
money on Saturday morning. Besides, it was a cheap place, kept
by an old woman with two sentimental daughters, who wore
their hair in curls and always smelt of sassafras soap. There were
various reasons which you will understand, without my telling
you, why my residence there grew at last to be insufferable. I
accidentally discovered that the owner of a corner grocery in
the Bowery had a vacant room over his store, with a separate
entrance from the cross-street, and that he could supply me, at
a cheap rent, with the most necessary furniture. The bargain

was soon made. The room and furniture cost me a dollar a week, and my food could be regulated according to my means. The common eating-houses supplied me, now and then, with a meal, but I oftenest bought my bread at the baker's, and filled my pitcher from the hydrant in the back-yard. I was also so far independent that I could choose my associates, and regulate my personal habits. I assure you that I never washed my face with sassafras soap."

Mrs. Waldo laughed heartily at this declaration, and Mrs. Merryfield innocently exclaimed : "Why, I'm sure it's very good for the skin."

"Meanwhile," Woodbury continued, "I still kept up intercourse with the circle in which my father moved, and which, at that time, would have been called 'fashionable.' Some families, it is true, felt a restraint towards me which I was too sensitive not to discover. The daughters had evidently been warned against too great a display of sympathy. On the other hand, I made new and delightful acquaintances, of equal social standing, by whom I was treated with a delicacy and a generous consideration which I shall never forget. In fact, whatever Christian respect I may exhibit, in my intercourse with others, I learned from those families. You may know what they were, Mr. Waldo, by imagining how you would treat me, now, if I should suddenly lose my property.

"I had been living in this manner for a year, or thereabouts, when the main incident of my story occurred. In the circle where I was most intimate, there were two or three wealthy bachelors, who had handsome residences in the neighborhood of Bleecker street (there was no Fifth Avenue then). These gentlemen had, in turn, given entertainments during the winter, and had taken such pains to make them agreeable to the young ladies, that they constituted a feature of the season. The company was small and select, on these occasions, two or three married pairs being present for the sake of propriety, but no society was ever more genial, joyous, and unconstrained in tone. At the last entertainment, our host finished by giving

us a choice supper, to which we sat down in order to enjoy it
thoroughly. I have had a prejudice against all ambulatory
suppers since. There were songs and toasts, and fun of the
purest and most sparkling quality. At last, one of the young
ladies said, with a mock despair: 'So, this is the end of our
bachelor evenings. What a pity! I am ready to wish that
you other gentlemen had remained single, for our sakes. You
know you cannot give us such delightful parties as this.'

"'Are there really no more bachelors?' exclaimed Miss
Remington, a tall, beautiful girl, who sat opposite to me.
'Must we sing: Lochaber no more? But that will never do:
some married man must retract his vow, for our sakes.'

"One of the latter, looking around the table, answered:
'Let us be certain, first, that we are at the end of the list.
Belknap, Moulton, Parks—yes—but stop! there's Woodbury!
too modest to speak for himself.'

"'Woodbury! Woodbury!' they all shouted, the young
ladies insisting that I *should* and *must* entertain them in my
turn. My heart came into my throat. I attempted to laugh
off the idea as a jest, but they were too joyously excited to
heed me. It was a cruel embarrassment, for none of the company even knew where I lived. My letters were always sent
to the office of my employer. Moreover, I had but five dollars, and had made a resolution never to live in advance of my
wages. What was I to do? The other guests, ignorant of
my confusion, or not heeding it, were already talking of the
entertainment as settled, and began to suggest the evening
when it should take place. I was meditating, in a sort of desperation, whether I should not spring up and rush out of the
house, when I caught Miss Remington's eye. I saw that she
understood my embarrassment, and wanted to help me. Her
look said 'Accept!'—a singular fancy darted through my
mind, and I instantly regained my self-possession. I informed
the company that I should be very happy to receive them, and
that my entertainment should bear the same proportion to my
means as that of our host. The invitations were given and

accepted on the spot, and an evening selected from the following week.

" 'But where is it to be?' asked one of the young ladies.

" ' Oh, he will let you know in time,' said Miss Remington, who took occasion to whisper to me, before the company separated : ' Come to me first, and talk the matter over.'

"I called upon her the next evening, and frankly confided to her my situation and means. She was three or four years older than myself, and possessed so much natural judgment and good sense, in addition to her social experience, that I had the utmost confidence in her advice. A woman of less tact would have offered to assist me, and that would have been an end of the matter. She saw at once what was best to be done, and we very soon agreed upon the preparations. Every thing was to be kept secret from the rest of the company, whom she determined to mystify to her heart's content. She informed them that the entertainment would be unlike any thing they had ever seen ; that the place was not to be divulged, but the guests were to assemble at her father's house on the appointed evening ; and that they must so dress as to do the highest honor to my hospitality. The curiosity of all was greatly excited ; the affair was whispered about, and others endeavored to join the party, but it was strictly confined to the original company.

" On my part I was not idle. Adjoining my chamber was a large room, in which the grocer kept some of his stores. This room I thoroughly cleaned, removing some of the articles, but retaining all the kegs and boxes. The grocer, an honest, amiable man, supposed that I was preparing a little festival for some of my relatives, and gave me the free use of his material. I arranged the kegs and boxes around the walls, and covered them with coarse wrapping-paper, to serve as seats. The largest box was stationed in a corner, with a keg on the top, as a post for the single musician I had engaged— an old Irish fiddler, whom I picked up in the street I went out towards Yorkville and brought home a bundle of cedar

boughs, with which I decorated the walls, constructing a large
green word—WELCOME—above the fireplace.   I borrowed
twelve empty bottles in which I placed as many tallow candles,
and disposed them about the room, on extemporized brackets.
For my own chamber, which was designed to answer as a dres-
sing-room for the ladies, I made candlesticks out of the largest
turnips I could find in the market.   In fact, I purposely removed some little conveniences I possessed, and invented substi-
tutes of the most grotesque kind.   I became so much interested in my preparations, and in speculating upon the effect
they would produce, that I finally grew as impatient as my
guests for the evening to arrive.

" Nine o'clock was the hour appointed, and, punctually to the
minute, five carriages turned out of the Bowery and drew up,
one after another, at the side-door.   I was at the entrance, in
complete evening dress, with white gloves (washed), to receive
my guests.   I held a tray, upon which there were as many
candles fixed in large turnips, as there were gentlemen in the
party, and begged each one to take a light and follow me.
The ladies, magnificently dressed in silks and laces, rustled
up the narrow staircase, too much amazed to speak.   As I
threw open the door of my saloon, the fiddler, perched near
the ceiling, struck up 'Hail to the Chief.'   The effect, I assure you, was imposing.   Miss Remington shook hands with
me, heartily, exclaiming: ' Admirable!   You could not have
done better.'   To be sure, there were some exclamations of
surprise, and perhaps one or two blank faces—but only for a
moment.   The fun was seen immediately, and the evening
commenced with that delightful social *abandon* in which other
evenings generally end.   The fiddler played a Scotch reel, and
the couples took their places on the floor.   Two of the older
gentlemen were familiar with both the Scotch and Irish dances,
and the younger ladies set about learning them with a spirit
which charmed the old musician's heart.   The superb silks
floated about the room to the jolliest tunes, or rested, in the
intervals, on the grocer's kegs, and once a string of pearls

broke and rolled into the fireplace. After a while, the grocer's boy, in his shirt-sleeves, made his appearance with a large
market-basket on his arm, containing a mixture of cakes,
raisins, and almonds. He was in great demand, especially
as I furnished no plates. It was then agreed to put the
basket on a keg, as a permanent refreshment-table, and the boy
brought in lemonade, in all kinds of drinking-vessels. I had
taken some pains to have them all of different patterns. There
were tin-cups, stoneware mugs, tea-cups, bowls, and even a
cologne bottle. By this time all had fully entered into the
spirit of the affair: I was not only at ease but jubilant. The
old fiddler played incessantly. Miss Remington sang 'The
Exile of Erin' to his accompaniment, and the old man cried:
we had speeches, toasts, recitations: we revived old games:
we told fortunes with cards (borrowed from the porter-house
across the way): in short, there was no bound to the extent of
our merriment, and no break in its flow.

"It occurred to some one, at last, to look at his watch.—
'God bless me! it's three o'clock!' he cried. Three!—and six
hours had already passed away! The ladies tore up my green
word 'WELCOME,' to get sprigs of cedar as souvenirs of the
evening: some even carried off the turnip-candlesticks. Miss
Remington laughed in her sleeve at the latter. 'I know better than to do that,' she said to me; 'turnips have a habit of
rotting.' It was unanimously voted that I had given them
the best entertainment of the season; and I am sure, for my
own part, that none had been so heartily enjoyed.

"The story, as you may suppose, soon became known; and
it was only by sheer resolution that I escaped a social popularity which might have turned my head at that age. I was
even asked to repeat the entertainment, so that others might
have a chance to participate in it; but I knew that its whole
success lay in the spontaneous inspiration which prompted,
and the surprise which accompanied it. The incident, however, proved to be one of the influences to which I must attribute my subsequent good fortune."

"Pray, how was that?" asked Mr. Waldo.

"My employer heard, in some way or other, that I had given a splendid entertainment. Knowing my means, and fearing that I had fallen into reckless habits, he called me into his private office and very seriously asked for an explanation of my conduct. I related the circumstances, precisely as they had occurred. He easily ascertained that my story was true, and from that day forward took an increased interest in me, to which I must attribute, in part, my rapid advancement. Now, if there is any moral in all this, I think you can easily find it. If there is not, perhaps you have been diverted enough to pardon me for talking so much about myself."

"Why, it's delightful! I never heard any thing better!" cried Mrs. Waldo.

"It shows, though," interposed Mrs. Merryfield, "how inconsistent those fashionable women are. They can be courageous and independent for the sake of pleasure, but they'd be horrified at venturing so far for the sake of principle."

"You are hardly just," said Hannah Thurston, addressing the last speaker; "Mr. Woodbury's story *has* a moral, and I am very glad he has given it to us."

Seth Wattles had been interested and amused, in spite of himself, but he was not the man to acknowledge it. He was endeavoring to find some point at which he might carp, with a show of reason, when Miss Carrie Dilworth entered the room, and presently Bute Wilson, who had driven from Lakeside to take Woodbury home.

"Mr. Max.!" cried the latter, whose face had a flushed, strange expression, "Diamond won't stand alone, and I must go out and hold him till you're ready."

"I'll come at once, then," said Woodbury, and took leave of the company.

CHAPTER XI.

CONTAINING TWO DECLARATIONS, AND THE ANSWERS THERETO.

As Bute, on entering the village, passed the Widow Thurston's cottage, he noticed a dim little figure emerging from the gate. Although the night was dark, and the figure was so muffled as to present no distinct outline, Bute's eyes were particularly sharp. Like the sculptor, he saw the statue in the shapeless block. Whether it was owing to a short jerking swing in the gait, or an occasional sideward toss of what seemed to be the head, he probably did not reflect; but he immediately drew the rein on Diamond, and called out " Miss Carrie!"

" Ah !" proceeded from the figure, as it stopped, with a start; " who is it ?"

Bute cautiously drove near the plank sidewalk, before answering. Then he said : " It's me."

" Oh, Bute," exclaimed Miss Dilworth, "how you frightened me ! Where did you come from ?"

" From home. I'm a-goin' to fetch Mr. Max., but there's no hurry. I say, Miss Carrie, wouldn't you like to take a little sleigh-ride ? Where are you goin' to ?"

" To Waldo's."

" Why, so am I ! Jump in, and I'll take you along."

Miss Dilworth, nothing loath, stepped from the edge of the sidewalk into the cutter, and took her seat. Bute experienced a singular feeling of comfort, at having the soft little body wedged so closely beside him, with the same wolf-skin spread over their mutual knees. His heart being on the side next

her, it presently sent a tingling warmth over his whole frame;
the sense of her presence impressed him with a vague physical
delight, and he regretted that the cutter was not so narrow as
to oblige him to take her upon his knees. It was less than
half a mile to the parsonage—about two minutes, as Diamond
trotted—and then the doors of heaven would close upon him.

"No! by Jimminy!" he suddenly exclaimed, turning
around in the track, at the imminent risk of upsetting the
cutter.

"What's the matter?" cried Miss Dilworth, a little alarmed
at this unexpected manœuvre.

"It isn't half a drive for you, Carrie," Bute replied. "The
sleddin's prime, and I'll jist take a circuit up the creek, and
across into the South Road. We'll go it in half an hour, and
there's plenty of time."

Miss Dilworth knew, better even than if he had tried to tell
her, that Bute was proud and happy at having her beside
him. Her vanity was agreeably ministered to; she enjoyed
sleighing; and, moreover, where was the harm? She would
not have objected, on a pinch, to be driven through Ptolemy
by Arbutus Wilson, in broad daylight; and now it was too
dark for either of them to be recognized. So she quietly
submitted to what was, after all, not a hard fate.

As they sped along merrily over the bottoms of East
Atauga Creek, past the lonely, whispering elms, and the
lines of ghostly alders fringing the stream, where the air
struck their faces with a damp cold, the young lady shuddered. She pressed a little more closely against Bute, as if
to make sure of his presence, and said, in a low tone: "I
should not like to be alone, here, at this hour."

Poor Bute felt that the suspense of his heart was no longer
to be borne. She had played with him, and he had allowed
himself to be played with, long enough. He would ask a
serious question and demand a serious answer. His resolution
was fixed, yet, now that the moment had arrived, his tongue
seemed to become paralyzed. The words were in his mind,

every one of them—he had said them over to himself, a hundred times—but there was a muzzle on his mouth which prevented their being put into sound. He looked at the panels of fence as they sped past, and thought, "so much more of the road has gone, and I have said nothing."

Miss Dilworth's voice was like a palpable hand stretched out to draw him from that quagmire of silence. "Oh, Carrie!" he exclaimed, "you needn't be alone, anywheres—leastways where there's any thing to skeer or hurt you."

She understood him, and resumed her usual tactics, half-accepting, half-defensive. "We can't help being alone sometimes, Bute," she answered, "and some are born to be alone always. Alone in spirit, you know; where there is no congenial nature."

"You're not one o' *them*, Carrie," said Bute, desperately. "You know you're not a genus. If you was, I shouldn't keer whether I had your good-will or not. But I want that, and more'n that, because I like you better than any thing in this world. I've hinted the same many a time, and you know it, and I don't want you to turn it off no longer."

The earnestness of his voice caused Miss Dilworth to tremble. There was a power in the man which she feared she could not withstand. Still he had made no definite proposal, and she was not bound to answer more than his words literally indicated.

"Why, of course I like you, Bute," said she; "everybody does. And you've always been so kind and obliging towards me."

"Like! I'd ruther you'd say *hate* than *like*. There's two kinds o' likin', and one of 'em's the kind that doesn't fit anybody that comes along. Every man, Carrie, that's wuth his salt, must find a woman to work for, and when he's nigh onto thirty, as I am, he wants to see a youngster growin' up, to take his place when he gits old. Otherways, no matter how lucky he is, there's not much comfort to him in livin'. Now, I'm awful serious about this. I don't care whether we're con-

7

genial spirits, or not, but I want you, Carrie, for my wife.
You may hunt far and wide, but you'll find nobody that'll
keer for you as I will. Perhaps I don't talk quite as fine as
some, but talkin's like the froth on the creek; maybe it's
shallow, and maybe it's deep, you can't tell. The heart's the
main thing, and, thank God, I'm right there. Carrie, this
once, jist this once, don't trifle with me."

Bute's voice became soft and pleading, as he closed. Miss
Dilworth was moved at last; he had struck through her affected sentimentalism, and touched the small bit of true womanly
nature beneath it. But the impression was too sudden. She
had not relinquished her ambitious yearnings; she knew and
valued Bute's fidelity, and, precisely for that reason, she felt
secure in seeming to decline it. She would have it in reserve,
in any case, and meanwhile, he was too cheerful and light-
hearted to suffer much pain from the delay. Had he taken
her in his arms, had he stormed her with endearing words,
had he uttered even one sentence of the hackneyed sentiment
in which she delighted, it would have been impossible to resist. But he sat silently waiting for her answer, while the
horse slowly climbed the hill over which they must pass to
reach the South Road; and in that silence her vanity regained
its strength.

"Carrie?" he said, at last.

"Bute?"

"You don't answer me."

"Oh, Bute!" said she, with a curious mixture of tenderness
and coquetry, "I don't know how. I never thought you
were more than half in earnest. And I'm not sure, after all,
that we were meant for each other. I like you as well as I
like anybody, but—"

Here she paused.

"But you won't have me, I s'pose?" said Bute, in a tone
that was both bitter and sad.

"I don't quite mean that," she answered. "But a woman
has so much at stake, you know. She must love more than a

man, I've been told, before she can give up her name and her life to him. I don't know, Bute, whether I should do right to promise myself to you. I've never thought of it seriously. Besides, you come upon me so sudden—you frightened me a little, and I really don't exactly know what my own mind is."

"Yes, I see," said Bute, in a stern voice.

They had reached the top of the hill, and the long descent to Ptolemy lay before them. Bute drew the reins and held the horse to his best speed. Some inner prop of his strong breast seemed to give way all at once. He took the thick end of his woollen scarf between his teeth and stifled the convulsive movements of his throat. Then a sensation of heat rushed through his brain, and the tears began to roll rapidly down his cheeks. He was grateful for the darkness which hid his face, for the bells which drowned his labored breathing, and for the descent which shortened the rest of the drive. He said nothing more, and Miss Dilworth, in spite of herself, was awed by his silence. By the time they had reached the parsonage he was tolerably calm, and the traces of his passion had disappeared from his face.

Miss Dilworth lingered while he was fastening the horse. She felt, it must be confessed, very uneasy, and not guiltless of what had happened. She knew not how to interpret Bute's sudden silence. It was probably anger, she thought, and she would therefore lay the first stone of a temple of reconciliation. She liked him too well to lose him wholly.

"Good-night, Bute!" she said, holding out her hand: "you are not angry with me, are you?"

"No," was his only answer, as he took her hand. There was no eager, tender pressure, as before, and the tone of his voice, to her ear, betrayed indifference, which was worse than anger.

After Woodbury had taken leave, there was a general movement of departure. The sempstress had come to spend a few days with Mrs. Waldo, and did not intend returning; it was rather late, and the Merryfields took the nearest road home, so

that Hannah Thurston must have walked back, alone, to her
mother's cottage, had not Seth Wattles been there to escort her.
Seth foresaw this duty, and inwardly rejoiced thereat. The
absence of Woodbury restored his equanimity of temper, and
he was as amiably disposed as was possible to his incoherent
nature. He was not keen enough to perceive the strong relief
into which his shapeless mind was thrown by the symmetry
and balance of the man whom he hated—that he lost ground,
even in his own circle, not merely from the discomfiture of the
moment, but far more from that unconscious comparison of the
two which arose from permanent impressions. He was not
aware of the powerful magnetism which social culture exer-
cises, especially upon minds fitted, by their honest yearning
after something better, to receive it themselves.

Seth was therefore, without reason, satisfied with himself as
he left the house. He had dared, at least, to face this self-
constituted lion, and had found the animal more disposed to
gambol than to bite. He flattered himself that his earnestness
contrasted favorably with the levity whereby Woodbury had
parried questions so important to the human race. Drawing
a long breath, as of great relief, he exclaimed:

"Life is real, life is earnest! We feel it, under this sky:
here the frivolous chatter of Society is hushed."

Hannah Thurston took his proffered arm, conscious, as she
did so, of a shudder of something very like repugnance. For
the first time it struck her that she would rather hear the
sparkling nothings of gay conversation than Seth's serious
platitudes. She did not particularly desire his society, just
now, and attempted to hasten her pace, under the pretext that
the night was cold.

Seth, however, hung back. "We do not enjoy the night as
we ought," said he. "It elevates and expands the soul. It is
the time for kindred souls to hold communion."

"Scarcely out of doors, in winter, unless they are disembod-
ied," remarked Miss Thurston.

Seth was somewhat taken aback. He had not expected so

light a tone from so grave and earnest a nature. It was unusual with her, and reminded him, unpleasantly, of Woodbury's frivolity.   But he summoned new courage, and continued:

"We can say things at night for which we have no courage
in daylight. We are more sincere, somehow—less selfish, you
know, and more affectionate."

"There ought to be no such difference," said she, mechanically, and again hastening her steps.

"I know there oughtn't. And I didn't mean that *I* wasn't
as true as ever; but—but there are chosen times when our
souls are uplifted and approach each other. This is such a
time, Hannah. We seem to be nearer, and—and—"

He could get no farther. The other word in his mind was
too bold to be used at the outset. Besides, having taken one
step, he must allow her to take the next: it would make the
crisis easier for both. But she only drew her cloak more
closely around her, and said nothing.

"The influences of night and—other things," he resumed,
"render us insensible to time and—temperature. There is
one thing, at least, which defies the elements. Is there not?"

"What is it?" she asked.

"Can't you guess?"

"Benevolence, no doubt, or a duty so stern and sacred that
life itself is subordinate to its performance."

"Yes, that's true—but I mean something else!" Seth exclaimed. "Something *I* feel, now, deep in my buzzum. Shall
I unveil it to your gaze?"

"I have no right to ask or accept your confidence," she
replied.

"Yes, you have. One kindred soul has the right to demand
every thing of the other. I might have told you, long ago,
but I waited so that you might find it out for yourself, without the necessity of words. Surely you must have seen it in my
eyes, and heard it in my voice, because every thing powerful
in us expresses itself somehow in spite of us. The deepest

emotions, you know, are silent; but you understand my silence now, don't you?"

Hannah Thurston was more annoyed than surprised by this declaration. She saw that a clear understanding could not be avoided, and nerved herself to meet it. Her feeling of repugnance to the speaker increased with every word he uttered; yet, if his passion were genuine (and she had no right to doubt that it was so), he was entitled at least to her respect and her pity. Still, he had spoken only in vague terms, and she could not answer the real question. Why? Did she not fully understand him? Was the shrinking sense of delicacy in her heart, which she was unable to overcome, a characteristic of sex, separating her nature, by an impassable gulf, from that of man?

"Please explain yourself clearly, Seth," she said, at last.

"Oh, don't your own heart explain it for you? Love don't want to be explained: it comes to us of itself. See here— we've been laboring together ever so long in the Path of Progress, and our souls are united in aspirations for the good of our fellow-men. All I want is, that we should now unite our lives in the great work. You know I believe in the equal rights of Woman, and would never think of subjecting you to the tyranny your sisters groan under. I have no objection to taking your name, if you want to make that sort of a protest against legal slavery. We'll both keep our independence, and show to the world the example of a true marriage. Somebody must begin, you know, as Charles Macky, the glorious poet of our cause, says in his Good Time Coming."

"Seth," said Hannah Thurston, with a sad, deliberate sweetness in her voice, "there is one thing, without which there should be no union between man and woman."

"What is that?" he asked.

"Love."

"How? I don't understand you. That is the very reason why——"

"You forget," she interrupted, "that love must be reciprocal. You have taken it for granted that I returned, in equal measure, the feelings you have expressed towards me. Where the fortune of a life is concerned, it is best to be frank, though frankness give pain. Seth, I do not, I never can, give you love. A coincidence of opinions, of hopes and aspirations, is not love. I believe that you have made this mistake in your own mind, and that you will, sooner or later, thank me for having revealed it to you. I have never suspected, in you, the existence of love in its holiest and profoundest meaning, nor have I given you reason to suppose that my sentiments towards you were other than those of friendly sympathy and good-will. I deeply regret it, if you have imagined otherwise. I cannot atone to you for the ruin of whatever hopes you may have cherished, but I can at least save you from disappointment in the future. I tell you now, therefore, once and forever, that, whatever may happen, however our fates may change, you and I can never, never be husband and wife."

Sweet and low as was her voice, an inexorable fate spoke in it. Seth felt, word by word, its fatal significance, as the condemned culprit feels the terrible phrases of his final sentence. He knew, instinctively, that it was vain to plead or expostulate. He must, perforce, accept his doom; but, in doing so, his injured self-esteem made a violent protest. It was the fretful anger of disappointment, rather than the unselfish sorrow of love. He could only account for the fact of his refusal by the supposition that her affections were elsewhere bestowed.

"I see how it is," said he, petulantly; "somebody else is in the way."

"Do not misunderstand me," she answered. "I, only, am responsible for your disappointment. You have no right to question me, and I might well allow your insinuation to pass without notice; but my silence may possibly mislead you, as it seems my ordinary friendly regard has done. I will, therefore, for my own sake no less than yours—for I desire, in so solemn a matter, to leave no ground for self-reproach—voluntarily say to you, that I know no man to whom I could surrender my life in the unquestioning sacrifice of love. I have long since renounced the idea of marriage. My habits of thought —the duties I have assumed—my lack of youth and beauty, perhaps" (and here the measured sweetness of her voice was interrupted for a moment), " will never attract to me the man, unselfish enough to be just to my sex, equally pure in his aspirations, equally tender in his affections, and wiser in the richness of his experience, whom my heart would demand, if it dared still longer to cherish a hopeless dream. I have not even enough of an ideal love remaining, to justify your jealousy. In my association with you for the advancement of mutual aims, as well as in our social intercourse, I have treated you with the kindly respect which was your due as a fellow-being, but I can never recognize in you that holy kinship of the heart, without which Love is a mockery and Marriage is worse than death !"

Seth felt it impossible to reply, although his self-esteem was cruelly wounded. She thought herself too good for him, then : that was it ! Why, the very man she had described, as the ideal husband she would never meet—it was exactly himself ! It was of no use, however, for him to say so. She had rejected him with a solemn decision, from which there was no appeal. He must, also, needs believe her other declaration, that she loved no one else. Her inordinate mental pride was the true explanation.

They had stopped, during the foregoing conversation. Hannah Thurston had dropped her hold on his arm, and stood, facing him, on the narrow sidewalk. The night was so dark that neither could distinctly see the other's face. A melancholy wind hummed in the leafless twigs of the elms above them, and went off to sough among a neighboring group of pines. Finding that Seth made no answer, Miss Thurston slowly resumed her homeward walk. He mechanically accompanied her. As they approached the widow's cottage, he heaved a long, hoarse sigh, and muttered :

" Well, there's another aspiration deceived. It seems

there's no quality of human nature which we can depend upon."

"Do not let this disappointment make you unjust, Seth," she said, pausing, with her hand upon the gate. "You have deceived yourself, and it is far better to become reconciled to the truth at once. If I have ignorantly, in any way, assisted in the deception, I beg you to pardon me."

She turned to enter the cottage, but Seth still hesitated. "Hannah," he said at last, awkwardly: "You—you won't say any thing about this?"

She moved away from him with an instant revulsion of feeling. "What do you take me for?" she exclaimed. "Repeat that question to yourself, and perhaps it may explain to you why your nature and mine can never approach!" Without saying good-night, she entered the house, leaving Seth to wander back to his lodgings in a very uncomfortable frame of mind.

Hannah Thurston found the lighted lamp waiting for her in the warm sitting-room; her mother was already in bed. She took off her bonnet and cloak, and seated herself in the widow's rocking-chair. Tears of humiliation stood in her eyes. "He does not deserve," she said to herself, "that I should have opened my heart before him. I wanted to be just, for I thought that love, however imperfect or mistaken, was always at least delicate and reverent. I thought the advocacy of moral truth presupposed some nobility of soul—that a nature which accepted such truth could not be entirely low and mean. I have allowed a profane eye to look upon sanctities, and the very effort I made to be true and just impresses me with a sense of self-degradation. What must I do, to reconcile my instincts with the convictions of my mind? Had I not suppressed the exhibition of my natural repugnance to that man, I should have been spared the pain of this evening—spared the shrinking shudder which I must feel whenever the memory of it returns."

Gradually her self-examination went deeper, and she con-
7*

fessed to herself that Seth's declaration of love was in itself her greatest humiliation. She had not told him the whole truth, though it had seemed to be so, when she spoke. She had *not* renounced the dream of her younger years. True, she had forcibly stifled it, trodden upon it with the feet of a stern resolution, hidden its ruins from sight in the remotest chamber of her heart—but now it arose again, strong in its immortal life. Oh, to think *who* should have wooed her under the stars, in far other words and with far other answers—the man whom every pulse of her being claimed and called upon, the man who never came! In his stead this creature, whose love seemed to leave a stain behind it—whose approach to her soul was that of an unclean footstep. Had it come to this? Was *he* the only man whom the withheld treasures of her heart attracted towards her? Did he, alone, suspect the splendor of passion which shone beneath the calmness and reserve of the presence she showed to the world?

It was a most bitter, most humiliating thought. With her head drooping wearily towards her breast, and her hands clasped in her lap, with unheeded tears streaming from her eyes, she sought refuge from this pain in that other pain of the imagined love that once seemed so near and lovely—lovelier now, as she saw it through the mist of a gathering despair. Thus she sat, once more the helpless captive of her dreams, while the lamp burned low and the room grew cold.

CHAPTER XII.

MOTHER AND DAUGHTER.

THE morning came, late and dark, with a dreary March rain, the commencement of that revolutionary anarchy in the weather, through which the despotism of Winter is over-thrown, and the sweet republic of Spring established on the Earth. Even Woodbury, as he looked out on the writhing trees, the dripping roofs, and the fields of soggy, soaked snow, could not suppress a sigh of loneliness and yearning. Bute, whose disappointment, bitter though it was, failed to counter-act the lulling warmth of the blankets after his ride home against the wind, and who had therefore slept soundly all night, awoke to a sense of hollowness and wretchedness which he had never experienced before. His duties about the barn attended to, and breakfast over, he returned to his bedroom to make his usual Sunday toilet. Mr. Woodbury had decided not to go to church, and Bute, therefore, had nothing but his own thoughts, or the newspapers, to entertain him through the day. Having washed his neck and breast, put on the clean shirt which Mrs. Babb took care to have ready for him, and combed his yellow locks, he took a good look at himself in the little mirror.

"I a'n't handsome, that's a fact," he thought to himself, "but nuther is she, for that matter. I've got good healthy blood in me, though, and if my face *is* sunburnt, it don't look like taller. I don't see why all the slab-sided, lantern-jawed, holler-breasted fellows should have no trouble o' gittin' wives, and me, of a darned sight better breed, though I do say it, to have sich bad luck! I can't stand it. I've got every thing here that a man could want, but 'ta'n't enough. O Lord! to think her children should have somebody else than me for a father!"

Bute groaned and threw himself on the bed, where he thrust both hands through his carefully combed hair. His strong masculine nature felt itself wronged, and the struggle was none the less severe, because it included no finer spiritual disappointment. He possessed only a true, honest, tender heart, as the guide to his instincts, and these, when baffled, suggested no revenge, such as might occur to a more reckless or more imaginative nature. His life had been blameless, heretofore, from the simple force of habit, and the pure atmosphere in which he lived. To confess the truth, he was not particularly shocked by the grosser experiences of some of his friends, but to adopt them himself involved a change so violent that he knew not where it might carry him. If the thought crossed his mind at all, it was dismissed without a moment's hospitality. He did not see, because he did not seek, any escape from the sore, weary, thirsty sensation which his disappointment left behind. The fibres of his nature, which were accustomed to give out a sharp, ringing, lusty twang to every touch of Life, were now muffled and deadened in tone : that was all.

It might have been some consolation to Bute, if he could have known that his presumed rival was equally unfortunate. In the case of the latter, however, there was less of the pang of blighted hopes than of the spiteful bitterness of wounded vanity. Seth Wattles was accustomed to look upon himself, and not without grounds of self-justification, as an unusual man. The son of a poor laborer, orphaned at an early age, and taken in charge by a tailor of Ptolemy, who brought him up to his own business, he owed his education mostly to a quick ear and a ready tongue. His brain, though shallow, was active, its propelling power being his personal conceit ; but he was destitute of imagination, and hence his attempted flights of eloquence were often hopelessly confused and illogical. The pioneer orators of Abolition and Temperance, who visited Ptolemy, found in him a willing convert, and he was quick enough to see and to secure the social consideration which he had gained in the small community of " Reformers"— an advantage which the conservative society of the village denied to him. Indeed, the abuse to which he was occasionally subjected, was in itself flattering ; for only men of importance, he thought, are thus persecuted. Among his associates, it was customary to judge men by no other standard than their views on the chosen reforms, and he, of course, stood among the highest. His cant, his presumption, his want of delicacy, were all overlooked, out of regard to an advocacy of " high moral truths," which was considered to be, and doubtless was, sincere.

Let us not, therefore, judge the disappointed tailor too harshly. His weaknesses, indeed, were a part of his mental constitution, and could, under no circumstances, have been wholly cured ; but it was his own fault that they had so thoroughly usurped his nature.

Whatever spiritual disturbance he might have experienced, on awaking next morning to the realities of the world, the woman who rejected him was much more deeply and painfully troubled. Years had passed since her heart had known so profound an agitation. She felt that the repose which she had only won after many struggles, had deceived herself. It was a false calm. The smooth mirror, wherein the sunshine and the stars saw themselves by turns, was only smooth so long as the south-wind failed to blow. One warm breath, coming over the hills from some far-off, unknown region, broke into fragments the steady images of her life. With a strange conflict of feeling, in which there was some joy and much humiliation, she said to herself : " I am not yet the mistress of my fate."

She rose late, unrefreshed by her short, broken sleep, and uncheered by the dark, cold, and wet picture of the valley. It was one of those days when only a heart filled to the brim

with unmingled happiness can take delight in life—when the
simplest daily duties present themselves as weary tasks—when
every string we touch is out of tune, and every work attempted is one discord the more. Descending to the sitting-
room, she found her mother in the rocking-chair, before a
brisk fire, while the little servant-girl was busy, preparing
the table for breakfast—a work which Hannah herself usually
performed.

"Thee's rather late, Hannah," said the widow. "I thought
thee might be tired, and might as well sleep, while Jane set
the table. She must learn it some time, thee knows."

"I'm obliged to thee, mother," the daughter replied. "I
have not slept well, and have a little headache this morning.
It is the weather, I think."

"Now thee mentions it, I see that thee's quite pale. Jane,
put two spoonfuls of tea in the pot; or, stay, thee'd better
bring it here and let me make it."

Hannah had yielded to the dietetic ideas of her friends, so
far as to give up the use of tea and coffee—a step in which
the widow was not able to follow her. A few months before,
the former would have declined the proposal to break her
habit of living, even on the plea of indisposition; she would
have resisted the natural craving for a stimulant or a sedative as something morbid; but now she was too listless,
too careless of such minor questions, to refuse. The unaccustomed beverage warmed and cheered her, and she rose
from the table strengthened to resume her usual manner.

"I thought it would do thee good," said the widow, noting
the effect, slight as it was, with the quick eye of a mother.
"I'm afraid, Hannah, thee carries thy notions about diet a
little too far."

"Perhaps thee's right, mother," was the answer. She had
no inclination to commence a new discussion of one of the few
subjects on which the two could not agree.

After the house had been put in order for the day, preparations made for the frugal dinner, and the servant-girl de-

spatched to the Cimmerian Church, Hannah took her usual seat by the window, saying: "Shall I read to thee, mother?"

"If thee pleases."

There was no Quaker Meeting nearer than Tiberius, and hence it had been the widow's custom, on "First-Days," to read, or hear her daughter read, from the classics of the sect. To Hannah, also, in spite of her partial emancipation, there was a great charm in the sweet simplicity and sincerity of the early Friends, and she read the writings of Fox, Barclay, Elwood, and William Penn, with a sense of refreshment and peace. To these were added some other works of a similar character, which the more cultivated Quakers have indorsed as being inspired by the true spirit—Thomas à Kempis, Jeremy Taylor, Madame Guyon, and Pascal. She now took the oft-read "No Cross, No Crown," of William Penn, the tone of which was always consoling to her; but this time its sweet, serious utterances seemed to have lost their effect. She gave the words in her pure, distinct voice, and strove to take them into her mind and make them her own: in vain! something interposed itself between her and the familiar meaning, and made the task mechanical. The widow felt, by a sympathetic presentiment, rather than from any external evidence which she could detect, that her daughter's mind was in some way disturbed; yet that respectful reserve which was habitual in this, as in most Quaker families, prevented her from prying into the nature of the trouble. If it was a serious concern, she thought to herself, Hannah would mention it voluntarily. There are spiritual anxieties and struggles, she knew, which must be solved in solitude. No one, not even a mother, should knock at the door of that chamber where the heart keeps its privacies, but patiently and silently wait until bidden to approach and enter.

Nevertheless, after dinner, when the household order was again restored, and Hannah, looking from the window upon the drenched landscape, unconsciously breathed a long, weary sigh, Friend Thurston felt moved to speak.

"Hannah," she said, gravely and softly, "thee seems to have something on thy mind to-day."

For a minute the daughter made no reply. Turning away from the window, she looked upon her mother's worn, pale face, almost spectral in the cloudy light, and then took her accustomed seat.

"Yes, mother," she answered, in a low voice, "and I ought to tell thee."

"If thee feels so, tell me then. It may lighten thy own burden, without making mine heavier."

"It is scarcely a burden, mother," said Hannah. "I know that I have done what is right, but I fear that I may have unconsciously brought it upon myself, when it might have been avoided." She then repeated the conversation which had taken place between Seth Wattles and herself, omitting only that secret, impassioned dream of her heart, a glimpse of which she had permitted to escape her. She did not dare to betray it a second time, and thus her own sense of humiliation was but half explained.

Friend Thurston waited quietly until the story was finished. "Thee did right, Hannah," she said, after a pause, "and I do not think thee can justly reproach thyself for having given him encouragement. He is a very vain and ignorant man, though well-meaning. It is not right to hold prejudice against any one, but I don't mind telling thee that my feeling towards him comes very near being that. Thee never could be happy, Hannah, with a husband whom thee did not respect: nay, I mean something more—whom thee did not feel was wiser and stronger than thyself."

A transient flush passed over the daughter's face, but she made no reply.

"Thee has a gift, I know," the widow continued, "and thee has learned much. There is a knowledge, though, that comes with experience of life, and though I feel my ignorance in many ways, compared to thy learning, there are some things which I am able to see more clearly than thee. It requires no book-learning to read the heart, and there is less difference in the hearts of women than thee may suppose. We cannot be wholly independent of the men : we need their help and companionship : we acknowledge their power even while we resist it. There are defects in us which we find supplied in them, as we supply theirs where marriage is perfect and holy. But we cannot know this, except through our own experience. I have agreed with thee in most of thy views about the rights of our sex, but thee never can be entirely wise on this subject so long as thee remains single. No, Hannah, thee won't think hard of me for saying it, but thee does not yet truly know either woman or man. I have often quietly wished that thee had not set thy heart against marriage. The Lord seems to have intended a mate for every one, so that none of His children should be left alone, and thee should not shut thy eyes against the signs He gives.

"Mother!"

Even while uttering this exclamation, into which she was startled by the unexpected words of her mother, Hannah Thurston felt that she was betraying herself.

"Child! child! thy father's eyes—thee has his very look! I am concerned on thy account, Hannah. Perhaps I have been mistaken in thee, as I was mistaken in him. Oh, if I could have known him in time! I shall not be much longer with thee, my daughter, and if I tell thee how I failed in my duty it may help thee to perform thine, if—if my prayers for thy sake should be fulfilled."

The widow paused, agitated by the recollections which her own words evoked. The tears trickled down her pale cheeks, but she quietly wiped them away. Her countenance thus changed from its usual placid repose, Hannah was shocked to see how weak and wasted it had grown during the winter. The parting, which she did not dare to contemplate, might be nearer than she had anticipated.

"Do not say any thing that might give thee pain," she said.

"Give thyself no concern, child. It will bring me relief. I have often felt moved to tell thee, but there seemed to be no fitting time before now."

"Is it about my father?" Hannah asked.

"Yes, Hannah. I wish he could have lived long enough to leave his face in thy memory, but it was not to be. Thee often reminds me of him, especially when I feel that there is something in thy nature beyond my reach. I was past thy age when we were married, and he was no longer a young man. We had known each other for some years, but nothing passed between us that younger persons would have called love. I was sincerely drawn towards him, and it seemed right that my life should become a part of his. It came to me as a natural change. Richard was not a man of many words; he was considered grave and stern; and when he first looked upon me with only a gentle smile on his face, I knew that his heart had made choice of me. From that time, although it was long before he spoke his mind, I accustomed myself to think of him as my husband. This may seem strange to thee, and, indeed, I never confessed it to him. When we came to live together, and I found, from every circumstance of our daily life, how good and just he was, how strong and upright and rigid in the ways that seemed right to him, I leaned upon him as a helper and looked up to him as a guide. There was in my heart quite as much reverence as love. An unkind word never passed between us. When I happened to be wrong in any thing, he knew how to turn my mind so gently and kindly that I was set right without knowing how. *He* was never wrong. Our married life was a season of perfect peace—yes, to me, because my own contentment made me careless, blind.

"I sometimes noticed that his eyes rested on me with a singular expression, and I wondered what was in his mind. There was something unsatisfied in his face, a look that asked for I knew not what, but more than the world contains. Once, when I said: 'Is any thing the matter, Richard?' he turned quickly away and answered sharply. After that, I said nothing, and I finally got accustomed to the look. I recollect when thy brother was born, he seemed like another man, though there was no outward change. When he spoke to me his voice was trembly, and sounded strange to my ears; but my own weakness, I thought, might account for that. He would take the babe to the window, before its eyes could bear the light; would pick it up when asleep, and hold it so tightly as to make the poor thing cry; then he would put it down quickly and walk out of the room without saying a word. I noticed all this, as I lay, but it gave me no concern: I knew not but that all men found their first children so strange and curious. To a woman, her first babe seems more like something familiar that is brought back to her, than something entirely new that is added to her life.

"I scarcely know how to make clear to thy mind another change that came over thy father while our little Richard still lived. I never could be entirely certain, indeed, when it commenced, because I fancied these things were passing moods connected with his serious thoughts—he was a man much given to reflection—and did not dream that they concerned myself. Therein, our quiet, ordered life was a misfortune. One day was like another, and we both, I think, took things as they were, without inquiring whether our knowledge of each other's hearts might not be imperfect. Oh, a storm would have been better, Hannah—a storm which would have shown us the wall that had grown up between us, by shaking it down! But thee will see that from the end—thee will see it, without my telling thee. Richard seemed graver and sterner, I thought, but he was much occupied with business matters at that time. After our child was taken from us, I began to see that he was growing thinner and paler, and often felt very uneasy about him. His manner towards me made me shy and a little afraid, though I could pick out no word or act that was not kind and tender. When I ventured to ask him what was the matter, he only answered: 'Nothing that can be helped.' I knew, after

that, that all was not right, but my eyes were not opened t
the truth."

Here Friend Thurston paused, as if to summon strength t
continue her narrative. Her withered hands were trembling
and she clasped them together in her lap with a nervous ene
gy which did not escape her daughter's eye. The latter ha
listened with breathless attention, waiting with mingled eage
ness and dread for the dénouement, which she felt must l
more or less tragic. Although her mother's agitation touche
her own heart with sympathetic pain, she knew that the stor
had now gone too far to be left unfinished. She rose, brough
a glass of water, and silently placed it on the little table besid
her mother's chair. When she had resumed her seat, the latte
continued :

" Within a year after our boy's death, thee was born.]
was a great consolation to me then, although it has been a muc
greater one since. I hoped, too, that it would have mad
Richard a little more cheerful, but he was, if any thing, quie
er than ever. I sometimes thought him indifferent both t
me and the babe. I longed, in my weakness and my comfor
to lay my head upon his breast and rest a while there.]
seemed a womanly fancy of mine, but oh, Hannah, if I had ha
the courage to say that much ! Once he picked thee uy
stood at the window for a long while, with thee in his arm:
then gave thee back to me and went out of the room withou
saying a word. The bosom of thy little frock was damp, an
I know now that he must have cried over thee.

" I had not recovered my full strength when I saw that h
was really ailing. I began to be anxious and uneasy, thoug
I scarcely knew why, for he still went about his business a
usual. But one morning—it was the nineteenth of the Fift
month, I remember, and on Seventh-day—he started to go t
the village, and came back to the house in half an hour, lool
ing fearfully changed. His voice, though, was as steady a
ever. ' I believe I am not well, Gulielma,' he said to me
' perhaps I'd better lie down a while. Don't trouble thyself—

it will soon be over.' I made him undress and go to bed, for my anxiety gave me strength. Then I sent for the doctor, without telling Richard what I had done. It was evening when the doctor came; thee was rather fretful that day, and I had taken thee into another room, for fear Richard might be disturbed. I only noticed that the doctor stayed a long time, but they were old friends, I thought, and might like to talk. By the time I had put thee to sleep, he had left and Richard was alone. I went directly to him. 'What is thee to take?' I asked. 'Nothing,' he said, so quietly that I ought to have been relieved, but—I do not know how it was—I turned to him trembling like a leaf, and cried out: 'Richard, thee has not told me all!'

"'Yes, all, Gulielma,' said he, 'nothing will help: I must leave thee.' I stared at him a while, trying to stand still, while every thing in the room went spinning around me, until I saw nothing more. I was lying beside him on the bed when I came to myself. My hair was wet: he had picked me up, poured water on his handkerchief and bathed my face. When I opened my eyes, he was leaning over me, looking into my eyes with a look I cannot describe. He breathed hard and painfully, and his voice was husky. 'I have frightened thee, Gulielma,' said he; 'but—but can thee not resign thyself to lose me?' His look seemed to draw my very soul from me; I cried, with a loud and bitter cry, 'Richard, Richard, take me with thee!' and threw my arms around his neck. Oh, my child, how can I tell thee the rest? He put away my arms, he held me back, and gasped, as he looked at me with burning eyes: 'Take care what thee says, Gulielma; I am dying, and thee dare not deceive me; does thee love me as I love thee—more than life, more, the Lord pardon me, more than heaven?' For the first time, I knew that I did. If it was a sin, it has been expiated. I cannot remember what was said, after that. It was all clear between us, and he would allow no blame to rest on me; but he could not speak, except at intervals. He held my hand all night, pressing it faintly in his sleep. The next day he died.

"He had loved me thus all the time, Hannah, and it was th
pride and the strength of his love which deceived me. H
would not ask for a caress or a tender word, because h
thought that a woman who loved would freely give it—no
would he offer one, so long as he suspected that the sacred ex
pression of his heart might be only passively received. Ah, i
was a sad doubt of me on his part, a sad blindness towards
him on mine. When he began to suffer from disease of the
heart, and knew that his life was measured, his self-torture in
creased. He purposely tried to subdue the mild, tempered
affection which he supposed I felt for him, in order that his
death might be a lighter grief to me. And I lived with him
day after day, never guessing that his stern, set manner was
not his real self! I do not dare to think on the cross he must
have borne: my own seems heavy, and my spirit sometimes
grows weary under it, and is moved to complain. Then I remember that by bearing it cheerfully I am brought nearer to
him, and the burden becomes light."

Hannah Thurston listened to the last words with her face
buried in her hands, and her heart full of pity and self-reproach.
What was the pang of her own fruitless dream, her baffled
ideal, beside the sharp, inconsolable sorrow which consumed
her mother's years? What availed her studies, her intellectual triumphs, her fancied comprehension of life, in comparison
with that knowledge of the heart of man thus fearfully won?
Humble, as when, a child, she listened to her mother's words
as the accents of infallible wisdom, she now bowed down
before the sanctity of that mother's experience.

The widow leaned back in her chair, with closed eyes, but
with a happy serenity on her weary face. Hannah took her
hand, and whispered, with a broken voice: "Thank thee,
mother!" The weak old arms drew her gently down, and
the pale lips kissed her own.

"Bless thee, my daughter. Now take thy book and let me
rest a while."

Hannah took the book, but not to read,

CHAPTER XIII.

IN WHICH SPRING OPENS.

The rainy Sunday was the precursor of a thaw, which lasted for a fortnight, and stripped the landscapes of Ptolemy of every particle of snow, except such as found a lodgment in fence-corners, behind walls, or in shaded ravines. The wands of the willow clumps along the streams brightened to a vivid yellow, and the myriad twigs of low-lying thickets blushed purple with returning sap. Frozen nights and muddy days enough were yet in store; but with every week the sun gained confidence in his own alchemy, and the edge of the north-wind was blunted. Very slowly, indeed, a green shimmer crept up through the brown, dead grass; the fir-woods breathed a resinous breath of awaking; pale green eyes peeped from the buds of the garden-lilacs, and, finally, like a tender child, ignorant of danger, the crocus came forth full blown and shamed the cowardly hesitation of the great oaks and elms.

During this season, Woodbury's intercourse with the society of the village was mostly suspended. After the termination of the Great Sewing-Union, families fell back into their narrower circles, and rested for a time both from their social and their charitable labors. Even the itinerant prophets and philanthropists ceased their visits, leaving Ptolemy in its normal darkness. Only Mr. Dyce, it was whispered, had again made his appearance at the Merryfields', where his spiritual sessions were attended by a select circle of the initiated. Neither Woodbury nor Mr. Waldo had been again invited to attend.

All minor gossip, however, was lost sight of, in the interest occasioned by an event which occurred about this time. Miss Eliza Clancy, to the surprise of everybody, had at last received "a call." During a visit to Syracuse, she had made the acquaintance of the Rev. Jehiel Preeks, a widower who, having been driven away from Tristan d'Acunha after losing his wife there, had been commissioned by the A. B. C. F. M. to a new field of labor in the Telugu country. His station was to be Cuddapah, only a day's journey from Jutnapore. Miss Eliza displayed such an intimate knowledge of the latter mission, derived from Mrs. Boerum's letters, and such a vital concern in the spiritual welfare of the Telugus, that the Rev. Jehiel, at their third interview, asked her to share his labors. There were persons in Ptolemy so malicious as to declare that the proposal really came from Miss Eliza herself; but this is not for a moment to be believed. The missionary made a better choice than such persons were willing to admit. Although verging on forty, and ominously thin, Miss Clancy was sincere, active, and patient, and thought more of the heathen souls whom she might enlighten than of the honors of her new position. When she returned to Ptolemy as Mrs. Preeks, with her passage engaged to Madras in the very vessel which was to carry out the contributions of the Mission Fund, she was too thoroughly happy to be disturbed by the village gossip. The other ladies of the Fund—foremost among them her sister spinsters, Miss Ann Parrott and Miss Sophia Stevenson—immediately resumed work, in order to provide her with a generous outfit for the voyage. Early in April the parting took place, with mutual tears, and thenceforth the pious patronage of Ptolemy was transferred from Jutnapore and Mrs. Boerum to Cuddapah and Mrs. Preeks.

The Hon. Zeno Harder occupied his seat in the Legislature, through the winter. Several times during the session Woodbury received the compliment of documents, one of them entitled: "Remarks of the Hon. Zeno Harder, of Atauga County, on the Mohawk and Adirondac Railroad Bill." Occasionally, also, the *Albany Cerberus* was sent to him with one of the leading editorials marked, by way of directing his attention to it. The Hon. Zeno looked upon Woodbury, who had been so long absent from the country as to have lost "the run" of politics, as fair prey. By securing him before the hostile party had a chance, he would gain two votes (one of them Bute's), and possibly more, besides a President of character and substance, for mass-meetings. Woodbury, however, was too shrewd, and the Member too clumsy in his diplomacy, for the success of this plan. The former, although foreseeing that he would be inevitably drawn to take sides, sooner or later, determined to preserve his independence as long as possible.

The churches in the village undertook their periodical "revivals," which absorbed the interest of the community while they lasted. It was not the usual season in Ptolemy for such agitations of the religious atmosphere, but the Methodist clergyman, a very zealous and impassioned speaker, having initiated the movement with great success, the other sects became alarmed lest he should sweep all the repentant sinners of the place into his own fold. As soon as they could obtain help from Tiberius, the Baptists followed, and the Rev. Lemuel Styles was constrained to do likewise. For a few days, the latter regained the ground he had lost, and seemed about to distance his competitors. Luckily for him, the Rev. Jehiel Preeks accompanied his wife on her farewell visit, and was immediately impressed into the service. His account of his sufferings at Tristan d'Acunha, embracing a description of the sickness and triumphant death of his first wife, melted the auditors to tears, and the exhortation which followed was like seed planted in well-ploughed ground. The material for conversion, drawn upon from so many different quarters, was soon exhausted, but the rival churches stoutly held out, until convinced that neither had any further advantage to gain over the other.

Mr. Waldo, of course, was not exempt from the general necessity, although conscious of the disadvantage under which he labored in representing so unimportant a sect. Its founder had been a man of marked character, whose strong, peculiar

8

intellect, combined with his earnestness of heart, wrought powerfully upon those with whom he came in personal contact, but his views were not broad enough to meet the wants of a large class. After his death, many of his disciples, released from the influence of his personality, saw how slight a difference separated them from their brethren, and yearned to be included in a more extensive fold. Among these was Mr. Waldo, whose native good sense taught him that minor differences in interpretation and observances do not justify Christians in dividing their strength by a multitude of separate organizations. His congregation, however, was very slowly brought to view the matter in the same light, and he was too sincerely attached to its members to give up his charge of them while any prospect of success remained.

On this occasion, nevertheless—thanks to the zeal of some of his flock, rather than his own power of wielding the thunderbolts of Terror—Mr. Waldo gained three or four solitary fish out of the threescore who were hauled up from the deeps by the various nets. The Cimmerian rite of baptism had this advantage, that it was not performed in public, and its solemnity was not therefore disturbed by the presence of a crowd of curious spectators, such as are especially wont to be on hand when the water is cold. Mr. Waldo even disregarded the peculiar form of initiation which characterized his sect, affirming that it added no sanctity to the rite.

During the period of the revivals, there was a temporary suspension of the social life of Ptolemy. Even kindred families rarely assembled at tea except to discuss the absorbing topic and compare the results obtained by the various churches. There was a great demand for Baxter's "Saint's Rest," Alleine's "Alarm," Young's "Night Thoughts," and Pollok's "Course of Time," at the little bookstore. Two feathers disappeared from the Sunday bonnet of Mrs. Hamilton Bue, and the Misses Smith exchanged their red ribbons for slate-colored. Still, it was not the habit of the little place to be sombre; its gayety was never excessive, and hence its serious moods never assumed a penitential character, and soon wore off. In this respect it presented a strong contrast to Mulligansville and Anacreon, both of which communities retained a severe and mournful expression for a long time after their revivals had closed.

By this time the meadows were covered with young grass, the willows hung in folds of misty color, and a double row of daffodils bloomed in every garden. The spring ploughing and all the other various forms of farm labor commenced in the valleys, and on the warm, frostless hillsides. The roads were again dry and hard; the little steamer resumed its trips on the lake; and a new life not only stirred within the twin valleys, but poured into them from without.

As the uniformity of winter life at Lakeside gave way to the changes exacted by the season, Woodbury became dimly sensible that Mrs. Fortitude Babb, with all her virtues as a housekeeper, stood too prominently in the foreground of his home. Her raw, angular nature came so near him, day by day, as to be felt as a disturbing element. She looked upon her dominion as reassured to her, and serenely continued the exercise of her old privileges. While entertaining the profoundest respect, not unmixed with a moderate degree of affection, for her master, she resisted any attempt to interfere with the regular course of household procedure which she had long since established. He was still too ignorant, indeed, to dispute her authority with any success, in-doors; but when the gardening weather arrived, and she transferred her rule to the open air, his patience was sometimes severely tried.

He knew, from his boyish days, every square foot in the sunny plot of ground—the broad alley down the centre, with flower-beds on either side, producing pinks, sweet-williams, larkspurs, marigolds, and prince's-feathers, in their succession; the clumps of roses at regular intervals; the low trellis, to be overrun with nasturtiums and sweet-peas; the broad vegetable beds, divided by rows of currant and gooseberry bushes, and the crooked old quince-trees against the northern wall.

There were they all, apparently unchanged; but, reverently
as he looked upon them for the sake of the Past, he felt that
if Lakeside was to be truly *his* home, its features must, to
some extent, be moulded by his own taste. The old arrangements could not be retained, simply for the sake of the old
associations; the place must breathe an atmosphere of life,
not of death. In spite of the admirable situation of the house,
its surroundings had been much neglected, and the trained
eye of its master daily detected new capacities for beauty.

Nothing of all this, however, suggested itself to the ossified
brain of the housekeeper. In her eyes, Woodbury was but a
tenant of Mrs. Dennison, and that lady would cry down from
Paradise to forbid the position of her favorite plants and her
trees from being changed. Hence, Mrs. Babb was almost
petrified with astonishment, one warm morning, on Woodbury
saying to her, as they stood in the garden :

"I shall extend the garden, so as to take in another half-
acre. The ground must be first prepared, so it can scarcely
be done this spring; but, at least, this first row of currants
can be taken up and set beyond the second. The vegetables
will then be partly hidden from sight, and these beds can be
planted with flowers."

"O, the land !" exclaimed the housekeeper. "Did a body
ever hear o' sich a thing ! Where'll you get your currans for
pies, I'd like to know ? They won't bear a mite if you take
'em up now. Besides, where am I to plant peas and early
beans, if you put flowers here ?"

"There," said Woodbury, pointing to the other end of the
garden.

"Why, I *had* 'em there last summer. Here, where these
cabbages was, is the right place. To my thinkin', there's
flowers enough, as it is. Not that I'd take any of 'em up:
she was always fond of 'em, and she was satisfied with my
fixin' of the garden. But there's them that thinks they knows
better. 'T'an't any too big as it was, and if you take off all
this here ground, we'll run out o' vegetables afore the sum-

mer's over. Then, I'll git the blame, all over the neighbor-hood. People knows *I* 'tend to it."

"Mrs. Babb," said Woodbury, a little sternly, "I shall take care that your reputation does not suffer. It is my intention to engage an experienced gardener, who will take all this work off your hands, for the future. But the improvements I intend to make cannot be carried out immediately, and I must ask you to superintend the planting, this spring. You shall have sufficient ground for all the vegetables we need, and it can make little difference to you where they grow."

The housekeeper did not venture upon any further remon-strance, but her heart was filled with gall and bitterness. She could not deny to herself Woodbury's right to do what he pleased with his own, but such innovations struck her as be-ing almost criminal. They opened the door to endless con-fusions, which it distressed her to contemplate, and the end whereof she could not foresee.

That evening, as Bute was shelling his seed-corn in the kitchen, he noticed that her thin lips were a little more tightly compressed than usual, while she plied her knitting-needles with an energy that betrayed a serious disturbance of mind. Bute gave himself no concern, however, well knowing that, whatever it was, he should hear it in good time.

Mrs. Babb sighed in her usual wheezy manner, drawing up and letting down her shoulders at the same time, and knit a few minutes longer, with her eyes fixed on the kitchen clock. At last she said : "Ah, yes, it's well she's gone."

Bute looked up, but as she was still inspecting the clock, he said nothing.

"I was afeard things couldn't stay as they was," she again remarked.

Bute picked up a fresh ear, and began grinding the butt-end with a cob, to loosen the grains.

"It's hard to see sich things a-comin' on, in a body's old days," groaned the housekeeper. This time her gaze was re-moved from the clock, and fell grimly upon her adopted son.

"What's the matter, Mother Forty?" he asked.

"Matter, Bute? I should think you'd ha' seen it, if you was in the habit o' seein' furder than your nose. Things is goin' to wrack, fast enough. He will have his way, no matter how onreasonable it is."

"Well, why shouldn't he? But as for bein' unreasonable, I don't see it. He's gettin' the hang of farmin' matters amazin'ly, and is goin' to let me do what I've been wantin' to, these five year. Wait till we get the gewano, and phosphate, and drainin' and deep ploughin', and you won't see such another farm in the hull county."

"Yes, and the garden all tore to pieces," rejoined the housekeeper; "if she could come out of her grave next year, she won't know it ag'in. And me, that's tended to it this ever so long, to have a strange man, that nobody knows, stuck over my head!"

Bute bent his face over the ear of corn, to conceal a malicious smile. He knew that all the housekeeper wanted, was to "speak out her mind"—after which she would resign herself to the inevitable. He accordingly made no further reply, and commenced whistling, very softly, "Barbara Allen," a tune which of late seemed to harmonize with his mood.

Woodbury, on his part, was conscious of a restless stirring of the blood, for which his contact with the housekeeper was in the least degree responsible. Her figure, nevertheless, formed a hard, sharp, rocky background, against which was projected, in double sweetness from the contrast, the soft outlines of a younger form, glimmering indistinctly through a mist which concealed the face.

He did not deceive himself. He saw that his apparent independence was a belligerent condition, in which he could never find adequate peace; but not for this reason—not from any cool calculations of prudence—did he long to see the household of Lakeside governed by its legitimate mistress. If the long years of summer had made his heart apathetic or indifferent, it had not deadened his nature to the subtle magic of spring. A more delicate languor than that of the tropics crept over him in the balmy mornings; all sounds and odors of the season fostered it, and new images began to obtrude upon his sleeping as well as his waking dreams. He knew the symptoms, and rejoiced over the reappearance of the old disease. It was not now the fever of youth, ignorantly given up to its own illusions. He could count the accelerated pulsations, hold the visions steadily fast as they arose in his brain, and analyze while he enjoyed them. Love and Experience must now go hand in hand, and if an object presented itself, the latter must approve while the former embraced.

Reviewing, in his mind, the women whom he knew, there was not one, he confessed to himself, whom he would ever, probably, be able to love. His acquaintances in New York were bright, lively girls—the associates of his nieces—in some of whom, no doubt, there was a firm basis of noble feminine character. It could not be otherwise; yet the woman who must share his seclusion, finding in him, principally, her society, in his home her recreation, in his happiness her own, could scarcely be found in that circle. Coming back to Ptolemy, his survey was equally discouraging. He could never overlook a lack of intellectual culture in his wife. Who possessed that, unless, indeed, Hannah Thurston? She, he admitted, had both exquisite taste and a degree of culture remarkable for the opportunities she enjoyed; but a union with her would be a perpetual torment. She, with her morbid notions of right, seeing an unpardonable sin in every innocent personal habit! What little she had observed of his external life had evidently inspired her with a strong dislike of him; how could she bear to know him as he was—to look over the pages of his past life? *His* wife, he felt, must be allowed no illusions. If she could not find enough of truth and manliness in his heart to counterbalance past errors and present defects, she should find no admittance there.

In spite of these unavailing reviews, one important result

was attained. He would no longer, as heretofore, shrink from the approach of love. From whatever quarter the guest might come, the door should be found open, and the word "Welcome," woven of the evergreen leaves of immortal longing, should greet the arrival.

CHAPTER XIV.

CONTAINING CONVERSATIONS MORE IMPORTANT THAN THEY SEEM TO BE.

ONE balmy afternoon, when the dandelions were beginning to show their golden disks among the grass, Woodbury started on foot for Ptolemy, intending to take tea with the Waldos, whom he had not seen for a fortnight. Sauntering along the road, at the foot of the eastern hill, with the dark, pine-fringed rocks and the sparkling cascade on one hand, and the fresh, breathing meadows on the other, he found himself, at last, at the end of the lane leading to the Merryfield farm-house, and paused, attracted by the roseate blush of a Judas-tree in the garden. The comfortable building, with its barn and out-houses, seemed to bask in happy warmth and peace, half-hidden in a nest of fruit-trees just bursting into bloom. The fences around them had been newly whitewashed, and gleamed like snow against the leafing shrubbery. An invigorating smell of earth came from the freshly-ploughed field to the south. Every feature of the scene spoke of order, competence, and pastoral contentment and repose.

In such a mood, he forgot the occasional tedium of the farmer's talk, and the weak pretensions of his wife, and only remembered that he had not seen them for some time. Turning into the lane, he walked up to the house, where he was cordially received by Mr. Merryfield. "Come in," said the latter: "Sarah's looking over seeds, or something of the kind, with Miss Thurston, but she'll be down presently. You recollect Mr. Dyce?" The last words were spoken as they entered the

8*

room, where the medium, with his sallow, unwholesome face, sat at an open window, absorbed in the perusal of a thick pamphlet. He rose and saluted Woodbury, though by no means with cordiality.

"How delightful a home you have here, Mr. Merryfield," Woodbury said. "You need not wish to change places with any one. An independent American farmer, with his affairs in such complete order that the work almost goes on of itself, from year to year, seems to me the most fortunate of men."

"Well—yes—I ought to be satisfied," answered the host: "I sometimes wish for a wider spere, but I suppose it's best as it is."

"Oh, be sure of that!" exclaimed Woodbury: "neither is your sphere a narrow one, if it is rightly filled."

"Nothing is best as it is," growled Mr. Dyce, from the window, at the same time; "private property, family, isolated labor, are all wrong."

Woodbury turned to the speaker, with a sudden doubt of his sanity, but Mr. Merryfield was not in the least surprised.

"You know, Mr. Dyce," said he, "that I can't go that far. The human race may come to that in the course of time, as it were, but I'm too old to begin."

"Nobody is too old for the Truth," rejoined the medium, so insolently that Woodbury felt an itching desire to slap him in the face,—"especially, when it's already demonstrated. Here's the whole thing," he continued, giving the pamphlet a whack on the window-sill: "read it, and you'll find how much better off we are without those selfish institutions, marriage and the right to property."

"What is it?" asked Woodbury.

"It's the annual report of the Perfectionists. They have a community near Aqueanda, where their principles are put in practice. Every thing is in common: labor is so divided that no one feels the burden, yet all live comfortably. The children are brought up all together, and so the drudgery of a family is avoided. Besides, love is not slavery, but freedom, and the affections are true because they do not wear legal chains."

"Good God! Is this true?" exclaimed Woodbury, turning to Mr. Merryfield.

"I believe it is," he answered. "I've read part of the report, and there are queer things in it. Even if the doctrine is right, I don't think mankind is fit for it yet. I shouldn't like, even, to let everybody read that book: though, to be sure, we might be much more outspoken than we are."

"Read it," said Mr. Dyce, thrusting the pamphlet into Woodbury's hand. "It's unanswerable. If you are not blinded by the lies and hypocrisies of Society, you will see what the true life of Man should be. Society is the Fall, sir, and we can restore the original paradise of Adam whenever we choose to free ourselves from its tyranny."

"No doubt, provided we are naturally sinless, like Adam," Woodbury could not help saying, as he took the pamphlet. He had no scruples in receiving and reading it, for he was not one of those delicate, effeminate minds, who are afraid to look on error lest they may be infected. His principles were so well-based that every shock only settled them the more firmly. He had never preferred ignorance to unpleasant knowledge, and all of the latter which he had gained had not touched the sound manliness of his nature.

"We are!" cried Mr. Dyce, in answer to his remark. "The doctrine of original sin is the basis of all the wrongs of society. It is false. Human nature is pure in all its instincts, and we distort it by our selfish laws. Our life is artificial and unnatural. If we had no rights of property we should have no theft: if we had no law of marriage we should have no licentiousness: if we had no Governments, we should have no war."

Mr. Merryfield did not seem able to answer these declarations, absurd as they were, and Woodbury kept silent, from self-respect. The former, however, was stronger in his instincts than in his powers of argument, and shrank, with a sense of painful repugnance, from a theory which he was unable to combat. Mr. Dyce's prolonged visit was beginning to be disagreeable to him. His ambition to be considered a prominent reformer was his weak side, and his freely-offered hospitality to the various apostles had given him a consideration which misled him. His kindness had thus frequently been imposed upon, but the secret fear of losing his place had prevented him, hitherto, from defending himself.

Mr. Dyce, on the other hand, was one of those men who are not easily shaken off. He led a desultory life, here and there, through New York and the New England States, presiding at spiritual sessions in the houses of the believers, among whom he had acquired a certain amount of reputation as a medium. Sometimes his performances were held in public (admittance ten cents), in the smaller towns, and he earned enough in this way to pay his necessary expenses. When he discovered a believing family, in good circumstances, especially where the table was well supplied, he would pitch his tent, for days, or weeks, as circumstances favored. Such an oasis in the desert of existence he had found at Mr. Merryfield's, and the discomfort of the meek host at his prolonged stay, which would have been sufficiently palpable to a man of the least delicacy of feeling, was either unnoticed by him, or contemptuously ignored.

Woodbury read the man at a glance, and received, also, a faint suspicion of Mr. Merryfield's impatience at his stay; but he, himself, had little patience with the latter's absurdities, and was quite content that he should endure the punishment he had invoked.

Putting the pamphlet in his pocket, and turning to Mr. Dyce, he said: "I shall read this, if only to find out the point at which Progress becomes Reaction—where Moral Reform shakes hands with Depravity."

The medium's sallow face grew livid, at the firm coolness with which these words were spoken. He half-started from his seat, but sank back again, and turning his head to the window, gave a contemptuous snort from his thin nostrils.

"There is mischief in that man," thought Woodbury.

Mr. Merryfield, in spite of his trepidation—for he was a thorough physical coward, and the moral courage on which he plumed himself was a sham article, principally composed of vanity—nevertheless felt a sense of relief from Woodbury's composed, indifferent air. Here, at least, was one man who could meet the vampire unconcernedly, and drive, if need be, a stake through his gorged carcass. For once, he regretted that he did not possess a similar quality. It was almost resistance, he was aware, and the man capable of it might probably be guilty of the crime (as he considered it) of using physical force; but he dimly recognized it in a refreshing element of strength. He did not feel quite so helpless as usual in Woodbury's presence, after that.

Still, he dreaded a continuance of the conversation. "Will you come, as it were"—said he; "that is, would you like"——

Woodbury, who had turned his back upon Mr. Dyce, after speaking, suddenly interrupted him with: "How do you do, Mrs. Merryfield?"

The mistress of the house, passing through the hall, had paused at the open door. Behind her came Hannah Thurston, in her bonnet, with a satchel on her arm.

After the greetings were over, Mrs. Merryfield said: "We were going into the garden."

"Pray, allow me to accompany you," said Woodbury.

"Oh, yes, if you care about flowers and things."

The garden was laid out on the usual plan: a central alley, bordered with flower-beds, vegetables beyond, and currants planted along the fence. It lay open to the sun, sheltered by a spur of the eastern ridge, and by the orchard to the left of the house. In one corner stood a Judas-tree, every spray thickly hung with the vivid rose-colored blossoms. The flowers were farther advanced than at Lakeside, for the situation was much lower and warmer, and there had been no late frosts. The hyacinths reared their blue and pink pagodas, filling the walk with their opulent breath; the thick green buds of the tulips began to show points of crimson, and the cushiony masses of mountain-pink fell over the boarded edges of the beds.

Mrs. Merryfield had but small knowledge of floriculture. Her beds were well kept, however, but from habit, rather than taste. "My pineys won't do well, this year, I don't think," said she : "this joon-dispray rose is too near them. Here's plenty of larkspurs and coreopsisses coming up, Hannah ; don't you want some ?"

"Thank you, my garden is wild with them," Miss Thurston answered, "but I will take a few plants of the flame-colored marigold, if you have them to spare."

"Oh, that's trash ; take them all, if you like."

"Miss Thurston," said Woodbury, suddenly, "would you like to have some bulbs of gladeolus and tiger-lily ? I have just received a quantity from Rochester."

"Very much indeed : you are very kind," she said. "How magnificent they are, in color!" The next moment, she was vexed at herself for having accepted the offer, and said no more.

Mrs. Merryfield, having found the marigolds, took up a number and placed them in a basket, adding various other plants of which she had a superfluity. As they left the garden, Woodbury quietly took the basket, saying : "I am walking to Ptolemy also, Miss Thurston."

It was impossible to decline his company, though the undefinable sense of unrest with which his presence always affected her, made the prospect of the walk far from agreeable. Side by side they passed down the lane, and had nearly gained the highway, when Woodbury broke the silence by saying :

"What do you think of Mr. Dyce?"

Hannah Thurston was a little startled by the unexpected question. "I have scarcely formed an opinion," she answered : "it may not be just to decide from impressions only. If I did so, the decision would not be favorable to him."

"You are right!" he exclaimed, with energy. "Do not speak to him again ! I beg pardon," he added, apologetically,

"I did not mean to be dictatorial; but the man is thoroughly false and bad."

"Do you know any thing of him?" she asked.

"Only what I have myself observed. I have learned to trust my instincts, because I find that what we call instinct is only a rapid and subtle faculty of observation. A man can never completely disguise himself, and we therefore see him most truly at the first glance, before his powers of deception can be exercised upon us."

"It may be true," she said, as if speaking to herself, "but one's prejudices are so arbitrary. How can we know that we are right, in yielding to them?"

For a moment, a sharp retort hovered on Woodbury's tongue. How can we know, he might have said, that we are right in accepting views, the extreme character of which is self-evident? How can we, occupying an exceptional place, dare to pronounce rigid, unmitigated judgment on all the rest of mankind? But the balmy spring day toned him to gentleness. The old enchantment of female presence stole over him, as when it surrounded each fair face with a nimbus, to the narcotized vision of youth. One glance at his companion swept away the harsh words. A tender gleam of color flushed her cheeks, and the lines of her perfect lips were touched with a pensive softness. Her eyes, fixed at the moment on the hill beyond the farther valley, were almost as soft as a violet in hue. He had never before seen her in the strong test of sunshine, and remarked that for a face like hers it was no disenchantment. She might be narrow and bigoted, he felt, but she was nevertheless true, earnest, and pure.

"We are *not* required to exhibit our prejudices," he said. "In Society, disagreeable persons are still individuals, and have certain claims upon us. But, after all the latitude we are required to grant, a basis of character must be exacted. Do you think a man consciously false and depraved should be tolerated on account of a coincidence in opinions?"

"Certainly not," she replied.

Woodbury then related the incident of the piano. He began to feel a friendly pity for the girl walking beside him. Her intense earnestness, he saw, and her ignorance of the true nature of men, were likely to betray her, as in the present case, into associations, the thought of which made him shudder. He would at least save her from this, and therefore told the story, with an uncomfortable sense, all the while, of the pamphlet in his pocket.

Hannah Thurston was unfeignedly shocked at the deception of Mr. Dyce. "I am glad you have told me this," said she, "for I wanted a justification for avoiding him. Have you mentioned it to the Merryfields?"

"No."

"Why not?"

"In the first place, you know that they are too infatuated with the spiritual delusion to believe it. He would have an explanation ready, as he had that night. Moreover, it would cost Bute, who gave me the details in confidence, the loss of two friends. For his sake let it still be confidential."

She met his deep brown eyes, and bowed in reply. He plucked the stalk of a dandelion, as they went along, pinched off the flower, split the lower end, and putting it into his mouth, blew a tiny note, as from a fairy trumpet. His manner was so serious that Hannah Thurston looked away lest he should see her smile.

"You are laughing, I know," said he, taking the stalk from his mouth, "and no wonder. I suddenly recollected having blown these horns, as a boy. It is enough to make one boyish, to see spring again, for the first time in fifteen years. I wonder if the willow switches are too dry. Henry Denison and I used to make very tolerable flutes of them, but we never could get more than four or five notes."

"Then you value your early associations?" she asked.

"Beyond all others of my life, I think. Is it not pleasant, to look back to a period when every thing was good, when all men and women were infinitely wise and benevolent, when life took care of itself and the future was whatever you chose to make it? Now, when I know the world—know it, Miss Thurston"—and his voice was grave and sad—"to be far worse than you, or any other pure woman suspects, and still keep my faith in the Good that shall one day be triumphant, I can smile at my young ignorance, but there is still a glory around it. Do you know Wordsworth's Ode?"

"Yes—'the light that never was on sea or land.'"

"Never—until after it has gone by. We look back and see it. Why, do you know that I looked on Mrs. Merryfield as a Greek must have looked on the Delphian Pythoness?"

Hannah Thurston laughed, and then suddenly checked herself. She could not see one of her co-workers in the Great Cause ridiculed, even by intimation. The chord he had touched ceased to vibrate. The ease with which he recovered from a deeper tone and established conversation again in mental shallows, annoyed her all the more, that it gratified some latent instinct of her own mind. She distrusted the influence which, in spite of herself, Woodbury exercised upon her.

"I see your eyes wander off to the hills," he said, after an interval of silence. "They are very lovely to-day. In this spring haze the West Ridge appears to be as high as the Jura. How it melts into the air, far up the valley! The effect of mountains, I think, depends more on atmosphere than on their actual height. You could imagine this valley to be one of the lower entrances to the Alps. By the way, Miss Thurston, this must have given you a suggestion of them. How did you manage to get such a correct picture in your mind?"

She turned her surprised face full towards him. The dreamy expression which softened its outline, and hovered in the luminous depth of her eyes, did not escape him.

"Oh, I know it," he added, laughing. "What was the song you sang at Mr. Bue's? Something about an Alpine hunter: it made me think I was standing on the Schei-

deck, watching the avalanches tumbling down from the Jung-
frau."

"You have been in Switzerland, Mr. Woodbury!" she
exclaimed, with animation.

"Yes, on my way from England to India."

He described to her his Swiss tour, inspired to prolong the
narrative by the eager interest she exhibited. The landscapes
of the higher Alps stood clear in his memory, and he had the
faculty of translating them distinctly into words. Commencing with the valley of the Reuss, he took her with him over
the passes of the Furca and the Grimsel, and had only reached
the falls of the Aar, when the gate of the Widow Thurston's
cottage shut down upon the Alpine trail.

"We will finish the trip another time," said Woodbury, as
he opened the gate for her.

"How much I thank you! I seem to have been in Switzerland, myself. I think I shall be able to sing the song better,
from knowing its scenery."

She offered him her hand, which he pressed cordially. "I
should like to call upon your mother again," he said.

"She will be very glad to see you."

As he walked down the street towards the Cimmerian parsonage, his thoughts ran somewhat in this wise: "How much
natural poetry and enthusiasm that girl has in her nature! It
is refreshing to describe any thing to her, she is so absorbed in
receiving it. What a splendid creature she might have become, under other circumstances! But here she is hopelessly
warped and distorted. Nature intended her for a woman and
a wife, and the *rôle* of a man and an apostle is a monstrous perversion. I do not know whether she most attracts me through
what she might have been, or repels me through what she is.
She suggests the woman I am seeking, only to show me how
vain the search must be. I am afraid I shall have to give it up."

Pursuing these reflections, he was about passing the parsonage without recognizing it, when a cheery voice rang out to
him from the open door:

"Have you lost the way, Mr. Woodbury?"

"'Not lost, but gone before,'" said he, as he turned back to the gate.

"What profanity!" exclaimed Mrs. Waldo, though she laughed at the same time. "Come in: our serious season is over. I suppose I ought to keep a melancholy face, for two weeks longer, to encourage the new converts, but what is one to do, when one's nature is dead against it?"

"Ah, Mrs. Waldo," replied Woodbury, "if you suffered under your faith, instead of rejoicing in it, I should doubt your Christianity. I look upon myself as one of your converts."

"I am afraid you are given to backsliding."

"Only for the pleasure of being reconverted," said he; "but come—be my mother-confessoress. I am in great doubt and perplexity."

"And you come to a woman for help? Delightful!"

"Even so. Do you remember what you said to me, when I picked you up out of the wreck, last winter? But I see you do not. Mrs. Fortitude Babb is a tyrant."

Mrs. Waldo was not deceived by this mock lamentation. He would not first have felt the tyranny now, she knew, unless a stronger feeling made it irksome.

"Ah ha! you have found it out," she said. "Well—you know the remedy."

"Yes, I know it; but what I do not know is—the woman who should take her place."

"Don't you?" said Mrs. Waldo, with a sigh, "then, of course, I do not."

"I walked from Merryfield's, this afternoon, with Hannah Thurston," he presently remarked.

"Well?" she asked eagerly.

"What a perversion of a fine woman! I lose my temper when I think of it. I came very near being rude to her."

"*You* rude?" exclaimed Mrs. Waldo, "then she must have provoked you beyond endurance."

"Not by any thing she said, but simply by what she is."

" What, pray ?"

" A ' strong-minded woman.' Heaven keep me from all
such! I have will enough for two, and my household shall
never have more than one head."

" That's sound doctrine," said Mr. Waldo, hearing the last
words as he entered the room.

CHAPTER XV.

WHICH COMES NEAR BEING TRAGIC.

In the beginning of June, the Merryfields received additional guests. Among their acquaintances in New York city were Mr. and Mrs. Whitlow, whom they had met during the Annual Convention of the Anti-Slavery Society. Mr. Whitlow was a prosperous grocer, who had profited by selling "free sugar" at two cents a pound more than the product of slave labor, although the former was an inferior article. He was very bitter in his condemnation of the Manchester manu facturers, on account of their consumption of cotton. The Merryfields had been present at a tea-party given by him to Mr. Wendell Phillips, and the circumstance was not forgotten by their hosts. When the latter shut up their house in the respectable upper part of Mercer street, in order to make a summer trip to Lake Superior by way of Niagara, they determined to claim a return for their hospitality. Tea in Mercer street was equivalent, in their eyes, to a week's entertainment at Ptolemy. If not, they could invite the Merryfields again, at the next Convention, which would certainly balance the account.

Accordingly, one fine evening, the stage from Atauga City brought to Ptolemy, and a carriage from Fairlamb's livery-stable forwarded to the Merryfield farm, Mr. and Mrs. Whitlow, and their two daughters, Mary Wollstonecraft Whitlow, aged thirteen, and Phillis Wheatley Whitlow, aged nine —together with four trunks. The good-natured host was overwhelmed with this large and unexpected visit, and feebly endeavored to obtain a signal from his wife as to whether they

could be conveniently accommodated, during the bustle of
arrival.

"If I had knowed, as it were, that you were coming,"
said he.

"Oh, we thought we would take you by surprise: it's so
much pleasanter," exclaimed Mrs. Whitlow, a tall, gaunt
woman, who displayed a pair of large feet as she clambered
down from the carriage. She thereupon saluted Mrs. Merryfield with a kiss which sounded like the splitting of a
dry chip.

Mary Wollstonecraft and Phillis Wheatley scampered off
around the house and into the garden as soon as they touched
ground. They amused themselves at first by pulling up the
early radishes, to see how long their roots were, but after a
while were attracted by the tulips, and returned to the house
with handfuls of the finest.

"Where did you get those?" said their mother; "I am
afraid they have taken too many," she added, turning towards
Mrs. Merryfield, "but the dear children are *so* fond of flowers.
I think it elevates them and helps to form their character.
The Beautiful and the Good, you know, are one and the same."

"Yes, but it ought to be directed," replied Mrs. Merryfield,
without exactly knowing what she was saying. She saw, in
imagination, her garden stripped bare, and was meditating
how she could prevent it. Her husband put a padlock on the
gate next morning, and in the course of the forenoon Phillis
Wheatley was discovered hanging by her frock from the
paling.

There was no help for it. The Whitlows had come to stay,
and they stayed. Mr. Dyce was obliged to give up his occupancy of the best bedroom, and take a small chamber under
the roof. Merryfield hoped, but in vain, that this new discomfort would drive him away. The new-comers were acquaintances of his, and although not spiritualists, yet they were
very free to discuss the peculiar doctrines of the Aqueanda
community.

Day by day, Mrs. Merryfield saw her choice hams and her cherished fowls disappearing before the onslaught of her guests. Her reserve of jams and marmalades was so drawn upon that she foresaw its exhaustion before the summer's fruit could enable her to replenish it. Mary Wollstonecraft and Phillis Wheatley were especially destructive, in this respect, and very frankly raised a clamor for "preserves," when there happened to be none on the table. Their mother mildly tolerated this infraction of good behavior on their part.

"They make themselves at home," she would remark, turning to the hostess with an amiable smile. "I think we should allow some liberty to the dietetic instincts of children. Alcott says, you know, that 'like feeds like—the unclean spirit licks carnage and blood from his trencher.'"

"Gracious me!" exclaimed Mrs. Merryfield, shuddering.

"Yes: and in the scale of Correspondences saccharine substances are connected with gentleness of heart. I rejoice to see this development in the dear children. Do you preserve with free sugar?"

"No," replied the hostess, with a faint salmon-colored blush, "we can't get it in Ptolemy. I should like to bear testimony in this way, if it was possible, but there are so few in this neighborhood who are interested in the cause of Humanity, that we cannot do as much as we desire."

"Why don't you apply to me?" said Mr. Whitlow. "Nothing easier than to buy two or three barrels at a time, and have it sent by rail. It will cost you no more than this"— putting a spoonful of quince jelly into his mouth—"which is stained with the blood of the slave." He said nothing, however, about the quality of the sugar, which was a very coarse, brown article, purporting to come from Port-au-Prince.

Fortunately, Mr. Merryfield's corn had been planted before the arrival of his guests. Otherwise, there would have been a serious interference with his farming operations. Every pleasant afternoon, the Whitlows laid claim to his carriage and horses, and, accepting the services of Mr. Dyce as coachman,

drove up and down the valleys, and even to the summits of
the hills, to obtain the best views. The very freedom with
which they appropriated to their use and comfort all the ap-
pliances which the farm furnished, imposed upon their kind-
hearted hosts. In the eyes of the latter, claims so openly
made involved the existence of a right of some kind, though
precisely what the right was, they could not clearly understand.

When Mrs. Whitlow, therefore, whose devotion to "Nature" was one of her expressed characteristics, proposed a
pic-nic for the following Saturday afternoon, it was accepted
without demur, as one of the ordinances of Destiny. The
weather had suddenly grown warm, and the deciduous trees
burst into splendid foliage, the luxuriant leaves of summer still
wearing the fresh green of spring-time. All the lower portion
of the valley, and its cleft branches beyond Ptolemy, from
rim to rim of the enclosing hills, hummed and stirred with
an overplus of life. The woods were loud with birds; a tiny
overture of insect horns and drums, in the meadows, preluded
the drama of their ephemeral life; the canes of maize shot the
brown fields with points of shining green, and the wheat began to roll in shallow ripples under the winds of the lake.
Mrs. Whitlow's proposal was well-timed, in a land where the
beautiful festival of Pentecost is unknown, and it did the
Merryfields no harm that they were forced, against their habit,
to celebrate the opening season.

Not more than a mile from the farm-house there was a spot
admirably adapted for the purpose. It was a favorite resort,
during the summer, of the young gentlemen and ladies of
Ptolemy, and sometimes, even, had been honored by the visit
of a party from Tiberius. Roaring Brook, which had its rise
some miles distant, among the hollows of the upland, issued
from a long glen which cleft East Atauga Hill at the point
where it bent away from the head of the lake, to make its
wider sweep around to the cape beyond Lakeside. At this
point there was a slightly shelving terrace, a quarter of a mile

in breadth, thrust out like the corner of a pedestal upon which
the hill had formerly rested. The stream, after lending a part
of its strength to drive a saw-mill at the mouth of the glen,
passed swiftly across the terrace, twisting its way through
broken, rocky ground, to the farther edge, whence it tumbled
in a cataract to the valley. The wall of rock was crowned
with a thick growth of pine, cedar, maple, and aspen trees, and
the stream, for the last hundred yards of its course, slid
through deep, cool shadows, to flash all the more dazzlingly
into the sunshine of its fall. From the brink there were lovely
views of the valley and lake; and even within the grove, as
far as a flat rock, which served as a table for the gay parties,
penetrated glimpses of the airy distance.

The other members of the little band of "Reformers" in
Ptolemy were invited to take part in the pic-nic. The Whitlows desired and expected this, and would have considered
themselves slighted, had the invitations been omitted. Mrs.
Waldo was included, at the request of Hannah Thurston, who
knew her need of recreation and her enjoyment of it. Besides, she was sure that Mr. Dyce would be there, and suspected the presence of Seth Wattles, and she felt the advantage of being accompanied by a brave and sensible friend.
Mr. Waldo was obliged to attend a meeting of the Trustees
of the Cimmerian Church, and so the two women, taking possession of his phlegmatic horse and superannuated gig, started
early in the afternoon for the appointed spot. Before reaching
the gate to the farm-house, they overtook Seth Wattles and
Mr. Tanner, on foot, the latter carrying his flute in his hand.
He was celebrated throughout the neighborhood for his performance of "*Love Not*" and "*The Pirate's Serenade*," on
that instrument.

The spot was reached by following the highway, past the
foot of Roaring Brook cataract, and then taking a side-road
which led across the embaying curve of the valley and, ascended to the saw-mill at the mouth of the glen. Some of the
party had gone directly across the fields from the Merryfield

9

farm-house, as there was one point in the rocky front of the
terrace where an ascent was practicable without danger. Thus
they nearly all met in the grove at the same time.

The day was warm and still, oppressively sultry in the sunshine, but there, under the trees and beside the mossy rocks,
the swift brook seemed to bring a fresh atmosphere with it,
out of the heart of the hills. A light wind, imperceptible elsewhere, softly rustled among the aspen-leaves, and sighed off
from the outer pine-boughs into the silence of the air. The
stream, swollen by late rains, yet cleansed of their stain, ran
deep and strong, curving like bent glass over the worn rocks
in its bed, with a suppressed noise, as if hoarding its shout for
the leap from the cliff. The shade was sprinkled with patches
of intense golden light, where the sun leaked through, and the
spirit of the place seemed to say, in every feature, "I wait
for color and life." Both were soon given. The Whitlow
children, in pink frocks, scampered here and there; Mrs.
Waldo's knot of crimson ribbon took its place, like a fiery tropical blossom, among the green; Mrs. Merryfield hung her
orange-colored crape shawl on a bough; and even Seth's ungainly figure derived some consistency from a cravat of sky-
blue satin, the ends of which hung over his breast. Mr. Tanner screwed together the pieces of his flute, wet his lips several
times with his tongue, and played, loud and shrill, the "Mac-
gregor's Gathering."

"The moon's on the lake and the mist's on the brae,"

sang Hannah Thurston to herself, as she stood on the edge of
the stream, a little distance from the others. The smell of the
moss, and of the woolly tufts of unrolling ferns, powerfully excited and warmed her imagination. She was never heard to
say, in such a spot, like many young ladies, "How romantic!"
but her eyes seemed to grow larger and darker, her pale cheek
glowed without an increase of color, and her voice was thrilled
with an indescribable mixture of firmness and sweetness. This
was her first true enjoyment of the summer. The anxiety oc-

casioned by her mother's failing health, the reawakening of dreams she had once conquered, the painful sense of incompleteness in her own aspirations, and the growing knowledge of unworthiness in others, which revealed more clearly her spiritual isolation, were all forgotten. She bathed her soul in the splendor of summer, and whatever pain remained was not distinguishable from that which always dwells in the heart of joy.

As she reached the line:

"O'er the peak of Ben Lomond the galley shall steer,"

a coarse bass voice behind her joined in the song. She turned and beheld Seth Wattles and Dyce, seated on a rock. They had been listening, and might have heard her to the end, had not the former been too anxious to display his accomplishments. Her repugnance to both the men had unconsciously increased, and she could no longer resist the impulse which prompted her to avoid them. Mary Wollstonecraft was fortunately at hand, in the act of chewing fern-stems, and Hannah Thurston, unacquainted with the young lady's "dietetic instincts," seized her arm in some alarm and conducted her to her mother.

"Let go!" cried the girl; "mamma lets me eat what I please."

"But, my dear," mildly expostulated the mother, "these are strange plants, and they might not agree with you."

"I don't care; they're good," was the amiable reply.

"Would you not rather have a cake?" said Mrs. Waldo, coming to the rescue. "I have some in my basket, and will bring you one, if you will not put those stems in your mouth."

"I was playing cow, but I'll stop if you'll bring me two."

Mrs. Waldo took her way towards the old gig, which was left, with the other vehicles, at the edge of the grove. As she emerged from the shade, and looked up towards the saw-mill, where the sawyer, in his shirt-sleeves, was tilting about over a pile of scantling, she saw a horseman coming down the glen

road. Something in his appearance caused her to stop and
scan him more closely. At the same instant he perceived her,
turned his horse out of the road, and cantered lightly up to
the grove.

"You here!" he exclaimed; "is it a camp-meeting?"

"You there, Mr. Woodbury! Where have *you* been?
Are you to monopolize all the secular enjoyments? No; it is
a pic-nic, small, but select, though I say it."

"Ah! who are here?" he asked, leaning forward on his
horse and peering into the shade—"My God!"

Mrs. Waldo, watching his countenance with merry eyes, saw
a flush of horror, quick as lightning, pass over it. With one
bound he was off the horse, which sprang away startled, and
trotted back towards the road. The next instant she saw him
plunge headlong into the stream.

Phillis Wheatley, in whom the climbing propensity was at
its height, had caught sight of a bunch of wild scarlet colum-
bine, near the top of a rock, around which the stream turned.
Scrambling up the sloping side, she reached down for the
flowers, which were still inaccessible, yet so near as to be tantalizing. She then lay down on her face, and, stretching her
arm, seized the bunch, at which she jerked with all her force.
The roots, grappling fast in the crevices of the rock, did not
give way as she expected. On the contrary, the resistance of
the plant destroyed her own balance, and she whirled over
into the water.

Woodbury saw her dangerous position on the rock, at the
very moment the catastrophe occurred. With an instant intu-
ition, he perceived that the nearest point of the stream was a
bend a little below; a few bounds brought him to the bank,
in time to plunge in and catch the pink frock as it was swept
down the swift current. He had no time to think or calculate
chances. The stream, although not more than four or five
feet deep and twenty in breadth, bore him along with such
force that he found it impossible to gain his feet. At the last
turn where the current sheered toward the opposite bank, a

shrub hung over the water. His eye caught it, and, half springing up as he dashed along, he seized it with one hand. The momentary support enabled him to resist the current sufficiently to get his feet on the bottom, but they could gain no hold on the slippery rock. As he slipped and caught alternately, in a desperate struggle, Phillis, struggling blindly with him, managed to get her arms around his neck. Thin as they were, they seemed to have the muscular power of snakes, and, in his hampered condition, he found it impossible to loosen her hold. The branch of the shrub gave way, and the resistless current once more bore them down.

Mrs. Waldo's fearful shriek rang through the grove, and startled the light-hearted company from their discussion of the evils of Society. Every one felt that something dreadful had happened, and rushed towards the sound in helpless and uncertain terror. She was already on the bank of the stream, her hair torn by the branches through which she had plunged, and her face deadly pale, as she pointed to the water, gasping, "Help!" One glance told the whole story. Mrs. Whitlow covered her face and dropped on the ground. Merryfield and the father ran down the bank, stretching out their hands with a faint hope of catching the two as the current brought them along. Hannah Thurston looked around in a desperate search for some means of help, and caught sight of a board which had been placed across two low rocks, for a seat. "The board—quick!" she cried, to Seth and Dyce, who stood as if paralyzed—" at the head of the fall!" Mechanically, but as rapidly as possible, they obeyed her.

Woodbury, after letting go his hold of the shrub, turned his face with the stream, to spy, in advance, some new point of escape. He saw, a hundred feet ahead, the sharp edge of silver where the sun played on the top of the fall: the sudden turns of the stream were all behind him, and it now curved gradually to the right, slightly widening as it approached the brink. His perceptions, acting with the rapidity of lightning, told him that he must either gain the left bank before making half the remaining distance, or keep in the middle of the current, and trust to the chance of grasping a rock which rose a little above the water, a few feet in advance of the fall. He was an experienced swimmer, but a few strokes convinced him that the first plan would not succeed. Before reaching the rock the water grew deeper, and the current whirled in strong eddies, which would give him some little power to direct his course. In a second they seethed around him, and, though the bottom fell away from under his feet, he felt a sudden support from the back water from the rock. One tremendous effort and he reached it.

To the agonized spectators on the bank, the scene was terrible. Unable to avert their eyes from the two lives sweeping like a flash to destruction—feeling, instinctively, that there was no instantaneous power of action which could save—they uttered low, incoherent cries, too benumbed to speak or think. Only Seth and Dyce, who had conveyed the board to the head of the fall, were hurriedly endeavoring to thrust it out over the water. In their excitement they had placed it too low to reach the rock.

"Bring it further up!" shouted Mr. Whitlow.

Seth, nervously attempting to slide it up the bank, allowed the outer end to drop into the current. It was instantly twisted out of his hands and whirled over the fall.

Woodbury had gained a firm hold of the rock, but the water was up to his shoulders, the conflicting currents tugged him this way and that, and he was unable to clasp his charge securely. Her arms were still tight about his neck, but if her strength should give way, their situation would become critical. He saw the effort made for their rescue, and its failure.

"Another board!" he shouted.

Seth and Dyce darted through the grove in search of one, while Merryfield, more practical, made off with his utmost speed for the saw-mill. Hannah Thurston, in spite of her relief at the escape, recognized the danger which still impended. A single glance showed her the difficulty under which Wood bury labored, and a sickening anxiety again overcame her. To stand still was impossible; but what could she do? On a stump near her lay a fragment of board about four feet in length. The distance from the bank to the rock was at least twelve. Another glance at the rapid current, and an idea, which, it seemed to her afterwards, some passing angel must have let fall, flashed through her brain. Snatching her silk summer-shawl from the bough where it hung, she tied one end of it tightly around the middle of the board, drawing it to a firm knot on the edge. Mrs. Waldo was no less quick in comprehending what she intended. By the time the knot was tied, her own and Mrs. Merryfield's shawls were brought and quickly fastened, one to another. By this means a length considerably greater than the breadth of the stream was obtained.

"One thing more," said Hannah Thurston, breathlessly, as she took the scarf from her neck. Knotting one end and drawing the other through, so as to form a running noose, she fastened it to her shawl, near the board. Her plan came to her in a complete form, and hence there was no delay in putting it into execution. Taking her stand on a point of the bank, some feet above the rock where Woodbury clung, she gathered the shawls in loose links and held the board ready to throw. Woodbury, whose position was such that he could see her movements without risking his hold, now called to her:

"As far as you can throw!"

Mrs. Waldo had followed to the bank, and stood behind Hannah Thurston, grasping a handful of her dress, lest she, too, should lose her balance. But excitement gave Hannah firmness of nerve, when other women trembled. She flung the board with a steady hand, throwing the weight of the shawls, as much as possible, with it. It fell beyond the centre of the current, whirled around once or twice upon an eddy, and was sheering back towards the bank again, when Woodbury, whispering to Phillis, "Hold fast, darling!" put out one hand and caught it. With some difficulty, and with more risk to himself than the two anxious women on the bank were aware of, he drew the wet, sticky slip-noose of the scarf over Phillis's head and one arm, bringing it under her elbow before he could loosen her hold upon his neck. Thrusting the board under this arm, it was an easier task to disengage the other.

"Wind the end of the shawl around that sapling beside you!" he called to Hannah Thurston. "One of you go below to meet her."

Mrs. Waldo was on the spot before his words were finished. "Now, hold fast, my little girl, and you will be safe in a minute. Ready!" he cried.

Phillis obeyed, rather through blind trust in him, than from her consciousness of what was going on. The poor creature was chilled and exhausted, half strangled by the water she had swallowed, and wild with terror. Her arms having once been loosened, she clasped them again around the board in a last convulsive effort of strength. Woodbury let go the frail raft, which, impelled by the dragging weight of the shawls, darted at once half-way across the stream. Then it began to move more slowly, and the force of the current seemed to ingulf it. For a moment the water rushed over the child's head, but her dress was already within reach of Mrs. Waldo's hand, and she was drawn upon the bank, gasping and nearly insensible. Mrs. Merryfield picked her up and carried her to the mother, who still lay upon the ground, with her face in her hands.

Woodbury, relieved of his burden, now held his position with less difficulty. The coldness of the water, not yet tempered by the few days of summer, nevertheless, began to benumb him, and he was obliged to struggle against a growing exhaustion. Hannah Thurston, as soon as the child was rescued, drew in the board, examined the knots of the shawls, and gathered them together for another throw; but at the same instant Mr. Merryfield, out of breath and unable to speak, appeared with a plank on his shoulder. With the aid of the others, the end was secured between two trees, and it was then run out above the water, a little below the rock, where the stream was shallower. Woodbury cautiously slid down, gained a firm foothold, and slowly crossed, walking sidewise, supported by the plank. As he neared the bank, he stretched out his left hand, which was grasped by Merryfield, who drew so tremendously that he almost lost his footing at the last moment. As he felt the dry earth under him, a singular numbness fell upon him. He saw, as in a dream, Mrs. Waldo and Hannah Thurston; the former streaming with grateful tears, the latter pale and glad, with a moist light in her eyes. He sat down upon the nearest rock, chilled to the bone; his lips were blue and his teeth chattered.

"It is cold bathing," said he: "have you any wine?"

"We do not use intoxicating beverages," said Mr. Whitlow, who could not forget, even in his gratitude for his daughter's rescue, the necessity of bearing testimony against popular vices.

Mrs. Waldo, however, hastily left the company. Mr. Merryfield took off his coat, and having removed Woodbury's with some little trouble, substituted it. The dry warmth began to revive him. "Where is my new acquaintance?" he asked.

Mrs. Whitlow, after an hysterical outburst of alternate laughter and tears, had wrapped Phillis Wheatley in the only remaining dry shawl and given her a saucer of marmalade; but the child was still too much frightened to eat. Her father brought her in his arms and set her down before Woodbury. "There, Phillis," said he, and his voice trembled a little, "you must thank the gentleman for saving your life."

"Thank you for saving my life!" said Phillis, in a rueful voice.

"Not me," said Woodbury, rising slowly and wearily, and turning towards Hannah, "but Miss Thurston. Your coolness and presence of mind saved both of us."

He took her hand. His fingers were as cold as ice, yet a warmth she never before felt streamed from them through her whole frame.

Mrs. Waldo suddenly made her appearance, as breathless as before Mr. Merryfield had been, with the plank on his shoulder. She carried in her hand a tumbler full of a yellowish liquid.

9*

" There," she panted, " drink it.   Thankful am I that there
are still sinners in the world.   The sawyer had a black jug.
It's poisonous stuff, I know—leads to the gates of death, and
all that—but I thanked God when I saw it."

" Good Samaritan!" exclaimed Woodbury fervently, as he
drank.   It was, in truth, the vilest form of whiskey, but it
steadied his teeth and thawed his frozen blood.

" Now for my horse and a gallop home!" he said.

" Where is the horse?" they asked.

" I'll get him," exclaimed Seth, with alacrity.

" Hadn't you better go up to Jones's, as it were," said
Merryfield   " He's stopped the saw-mill, and run to the house
to get a fire kindled.   You can dry yourself first, and Sarah
can make you some tea or coffee."

Jones made his appearance at almost the same instant.
" I ketched y'r horse, Mr. Maxwood," said he, running the
names together in his excitement.   " He's all right.   Come up
t' th' house : Mary Jane's made a rousin' fire, and you kin
dry y'rself."

" Thank you, my friends," Woodbury answered.   " Your
whiskey has done me great service, Mr. Jones, and what I now
want more than any thing else is a little lively motion.   Will
you please lend Mr. Merryfield one of your coats, since he has
kindly given me his?   I shall ride over and see you to-
morrow ; but now let me get to my horse as soon as possible."

He put his hand on the sawyer's shoulder, to steady himself, for his steps were still tottering, and was turning away,
when he perceived his wet coat, spread out on a rock.   Picking it up, he took a note-book and some pulpy letters from the
breast-pocket.   After examining the latter, he crushed them
in his hand, and tossed them into the stream.   He then felt
the deep side-pockets : in one there was a wet handkerchief,
but on reaching the other he dropped the coat.

" There, Mr. Dyce," said he, " you will find your pamphlet.
I had it in my pocket, intending to leave it with Mr. Merryfield this afternoon.   It is pretty thoroughly soaked by this

time, but all the waters of Roaring Brook could not wash it clean."

Nodding a cheerful good-by to Mrs. Waldo, a respectful one to Hannah Thurston, and giving Phillis a kiss which left her staring at him in open-mouthed astonishment, he left the company. The sawyer, with a rough tenderness, insisted on keeping his arm around Woodbury's waist, and on reaching the mill produced the black jug, from which it was impossible to escape without a mild libation. Woodbury repaid it the next day with a bottle of smoky "Islay," the remembrance of which made Jones's mouth water for years afterwards.

The pic-nic, of course, was at an end. Without unpacking the refreshments, the party made immediate preparations to return. The fire Mrs. Jones had kindled was employed to dry Phillis and the shawls, while the gentlemen harnessed the horses. Mr. Merryfield went about in the sawyer's Sunday coat, which had been first made for his wedding, sixteen years before. It was blue, with brass buttons, a high rolling collar, very short waist, and tails of extraordinary length. No one laughed, however, except Mary Wollstonecraft.

In spite of the accident, which left an awed and subdued impression upon all minds, the ride home was very animated. Each was anxious to describe his or her feelings, but Mrs. Whitlow was tacitly allowed to play the chief part.

"You were all running here and there," said she, "and the movement was some relief. What *I* suffered, no tongue can describe. But I am reconciled to it now. I see in it a mysterious sign that Phillis Wheatley is to have an important mission in the world, and my duty is to prepare her for it."

Fortunately, no injury resulted to the girl thus mysteriously commissioned, from the manner in which it was done. She was obliged, very much against her will, to lie down for the rest of the day; but the next morning she was discovered in the stable, pulling the tail-feathers out of an old cock she had caught.

On Monday, the Wintlows took their departure for Niagara, greatly to the relief of their hosts. As they do not appear again in the course of this history, we may hope that the remainder of their journey was agreeable.

CHAPTER XVI.

CONCERNING AN UNEXPECTED JOURNEY TO TIBERIUS.

Two days after the departure of the Whitlows, Mr. Dyce, during breakfast, announced his intention of leaving Ptolemy. "I have promised to visit the Community," said he, "and it is now a pleasant time to be there. Could you lend me your horse and carriage as far as Tiberius, Merryfield?"

"Not to-day, I guess," said the farmer; "I must go to Mulligansville this afternoon, to see about buying another cow, and Henry has the hill-field to hoe. You could take Jinny and the carriage, but how would I get them back again?"

"I will go," said his wife, with an unusual eagerness. "I must go there soon, any way. I've things to buy, you know, James, and there's Mrs. Nevins that I've been owing a visit to, this ever so long."

"Well, if you want to, Sarah," he answered, "I've nothing against it. Are you sure it won't be too much for you? You know you've been having extra work, and you're not strong."

Mrs. Merryfield drew up the corners of her mouth, and gave a spasmodic sob. "Yes, I know I am the weaker vessel," she wailed, "and my own judgment don't pass for any thing."

"Sarah, Sarah, don't be foolish!" said her husband; "you know I never interfere unreasonably with your ways. You can do as you please. I spoke for your own good, and you needn't cry about it."

He rose with an impatient air, and left the table. He could not but admit to himself, sometimes, that the happiness of his married life had not increased in proportion to his progress in the knowledge of Reform. When he looked back and recalled the lively, rosy young woman, with her first nuptial bashfulness and air of dependence on her husband fresh about her, whom he had brought to the farm-house twenty-five years before, when they lived in utter ignorance of diètetic laws and solemn duties towards the Human Race, he could not repress a feeling of pain. The sallow, fretful woman, who now considered her years of confiding love as a period of servitude, which she strove to balance by claiming more than an equal share in the direction of the household, was another (and less agreeable) creature, in comparison with her former self. Of late, she had grown more than usually irritable and unsatisfied, and, although he had kindly ascribed the fact to housekeeping perplexities, his patience was sorely tried. There was no remedy but endurance, so far as he could see. It was impossible, now, to change his convictions in regard to woman's rights, and he was too sincere to allow the practice of his life to be inconsistent with them.

When he returned at noon from a distant field, where he had been engaged all the morning, he was surprised to find the carriage still at home, although his man Henry was engaged in greasing the hubs of the wheels. "Why, Sarah," said he, as he sat down to dinner, "I thought you would have been off."

"I couldn't get ready," she answered, rather sullenly. "But I need not come back to-night. It will be better for Jinny, anyhow."

Mr. Dyce was unusually talkative on the subject of the Community, the charms of which he painted in the liveliest colors. His host was tired of the subject, but listened with an air of tolerance, as he was so soon to get rid of the speaker.

Bidding the latter good-by, immediately after dinner, he saddled his horse and rode to Mulligansville. The new cow met his requirements, and a bargain was soon concluded. She was to be brought to the farm next day, when the price agreed upon would be paid. Mr. Merryfield had adopted the sensible rule of defraying all such expenses as they arose. Hence his crops were never mortgaged in advance, and by waiting until they could be sold to the best advantage, he prospered from year to year.

When he reached home again, it was nearly four o'clock. Putting up his horse, he entered the house and went directly to the old-fashioned mixture of book-case, writing-desk, and chest of drawers, which stood in a corner of the sitting-room. He must make a note of the purchase, and, since he was alone, might as well spend an hour, he thought, in looking over his papers and making his calculations for the summer.

He was very methodical in his business arrangements, and the desk was in such perfect order that he always knew the exact place of each particular paper. This was one of the points of controversy with his wife, which he never yielded: he insisted that she should not open the desk in his absence. This time, however, as he seated himself, drew out the supports for the lid, and let it down upon them, his exact eye showed him that something had been disturbed. The papers in one of the pigeon-holes projected a little further than usual, and the corners were not square as they should be. Besides, the pile appeared to be diminished in height. He knew every paper the pigeon-hole contained, took them out and ran rapidly through them. One was missing!—an envelope, containing bonds of the New York Central Railroad, to the amount of three thousand dollars, the private property of his wife. It was the investment of a sum which she had inherited at her father's death, made in her own name, and the interest of which she had always received for her separate use.

He leaned back in his chair, thunderstruck at the discovery. Could one of the servants have taken the envelope? Impossible. Dyce?—how should he know where to find it? Evidently, nothing else had been touched. Had his wife, perhaps, taken it with her, to draw the semi-annual interest at Tiberius? It was not yet due. Mechanically, hardly conscious of what he suspected or feared, he arose and went up-stairs. In the bed-

room which Dyce had last occupied, every thing was in order.
He passed into his own, opening closets and wardrobes, expecting either to find or miss something which might enlight-
en him. In his wife's wardrobe three pegs, upon which dresses
had hung, were empty. He jerked open, in haste, the drawers of her bureau: many things had apparently been removed.
Closing them again, he raised his head, and a little note, stick-
ing among the bristles of the hair-brush, which lay on its back
in front of the looking-glass, caught his eye. He seized it, unfolded it with shaking hands, put on his spectacles and read.
There were but two lines:

"Send to Tiberius for the carriage. I am going to the
Community."

It was a hard blow for the poor man. The idea of conjugal
infidelity on the part of his wife was simply incredible, and no
suspicion of that nature entered his mind. It was a deliberate
case of desertion, and the abstraction of the bonds indicated
that it was meant to be final. What her motives were, he
could only guess at in a confused way; but he knew that she
would never, of her own accord, have determined upon a course
so mad and ruinous. Many things were suddenly clear to him.
The evil influence of Dyce, strengthened by his assumed power, as a medium, of bringing her children near to her; the magnetic strength, morbid though it was, of the man's words and
presence; the daily opportunities of establishing some intan-
gible authority over the wife, during her husband's absence,
until she became, finally, the ignorant slave of his will—all this,
or the possibility of it, presented itself to Merryfield's mind in
a rush of dim and tangled impressions. He had neither the
time nor the power to unravel them, but he felt that there was
truth at the core. Following this conviction came the determination to save her—yes! save her at once. There was no
time to be lost. Tiberius was eighteen miles distant, and they
could not yet have arrived there. He must follow instantly,
and overtake them, if possible, before the departure of the train
from the west.

Why was he delaying there? The ten minutes that he had been standing, motionless, in the centre of the room, with the note in his hand, his eyes mechanically reading the two lines over and over, until the first terrible chaos of his feelings subsided, had lengthened themselves into hours. Breaking the spell at last, he drew a long breath, which resolved itself into a groan, and lifted his head. The little looking-glass on the bureau was before him: moving a step nearer, he examined hi own face with a pitiful curiosity. It looked old and haggard; the corners of his mouth were rigidly drawn and tightened, and the pinched nostrils twitched in spite of himself, but his eyes were hard and dry.

"It don't make much difference in my looks, after all," he said to himself, with a melancholy laugh; and the next instant the eyes overflowed.

After this brief outbreak, he recovered some strength and steadiness, and rapidly arranged in his mind what was first to be done. Taking off his work-day clothes, he put on a better suit, and descended the stairs. Calling to the servant-girl in the kitchen, he informed her, in a voice which he strove to make natural and unconcerned, that he was suddenly obliged to visit Tiberius on business, but would return the next day, with his wife. He left directions with her for Henry, the field-hand, regarding the morrow's work, then resaddled his horse and rode rapidly to Ptolemy.

On the way, his thoughts involuntarily went in advance, and he endeavored to prefigure the meeting with his wife. It was impossible for him, however, to decide what course he should pursue in case she should persist in her determination. It was not enough to overtake her; he must be armed at all points to subdue and reclaim her. She had a stubborn power of resistance with which he was well acquainted; and, moreover, Dyce would be ready enough to assist her. He foreboded his own helplessness in such a case, though the right was on his side and the flagrant wrong on hers.

"It's my own fault," he groaned, bitterly; "I've given

way to her so long that I've lost my rightful influence over her."

One means of help suggested itself to his mind, and was immediately accepted. Leaving his horse at the livery stable, and ordering a fast, fresh animal and a light buggy to be sent to the Cimmerian Parsonage, he proceeded thither on foot.

Mr. Waldo was in his "study," which was one corner of his wife's sitting-room. He was engaged in an epistolary controversy with a clergyman of the Free-will Baptists, occasionally reading aloud a paragraph as he wrote. His wife, busily at work in remaking an old dress, listened and commended. They were both startled by the entrance of Mr. Merryfield, whose agitation was apparent in his face, and still more so in his voice, as he greeted them.

"What has happened?" exclaimed Mrs. Waldo.

"I don't hardly know, as yet," he stammered. "I want your help, Mr. Waldo. Come with me—I'm going to Tiberius. My wife"—— Here he paused, blushing with utter shame for *her*.

"Would you rather speak to my husband alone?" said Mrs. Waldo, rising from her seat.

"No, you must hear the rest, now," he answered. "You're a good woman, Mrs. Waldo—good and true, and perhaps you, too, can help. Sarah wants to leave me, and I must bring her back—I *must*, this night."

He then told them, briefly and brokenly, his painful story. Amazement and pity filled the hearts of the two good people, who felt his misfortune almost as keenly as if it were their own. Mrs. Waldo commenced making the few preparations necessary for her husband's departure, even before his consent was uttered. When the team was announced as ready, she took Mr. Merryfield's hand and bade him God-speed, with tears in her eyes. The poor man was too much moved to reply. Then, catching her husband's arm, as he was issuing from the room, she whispered earnestly, "No harshness—I know her: she must be coaxed and persuaded."

"I wish it were you who were going, my good wife," said Mr. Waldo, kissing her; "*you* would make no mistake. But be sure that I will act tenderly and carefully."

They drove away. She watched them turn the next corner, and went into the house powerfully excited by such a sudden and singular catastrophe. Her quick, intuitive mind, and her knowledge of Mrs. Merryfield's weak points, enabled her to comprehend the action more correctly than the husband himself. This very knowledge was the source of her greatest anxiety; for she saw that the success of the journey hung by a hair. Having already committed herself, Mrs. Merryfield, she foresaw, would not give up her plan from the discovery of it, merely. She was not the woman to fall at her husband's feet, repentant, at the first sight of him, and meekly return to her forsaken home. The utmost tact would be required—tact of a kind, of which, with all her respect for the sex, she felt that a man was not capable.

The more she pondered on the matter, the more restless and anxious she grew. Her husband's last words remained in her ears: "*You* would make no mistake." That was not certain, but she would make none, she knew, which could not at once be rectified. An inner voice continually said to her, "Go!" Her unrest became at last insupportable; she went to the stable, and harnessed their horse to the old gig with her own hands. Then taking her shawl, and thrusting some refreshments into a basket—for she would not delay even long enough to make a cup of tea—she clambered into the creaking vehicle, and drove off.

Mrs. Waldo, however, like many good women whose moral courage is equal to any emergency, was in some respects a ridiculous coward. Even in company with her husband, she never passed along the country roads, at night, without an incessant sensation of fear, which had no positive shape, and therefore could not be battled against. It was now six o'clock, and the darkness would be upon her long before she could reach Tiberius. The thought of making the journey alone,

was dreadful ; if the suspended fate of the Merryfields was to
be decided by her alone, she would have been almost ready
to hesitate.   There was but one person in Ptolemy to whom
she dared tell the story, and who was equally authorized with
herself, to go—that person was Hannah Thurston.

All these thoughts passed through her mind, and her resolution was taken, while she was harnessing the horse.   She
drove at once to the Widow Thurston's cottage, and was fortunate enough to find her and her daughter at their early tea.
Summoning them into the next room, out of ear-shot of the
little servant, she communicated the story and her request in
the fewest possible words.   She left them no time to recover
from the news.   " Don't stop to consider, Hannah," she said,
" we can talk on the way.   There is not a moment to lose."

Miss Thurston hesitated, overcome by a painful perplexity.
The matter had been confided to her, without the knowledge
of the principal actors, and she was not sure that her unexpected appearance before them would lead to good.   Besides,
Mrs. Merryfield's act was utterly abhorrent to all her womanly
instincts, and her virgin nature shrank from an approach to it,
even in the way of help.   She stood irresolute.

The widow saw what was passing in her mind.   " I know
how thee feels, Hannah," said she, " and I would not advise
thee, if thy way were not clear to my mind.   I feel that it is
right for thee to go.   The Saviour took the hand of the fallen
woman, and thee may surely take Sarah's hand to save her,
maybe, from falling.   Now, when thy gift may be of service
—now is the time to use it freely.   Something tells me that
thy help will not be altogether in vain."

" I will go, mother," the daughter replied.   " Thy judgment is safer than mine."

In five minutes more the two women were on their way.
The loveliest evening sunshine streamed across the valley,
brightening the meadows and meadow-trees, and the long,
curving sweep of the eastern hill.   The vernal grass, which, in
its flowering season, has a sweeter breath than the roses of Gu-

listan, was cut in many places, and lay in balmy windrows. The air was still and warm, and dragon-flies, emitting blue and emerald gleams from their long wings, hovered in zigzag lines along the brooksides. Now and then a thrush fluted from the alder-thickets, or an oriole flashed like a lighted brand through the shadows of the elms. The broad valley basked in the lazy enjoyment of its opulent summer hues; and whatever sounds arose from its bosom, they all possessed a tone of passive content or active joy. But the travellers felt nothing of all this beauty: that repose of the spiritual nature, in which the features of the external world are truly recognized, had been rudely disturbed.

They passed the Merryfield farm-house. How sadly at variance with its sunny air of peace was the tragic secret of its owners, which the two women carried with them! The huge weeping willow trailed its hanging masses of twigs against the gable, and here and there a rose-tree thrust its arm through the white garden paling and waved a bunch of crimson, as if to say: " Come in and see how we are blooming!" Towards the barn, the field-hand was letting down bars for the waiting cows, and the servant-girl issued from the kitchen-door with her tin milk-kettle, as they gazed. What a mockery it all seemed!

A little further, and the cataract thundered on their right. All below the rocky wall lay in shadow, but the trees on its crest were still touched by the sun, and thin wreaths of spray, whirling upward, were suddenly converted into dust of gold. Hannah Thurston looked up at the silent grove, and shuddered as she recalled the picture she had last seen there. The brook could never again wear to her its former aspect of wayward, impetuous jubilation. Under its green crystal and glassy slides lurked an element of terror, of pitiless cruelty. Yet even the minutes of agonizing suspense she had there endured were already softened in her memory, and seemed less terrible than the similar trial which awaited her.

Near the entrance to Lakeside they met Bute Wilson, with

a yoke of oxen. He recognized the old gig, and with a loud
" Haw, Buck,—come hither!" drew his team off the road."

"Takin' a drive, are ye? How d'you do, Mrs. Waldo—
Miss Hannah?"

"Good-evening, Bute!" said Mrs. Waldo. "How is Mr.
Woodbury? I hope he has not suffered from being so long
in the water."

"Bless you, no! Mr. Max. is as sound as a roach. He rid
over to Tiberius this afternoon. I say, wasn't it lucky that
jist *he* should ha' come along at the right time?" Bute's face
glowed with pride and delight.

"It was Providential: good-by!"

Slowly climbing the long ravine, through dark woods, it
was after sunset when they reached the level of the upland.
The village of Anacreon soon came in sight, and they drove
rapidly through, not wishing to be recognized. Beyond this
point the road was broad, straight, and firm, and they could
make better progress. A low arch of orange light lingered
in the west, but overhead the larger stars came out, one after
another. Belts of warm air enveloped them on the heights,
but the dusky hollows were steeped in grateful coolness, and
every tree by the roadside gave out its own peculiar odor.
The ripe, antique breath of the oak, the honeyed bitter of the
tulip-tree, and the perfect balsam of the hickory, were breathed
upon them in turn. A few insects still chirped among the
clover, and the unmated frogs serenaded, by fits, their reluctant
sweethearts. At one of the farm-houses they passed, a girl,
seated in the porch, was singing:

> "We have lived and loved together,
> Through many changing years."

Every circumstance seemed to conspire, by involuntary contrast, to force the difficult and painful task they had under-
taken more distinctly upon their minds. After Mrs. Waldo
had imparted all she knew, with her own conjectures of the

causes of the desertion, both women were silent for a long time, feeling, perhaps, that it was impossible to arrange, in advance, any plan of action. They must trust to the suggestions which the coming interview would supply.

"I cannot understand it," said Hannah Thurston, at last. "After so many years of married life—after having children born to them, and lost, uniting them by the more sacred bond of sorrow—how is it possible? They certainly loved each other: what has become of her love?"

"She has it somewhere, yet, you may be sure," said Mrs. Waldo. "She is weak and foolish, but she does not mean to be criminal. Dyce is a dangerous man, and he has led her to the step. No other man she knows could have done it."

"Can she love him?"

"Probably not. But a strong, unscrupulous man who knows our sex, Hannah, has a vast power which most women do not understand. He picks up a hundred little threads of weakness, each of which is apparently insignificant, and twists them into a chain. He surprises us at times when our judgment is clouded, his superior reason runs in advance of our thoughts—and we don't think very hard, you know—and will surely bind us hand and foot, unless some new personality comes in to interrupt him. We women are governed by personal influences—there is no use in denying the fact. And men, of course, have the strongest."

"I have sometimes feared as much," said Hannah Thurston, sadly, "but is it not owing to a false education? Are not women trained to consider themselves inferior, and thus dependent? Do not the daughters learn the lesson of their mothers, and the fathers impress the opposite lesson on their sons?"

"I know what you mean, and you are partly right. But that is not all. There are superior women whom we look up to—I look up to you, Hannah, who are, intellectually, so far above me—but they never impress us with the same sense of power, of protecting capacity, that we feel in the presence of almost any man. It is something I cannot explain—a sort of physical magnetism, I suppose. I respect men: I like them because they are men, I am not ashamed to confess: and I am not humiliated as a woman, by acknowledging the difference."

"Habit and tradition!" Hannah Thurston exclaimed.

"I know you *will* think so, Hannah, and I am not able to answer you. When I hear you speak, sometimes, every word you say seems just and true, but my instincts, as a woman, remain the same. Your life has been very different from mine, and perhaps you have taken, without knowing it, a sort of warlike position towards men, and have wilfully resisted their natural influence over you. For your sake, I have often longed—and you must pardon me, if I ought not to say such a thing—that some man, in every respect worthy of you, should come to know you as you are, and love you, and make you his wife."

"Don't—don't speak of that," she whispered.

"I couldn't help it, to-night, dear," Mrs. Waldo soothingly replied. "I have been thinking as I came along, what cause I have to thank God for having given me a good and faithful husband. *I* should never have been happy as a single woman, and for that reason, no doubt, your life seems imperfect to me. But we cannot always judge the hearts of others by our own."

By this time the glimmering arch of summer twilight had settled behind the hills, and only the stars lighted them on their way. The road stretched before them like a dusky band, between the shapeless darkness of woods and fields, on either side. Indistinct murmurs of leaves and rustlings among the grass began to be heard, and at every sound Mrs. Waldo started nervously.

"Was there ever such a coward as I am!" she exclaimed, in a low voice. "If you were not with me, I should go wild with fear. Do you suppose any man in the world is so timid?"

"There, again, I cannot judge," Miss Thurston answered. I only know that I am never alarmed at night, and that this journey would be a perfect enjoyment, if we were not going on such an unfortunate errand."

"I always knew you were an exception among women. Your nerves are like a man's, but mine are altogether feminine, and I can't help myself."

The horse stopped at a toll-gate. They were only two miles from Tiberius, and the road descended the greater part of the way. Mrs. Waldo recovered her courage, for the houses were now more thickly scattered, and the drive would soon be at an end. The old horse, too, had by this time recognized the extent of his task, and determined to get through with it. They rattled rapidly onwards, and from the next rise saw the lights of the town, twinkling around the foot of Atauga Lake.

As they reached the suburban belt, where every square, flat-roofed, chocolate-colored villa stood proudly in the centre of its own square plot of ground, Hannah Thurston asked:

"Where shall we go?"

"Bless me, I never thought of that. But I think my husband generally stops at 'The Eagle,' and we can at least leave the horse there. Then we must try to find him and—the others. I think our best plan would be to go to the railroad station."

The gardens and villas gradually merged into the irregular, crowded buildings which lined the principal street. Many stores were open, the side-walks were lively with people, transparencies gleamed before ice-cream saloons, and gas-lamps burned brilliantly at the corners.

"What time is it?" asked Mrs. Waldo.

Hannah Thurston looked at her watch. "A quarter past nine."

"We have made good time," said her companion; "Heaven grant that we are not too late!"

10

CHAPTER XVII.

WHICH SOLVES THE PRECEDING ONE.

MRS. MERRYFIELD, on forsaking her home, had not anticipated the possibility of an immediate pursuit. She supposed, of course, that her husband would first discover her intention the next morning, when he would have occasion to use the hairbrush. He would then, sooner or later, she believed, follow her to the Community, where the sight of a Perfect Society, of an Eden replanted on the Earth, would not only convince him of the wisdom of her act, but compel him to imitate it. If their convictions had been reversed, and *he* had desired to try the new social arrangement, could he not have done so with impunity, regardless of her opposition? Then, their rights being equal, why should she consult his pleasure?

Thus she reasoned, or, rather, Dyce reasoned for her. She was a very weak and foolish woman, afflicted with that worst of temperaments which is at the same time peevish and stubborn, and did not at all appreciate the gravity of the step she had taken. An inner voice, indeed, told her that its secrecy was unjustifiable—that she should openly and boldly declare her intention to her husband; but her base friend easily persuaded her that it was better to draw him after her when she had reached the Community, and settle the difference there. His own eyes would then convince him of her wisdom: opposition would be impossible, with the evidence before him. She would thus spare herself a long and perhaps fruitless encounter of opinions, which, owing to the finer organization of her spiritual nature, she ought to avoid. Such differences, he said, disturbed the atmosphere in which spirits most readily approached and communicated with her. In the pure and harmonious life of the Community, she might perhaps attain to the condition of a medium, and be always surrounded by angelic company.

The afternoon was hot and they drove slowly, so that even before they reached Tiberius, the two parties of pursuers were on the way. Just as they entered the town, Mr. Woodbury passed the carriage on horseback. Glancing at its occupants, he recognized Mrs. Merryfield, bowed, and reined in his horse as if to speak, but seeing Dyce, his cordial expression became suddenly grave, and he rode on. This encounter troubled Mrs. Merryfield. A secret uneasiness had been growing upon her during the latter part of the way, and Woodbury's look inspired her with a vague fear. She involuntarily hoped that she might not meet him again, or any one she knew, before leaving Tiberius. She would not even visit Mrs. Nevins, as she had proposed. Moreover, Woodbury would probably put up at the hotel which she and her husband usually visited. Another must be selected, and she accordingly directed Dyce to drive through the town to a tavern on its northern side, not far from the railroad station.

At half-past eight in the evening her husband and Mr. Waldo alighted in front of "The Eagle." As the former was giving orders about the horse to the attendant ostler, Woodbury came down the steps and immediately recognized the new arrivals.

"What!" he exclaimed, "is all Ptolemy coming to Tiberius to-day? Your wife has the start of you, Mr. Merryfield: I passed her this evening"——

A violent grasp on his arm interrupted him. "Where is she? Have they left?" the husband hoarsely asked.

The light from the corner-lamp fell full upon his face. Its expression of pain and anxiety was unmistakable, and a presentiment of the incredible truth shot through Woodbury's mind.

"Hush, my friend!" said Mr. Waldo. "Control yourself

while we register our names, and then we will go to work.
It is fortunate that you have betrayed yourself to Mr. Woodbury instead of some one else. Come with us!" he added,
turning to the latter; "you must now know the rest. We
can trust every thing to your honor."

They entered the office of the hotel. Merryfield, after
drinking a large tumbler of ice-water, recovered some degree
of composure. Mr. Waldo ascertained from the landlord that
the next train for the east would leave at midnight, the previous train having left at five o'clock. Woodbury, seeing the
necessity of a private understanding, invited them both to his
room, where the whole affair was explained to him, and he
was able to assure them, by recalling the hour of his own arrival, that Dyce and Mrs. Merryfield must be still in the town.

"We have three hours," said he, "and they must be found
in half the time. There must not be a meeting at the station.
Have you no idea, Mr. Merryfield, where your wife would go?"

"She spoke of visiting Mrs. Nevins, as it were," he replied.

"Then it is quite unlikely that she is there," said Woodbury.
"But we must first settle the point. Let us go at once: where
is the house?"

Merryfield led the way, much supported and encouraged by
Woodbury's prompt, energetic manner. He had now less
dread of the inevitable encounter with Dyce.

A walk of ten minutes brought them to the Nevins mansion.
It was a small villa, with a Grecian portico, seated in a diminutive garden. There was a light in the front room. Mr.
Waldo was unacquainted with the inmates, and afraid to
allow Merryfield to enter the house alone. There was a
moment of perplexity.

"I have it," said Woodbury, suddenly. "Move on a little,
and wait for me." He boldly entered the garden and stepped
upon the Grecian portico. The windows had muslin curtains
across their lower half, but he easily looked over them into
the room. A middle-aged woman, in a rocking-chair, was
knitting some worsted stuff with a pair of wooden needles.

On the other side of the lamp, with his back to her, sat a man, absorbed in a newspaper. A boy of ten years old lay asleep on the carpet. Noting all this at a glance, Woodbury knocked at the door. A rustling of the newspaper followed, footsteps entered the hall, and the outer door was opened.

Woodbury assumed a natural air of embarrassed disappointment. "I am afraid," said he, "that I have made a mistake. Does Mr. Israel Thompson live here?"

"Israel Thompson? I don't know any such person. There's James Thompson, lives further down the street, on the other side."

"Thank you. I will inquire of him. I am a stranger here," and he rejoined his friends. "Now," said he, "to save time, Mr. Waldo, you and I must visit the other hotels, dividing them between us. Mr. Merryfield had better not take any part in the search. Let him wait for us on the corner opposite 'The Eagle.' We can make our separate rounds in twenty minutes, and I am sure we shall have discovered them by that time."

An enumeration of the hotels was made, and the two gentlemen divided them in such a manner as to economize time in making their rounds. They then set out in different directions, leaving Merryfield to walk back alone to the rendezvous. Hitherto, the motion and excitement of the pursuit had kept him up, but now he began to feel exhausted and desponding. He had not eaten since noon, and experienced all the weakness without the sensation of hunger. A powerful desire for an artificial stimulant came over him, and, for a moment, he halted before the red light of a drinking-saloon, wondering whether there was any one inside who could recognize him. The door opened, and an atmosphere of rank smoke, tobacco-soaked sawdust, and pungent whiskey gushed out; oaths and fragments of obscene talk met his ears, and he hurried away in disgust. At "The Eagle" he fortified himself again with ice-water, and then took his stand on the opposite corner, screened from the lamp-light by an awning-post.

The late storekeepers up and down the street were putting up their shutters, but the ice-cream transparencies still shone brightly, and the number of visitors rather increased than diminished. From a neighboring house came the sound of a piano, and presently a loud, girlish voice which sang: "I dreamt that I dwe-helt in ma-harble halls." What business, he thought, had people to be eating ice-cream and singing songs? It was an insulting levity. How long a time his friends had been absent! A terrible fear came over him—what if he should not find his wife? At night—no, he dared not think of it. He looked down the crossing streets, in all four directions, as far as his eye could pierce, and inspected the approaching figures. Now he was sure he recognized Woodbury's commanding form; now the brisk gait of the short clergyman. But they came nearer and resolved themselves into strangers. Then he commenced again, striving to keep an equal watch on all the streets. The appointed time was past, and they did not come! A cold sweat began to gather on his forehead, and he was ready to despair. All at once, Mr. Waldo appeared, close at hand, and hurried up to him, breathless.

"I have finished my list," said he.

"Have you found them?"

"No, but——what does this mean!" cried the clergyman, starting. "That is my horse, certainly—and the old gig! Can my wife"——

He did not finish the sentence, but sprang into the street and called. The horse turned his head from a sudden jerk of the lines, and in a moment was drawn up beside the pavement.

"How glad I am we have met you! I *could not* stay at home, indeed. You will let us help, will you not? Are we in time?" cried Mrs. Waldo, apology, entreaty, and anxiety all mingling in her voice.

"With God's favor, we are still in time," her husband answered.

"I thank you for coming—you and Hannah, both," Merry-field sadly added, "but I'm afraid it's no use."

"Cheer up," said the clergyman, "Mr. Woodbury will be here in a moment."

"He is here already," said Woodbury, joining them at the instant. "I have"—— He paused, recognizing the gig and its occupants, and looked inquiringly at Mr. Waldo.

"They know it," answered the latter, "and for that reason they have come."

"Brave women! We may need their help. I have found the persons we are looking for—at the Beaver House, in the second-story parlor, waiting for the midnight train."

"Then drive on, wife," said Mr. Waldo; "you can put up the horse there. You are known at the Eagle, and we had better avoid curiosity. Follow us: Mr. Woodbury will lead the way."

They passed up the street, attracting no notice, as the connection between the movements of the women in the gig, and the three men on the sidewalk, was not apparent. In a short time they reached the Beaver House, a second-rate hotel, with a deserted air, on a quiet street, and near the middle of the block. Two or three loafers were in the office, half sliding out of the short arm-chairs as they lounged, and lazily talking. Woodbury called the landlord to the door, gave the horse into his charge, and engaged a private room until midnight. There was one, he had already ascertained, adjoining the parlor on the second story. He offered liberal pay, provided no later visitors were thrust upon them, and the landlord was very willing to make the arrangement. It was not often that he received so much patronage in one evening.

After a hurried consultation, in whispers, they entered the house. The landlord preceded them up-stairs with a lamp, and ushered them into the appointed room. It was a small oblong chamber, the floor decorated with a coarse but very gaudy carpet, and the furniture covered with shiny hair-cloth, very cold, and stiff, and slippery. There was a circular table of mahogany, upon which lay a Bible, and the Odd-Fellow's

Annual, bound in red. Beside it was a huge spittoon of brown stone-ware. Folding-doors connected with the adjoining parlor, and the wood-work, originally of unseasoned pine, gotten up without expense but regardless of durability, was so warped and sprung that these doors would not properly close. Privacy, so far as conversation was concerned, was impossible. In fact, no sooner had the landlord departed, and the noise of entrance subsided a little, than Dyce's voice was distinctly heard:

"You should overcome your restlessness. All pioneers in great works have their moments of doubt, but they are caused by the attacks of evil spirits."

Merryfield arose in great agitation. Perhaps he would have spoken, but Mr. Waldo lifted his hand to command silence, beckoned to his wife, and the three left the room. At the door the clergyman turned and whispered to Woodbury and Hannah Thurston: "You may not be needed: wait until I summon you."

The next instant he knocked on the door of the parlor. Dyce's voice replied: "Come in." He entered first, followed by his wife, and, last of all, the injured husband. Dyce and Mrs. Merryfield were seated side by side, on a sofa. Both, as by an involuntary impulse, rose to their feet. The latter turned very pale; her knees trembled under her, and she sank down again upon her seat. Dyce, however, remained standing, and, after the first surprise was over, regained his brazen effrontery.

Merryfield was the first to speak. "Sarah," he cried, "What does this mean?"

She turned her head towards the window, and made no answer.

"Mrs. Merryfield," said Mr. Waldo, gravely, yet with no harshness in his tone, "we have come, as your friends, believing that you have taken this step hastily, and without considering what its consequences would be. We do not think you appreciate its solemn importance, both for time and for eternity.   It is not yet too late to undo what you have done, and we are ready to help you, in all kindness and tenderness."

"I want nothing more than my rights," said Mrs. Merryfield, in a hard, stubborn voice, without turning her head.

"I will never interfere with your just rights, as a woman, a wife, and an immortal soul," the clergyman replied.   "But you have not alone rights to receive: you have duties to perform.   You have bound yourself to your husband in holy marriage; you cannot desert him, whose faith to you has never been broken, who now stands ready to pardon your present fault, as he has pardoned all your past ones, without incurring a greater sin than infidelity to him.   Your married relation includes both the moral laws by which society is bound, and the Divine laws by which we are saved."

"The usual cant of theologians!" interrupted Dyce, with a sneer.   "Mrs. Merryfield owes nothing to the selfish and artificial machinery which is called Society.   Marriage is a part of the machinery, and just as selfish as the rest.   She claims equal rights with her husband, and is doing no more than he would do, if he possessed all of her convictions."

"I would never do it!" cried Merryfield,—"not for all the Communities in the world!   Sarah, I've been faithful to you, in every thought, since you first agreed to be my wife.   If I've done you wrong in any way, tell me!"

"I only want my rights," she repeated, still looking away.

"If you really think you are deprived of them," said Mr. Waldo, "come home with us, and you shall be fairly heard and fairly judged.   I promise you, as an impartial friend, that no advantage shall be taken of your mistake: you shall be treated as if it had not occurred.   Have you reflected how this act will be interpreted, in the eyes of the world?   Can you bear, no matter how innocent you may be, to be followed, through all the rest of your life, by the silent suspicion, if not the open reproach, of the worst shame that can happen to woman?   Suppose you reach your Community.   These experiments have often been tried, and they have always failed.

10*

You might hide yourself for a while from the judgment of the world, but if the association should break to pieces—what then? Does the possession of some right which you fancy is withheld, compensate you for incurring this fearful risk—nay, for enduring this fearful certainty?"

"What do you know about it?" Dyce roughly exclaimed. "You, a petrified fossil of the false Society! What right have you to judge for her? She acts from motives which your narrow mind cannot comprehend. She is a disciple of the Truth, and is not afraid to show it in her life. If she lived only for the sake of appearances, like the rest of you, she might still be a Vegetable!"

Mrs. Merryfield, who had colored suddenly and violently, as the clergyman spoke, and had turned her face towards him, for a moment, with an agitation which she could not conceal, now lifted her head a little, and mechanically rocked on her lap a travelling-satchel, which she had grasped with both hands. She felt her own inability to defend herself, and recovered a little courage at hearing it done so fiercely by her companion.

Mr. Waldo, without noticing the latter, turned to her again. "I will not even condemn the motives which lead you to this step," said he, "but I must show you its inevitable consequences. Only the rarest natures, the most gifted intellects, may seem to disregard the ruling habits and ideas of mankind, because God has specially appointed them to some great work. You know, Mrs. Merryfield, as well as I do, that you are not one of such. The world will make no exception in your favor. It cannot put our kindly and tolerant construction upon your motives: it will be pitiless and inflexible, and its verdict will crush you to the dust."

"Sarah," said her husband, more in pity than in reproach, "do stop and think what you are doing! What Mr. Waldo says is true: you will bring upon yourself more than you can bear, or I can bear for you. _I_ don't charge you with any thing wrong; _I_ don't believe you would be guilty of—of—I can't say it—but I couldn't hold up my head, as—as it were, and defend you by a single word."

"Oh, no! of course *you* couldn't!" Dyce broke in again, with an insufferable impudence. " *You* know, as well as I do, —or Mr. Waldo, for that matter,—what *men* are. Don't brag to me about your morality, and purity, and all that sort of humbug: what's fit for one sex is fit for the other. Men, *you* know, have a natural monopoly in the indulgence of passion: it's allowed to them, but woman is damned by the very suspicion. You know, both of you, that any man would as lief be thought wicked as chaste—that women are poor, ignorant fools"——

One of the folding-doors which communicated with the adjoining room was suddenly torn open, and Woodbury appeared. His brown eyes, flashing indignant fire, were fixed upon Dyce. The sallow face of the latter grew livid with mingled emotions of rage and fear. With three strides, Woodbury was before him.

"Stop!" he cried, "you have been allowed to say too much already. If *you*," he added, turning to the others, "have patience with this beast, I have not."

"Ah! he thinks he's among his Sepoys," Dyce began, but was arrested by a strong hand upon his collar. Woodbury's face was pale, but calm, and his lips parted in a smile, the expression of which struck terror to the heart of the medium.

"Now, leave!" said he, in a low, stern voice, "leave, or I hurl you through that window!" Relinquishing his grasp on the collar, he opened the door leading to the staircase, and waited. For a moment, the eyes of the two men met, and in that moment each took the measure of the other. Dyce's figure seemed to contract; his breast narrowed, his shoulders fell, and his knees approached each other. He walked slowly and awkwardly to the end of the sofa, picked up his valise, and shuffled out of the room without saying a word. Woodbury followed him to the door, and said, before he closed it:

"Recollect, *you* leave here by the midnight train." None

of those who heard it had any doubt that the command would
be obeyed.

Mr. Merryfield experienced an unbounded sensation of relief
on Dyce's departure; but his wife was only frightened, not
conquered. Although pale and trembling, she stubbornly held
out, her attitude expressing her collective defiance of the company. She avoided directly addressing or meeting the eyes
of any one in particular. For a few moments there was silence
in the room, and she took advantage of it to forestall the
appeals which she knew would be made, by saying :

"Well, now you've got me all to yourselves, I suppose you'll
try to bully me out of my rights."

"We have no intention to meddle with any of your rights,
as a wife," Mr. Waldo answered. "You must settle that
question with your husband. But does not your heart tell
you that he has rights, as well? And what has he done to
justify you in deserting him?"

"He needn't be deserted," she said ; "he can come after me."

"Never!" exclaimed her husband. "If you leave me now,
and in this way, Sarah, you will not see me again until you
voluntarily come back to me. And think, if you go to that
place, what you must then seem to me ! I've defended you,
Sarah, and will defend you against all the world ; but if you
go on, you'll take the power of doing it away from me.
Whether you deserve shame, or not, it'll come to you—and
it'll come to me, just the same."

The deluded wife could make no reply. The consequences
of her step, if persisted in, were beginning to dawn upon her
mind, but, having defended it on the ground of her equal
rights as a woman, a pitiful vanity prevented her from yielding. It was necessary, therefore, to attack her from another
quarter. Hannah Thurston felt that the moment had arrived
when she might venture to speak, and went gently forward to
the sofa.

"Sarah," she said, " I think you feel that I am your friend.
Will you not believe me, then, when I say to you that we

have all followed you, prompted only by the pity and distress which we feel for your sake and your husband's? We beg you not to leave us, your true friends, and go among strangers. Listen to us calmly, and if we convince you that you are mistaken, the admission should not be difficult."

"You, too, Hannah!" cried Mrs. Merryfield. "You, that taught me what my rights were! Will you confess, first, that *you* are mistaken?"

An expression of pain passed over Hannah Thurston's face. "I never meant to claim more than natural justice for woman," said she, "but I may have been unhappy in my advocacy of it. I may even," turning towards Mrs. Waldo, "have seemed to assume a hostile position towards man. If so, it was a mistake. If what I have said has prompted you to this step, I will take my share of humiliation. But we will not talk of that now. Blame me, Sarah, if you like, so you do not forget the tenderness you cannot wholly have lost, for him whose life is a part of yours, here and hereafter. Think of the children who are waiting for you in the other life—waiting for *both* parents, Sarah."

The stubborn resistance of the wife began to give way. Tears came to her eyes, and she shook as if a mighty struggle had commenced in her heart. "It was for them," she murmured, in a broken voice, "that I was going. He said they would be nearer to me."

"Can they be nearer to you when you are parted from their father? Was it only your heart that was wrung at their loss? If all other bonds were broken between you, the equal share in the beings of those Immortals should bind you in life and death! Pardon me for renewing your sorrow, but I must invoke the purer spirit that is born of trial. If your mutual watches over their cradles cannot bring back the memory of your married love, I must ask you to remember who held your hand beside their coffins, whose arm supported you in the lonely nights!"

The husband could endure no more. Lifting his face from

his hands, he cried: "It was me, Sarah. And now, if you leave me, there will be no one to talk with me about Absalom, and Angelina, and our dear little Robert. Don't you mind how I used to dance him on my knee, as—as it were, and tell him he should have a horse when he was big? He had such pretty hair; you always said he'd make a handsome man, Sarah: but now they're all gone. There's only us two, now, as it were, and we can't—no, we daren't part. We won't part, will we?"

Mrs. Waldo made a quiet sign, and they stole gently from the room. As he closed the door, Woodbury saw the conquered and penitent wife look up with streaming eyes, sobbing convulsively, and stretch out her arms. The next instant, Mrs. Waldo had half embraced him, in the rush of her pent-up gratitude.

"Oh!" she exclaimed, striving to subdue her voice, "how grand it was that you put down that—that *man*. I never believed in non-resistance, and now I know that I am right."

Hannah Thurston said nothing, but her face was radiant with a tranquil light. She could not allow the doubts which had arisen in her mind—the disturbing influences which had, of late, beset her, to cloud the happy ending of such a painful day. A whispered conversation was carried on between Woodbury and the Waldos, so as not to disturb the low voices in the next room; but at the end of ten minutes the door opened and Merryfield appeared.

"We will go home to-night, as it were," said he. "The moon rises about this time, and the night is warm."

"Then we will all go!" was Mrs. Waldo's decision. "The carriages will keep together—husband, you must drive one of them, alone—and I shall not be so much alarmed. It is better so: curious folks will not see that we have been absent, and need not know."

Woodbury whispered to her: "I shall wait until the train leaves."

"Will you follow, afterwards?"

"Yes—but no : my intention to stay all night is known, and I ought properly to remain, unless you need my escort."

"Stay," said Hannah Thurston.

The vehicles left the two hotels with the same persons who had arrived in them—Dyce excepted. Outside of Tiberius they halted, and Merryfield joined his wife. The two women followed, and Mr. Waldo, alone, acted as rear-guard. Thus, in the silent night, over the moonlit hills, and through the rustling darkness of the woods, they went homewards.

Vague suspicions of *something* haunted the community of Ptolemy for a while, but nothing was ever discovered or betrayed which could give them a definite form. And yet, of the five persons to whom the truth was known, three were women.

CHAPTER XVIII.

ONE OF THE SUMMER DIVERSIONS OF PTOLEMY.

TEN days after the journey to Tiberius, the highways in both valleys, and those descending from the hills on either side, were unusually thronged. Country carriages, buggies of all fashions, and light open carts, rapidly succeeded each other, all directing their course towards the village. They did not halt there, however, but passed through, and, climbing the gentle acclivity of the southern hill, halted at a grove, nearly a mile distant. Here the Annual Temperance Convention of Atauga County was to be held. The cause had been languishing for the past year or two; many young men had become careless of their pledges, and the local societies were beginning to fall to pieces, because the members had heard all that was to be said on the subject, and had done all that could conveniently be done. The plan of procuring State legislation in their favor rendered it necessary to rekindle, in some measure, the fires of zeal—if so warm an expression can be applied to so sober a cause—and one of the most prominent speakers on Temperance, Mr. Abiram Stokes, was called upon to brush up his well-used images and illustrations for a new campaign.

It was announced, by means of large placards, posted in all the village stores, post-offices, and blacksmiths' shops, far and wide, that not only he, but Mr. Grindle and several other well-known speakers were to address the Convention. Strange as it may seem, the same placard was conspicuously displayed in the bar-room of the Ptolemy House, the landlord candidly declaring that he would be glad if such a convention were held every week, as it brought him a great deal of custom. The friends of the cause were called upon for a special effort; the day was carefully arranged to come at the end of haying, yet before the wheat-harvest had fairly commenced; moreover, it was Saturday, and the moon was nearly full. The weather favored the undertaking, and by noon the line of the roads could be distinguished, at some distance, by the dust which arose from the strings of vehicles.

The principal members of the local societies—especially those of Atauga City, Anacreon, Nero Corners, Mulligansville, and New Pekin—came in heavy lumber-wagons, decorated with boughs of spruce and cedar, carrying with them their banners, whenever they had any. With some difficulty, a sufficient sum was raised to pay for the services of the Ptolemy Cornet Band, in performing, as the placard stated, "melodies appropriate to the occasion." What those melodies were, it was not very easy to determine, and the managing committee of the Ptolemy Society had a special meeting on the subject, the night before. A wag suggested "The Meeting of the Waters," which was at once accepted with delight. "Bonny Doon" found favor, as it "minded" the hearers of a Scottish brook. "The Campbells are Comin'" was also on the list, until some one remembered that the landlord of the Ptolemy House bore the name of that clan. "A wet sheet and a flowing sea" hinted too strongly at "half-seas over," and all the familiar Irish airs were unfortunately associated with ideas of wakes and Donnybrook Fairs. After much painful cogitation, the "Old Oaken Bucket," "Allan Water," "Zurich's Waters," and "The Haunted Spring" were discovered; but the band was not able to play more than half of them. Its most successful performance, we are bound to confess, was the air of "Landlord, fill the flowing bowl," which the leader could not resist giving once or twice during the day, to the great scandal of those votaries of the cause who had once been accustomed to sing it in character.

The grove was a beautiful piece of oak and hickory timber,

sloping towards the north, and entirely clear of underbrush.
It covered about four acres of ground, and was neither so
dense nor fell so rapidly as to shut out a lovely glimpse of
the valley and the distant, dark-blue sheet of the lake, between
the boles. It was pervaded with a grateful smell, from the
trampled grass and breathing leaves; and wherever a beam of
sunshine pierced the boughs, it seemed to single out some bit
of gay color, in shawl, or ribbon, or parasol, to play upon and
utilize its brightness. At the bottom of the grove, against
two of the largest trees, a rough platform was erected, in
front of which, rising and radiating amphitheatrically, were
plank benches, capable of seating a thousand persons. Those
who came from a distance were first on hand, and took their
places long before the proceedings commenced. Near the
main entrance, venders of refreshments had erected their
stands, and displayed to the thronging visitors a tempting
variety of indigestible substances. There was weak lemonade,
in tin buckets, with huge lumps of ice glittering defiantly at
the sun; scores of wired bottles, filled with a sarsaparilla mixture, which popped out in a rush of brown suds; ice-cream,
the cream being eggs beaten up with water, and flavored with
lemon sirup; piles of dark, leathery ginger-cakes, and rows
of glass jars full of candy-sticks; while the more enterprising
dealers exhibited pies cut into squares, hard-boiled eggs, and
even what they called coffee.

Far down the sides of the main road to Ptolemy the vehicles
were ranged, and even inside the adjoining fields—the owner
of which, being a friend to the cause, had opened his bars to
the multitude. Many of the farmers from a distance brought
their own oats with them, and unharnessed and fed their horses
in the fence-corners, before joining the crowd in the grove.
Then, accompanied by their tidy wives, who, meanwhile, examined the contents of the dinner-baskets and saw that every
thing was in order, they approached the meeting with satisfied
and mildly exhilarated spirits, occasionally stopping to greet
an acquaintance or a relative. The daughters had already pre-

ceded them, with their usual independence, well knowing the impatience of the young men, and hoping that the most agreeable of the latter would discover them before the meeting was called to order. This was the real charm of the occasion, to old as well as young. The American needs a serious pretext for his recreation. He does not, in fact, recognize its necessity, and would have none at all, did not Nature, with benevolent cunning, occasionally furnish him with diversion under the disguise of duty.

As the banners of the local societies arrived, they were set up in conspicuous positions, on and around the speaker's platform. That of Tiberius was placed in the centre. It was of blue silk, with a gold fringe, and an immense geyser-like fountain in its field, under which were the words: "Ho! every one that thirsteth!" On the right was the banner of Ptolemy—a brilliant rainbow, on a white ground, with the warning: "Look not upon the Wine when it is Red." What connection there was between this sentence and the rainbow was not apparent, unless the latter was meant to represent a watery deluge. The banner of Anacreon, on the left, held forth a dancing female, in a crimson dress. One foot was thrown far out behind her, and she was violently pitching forward; yet, in this uncomfortable position, she succeeded in pouring a thick stream of water from a ewer of blue china into the open mouth of a fat child, who wore a very scanty dress. The inscription was: "The Fountain of Youth." The most ingenious device, however, was that from Nero Corners. This little community, too poor or too economical to own a temperance banner, took a political one, which they had used in the campaign of the previous year. Upon it were the names of the candidates for President and Vice-President: "PIERCE and KING." A very little alteration turned the word "Pierce" into "Prince," and the word "WATER" being prefixed, the inscription became: "Water,—Prince and King." Those from other neighborhoods, who were not in the secret, greatly admired the simplicity and force of the expression.

Woodbury, who was early upon the ground, was much interested in the scene. Between two and three thousand persons were present, but an order and decorum prevailed, which
would be miraculous in lands where the individual is not permitted to grow up self-ruled, or swayed only by the example
of his fellows, and self-reliant. No servant of the law was present to guard against disorder, because each man was his own
policeman. Even some tipsy rowdies, who came out from
Ptolemy towards the close of the afternoon, were sobered
by the atmosphere of the place, and had no courage to make
their intended interruptions. The effect of such meetings,
Woodbury confessed to himself, could not be otherwise
than good; the reform was necessary among a people whose
excitable temperament naturally led them to excesses, and
perhaps it was only one extreme which could counteract
the other. There was still too little repose, too little mental
balance among them, to halt upon the golden middle-ground
of truth.

The band occupied the platform for some time after he arrived, and its performances gave intense satisfaction to the
people. The clear tones of the horns and clarionets pealed
triumphantly through the shade, and an occasional slip in an
instrument was unnoticed in the hum of voices. Gradually,
the hearers were lifted a little out of the material sphere in
which they habitually moved, and were refreshed accordingly.
They were made capable, at least, of appreciating some sentiment and imagination in the speakers, and words were now
heard with delight, which, in their common moods, would have
been vacant sound. They touched, in spite of themselves, that
upper atmosphere of poetry which hangs over all human life—
where the cold marsh-fogs in which we walk become the rosy
cloud-islands of the dawn!

At two o'clock, the band vacated the platform, and the Convention was called to order. After an appropriate prayer by
the Rev. Lemuel Styles, a temperance song was sung by a large
chorus of the younger members. It was a parody on Hoff-

man's charming anacreontic: "Sparkling and Bright," the
words of which were singularly transformed.　Instead of:

> " As the bubbles that swim on the beaker's brim,
> 　And break on the lips at meeting,"

the refrain terminated with:

> " There's nothing so good for the youthful blood,
> 　Or so sweet as the sparkling water!"

—in the style of a medicinal prescription.　Poor Hoffman!
Noble heart and fine mind, untimely darkened!　He was at
least spared this desecration; or perhaps, with the gay humor
with which even that darkness is still cheered, he would have
parodied the parody to death.

The Annual Report was then read.　It was of great length,
being mainly a furious appeal to voters.　The trick of basing
a political issue upon a personal habit was an innovation in the
science of government, which the natural instincts of the people were too enlightened to accept without question.　The
County Committee, foreseeing this difficulty, adopted the usual
tactics of party, and strove to create a headlong tide of sympathy which would overbear all hesitancy as to the wisdom of
the movement, or the dangerous precedent which it introduced
into popular legislation.　"Vote for the Temperance Candidates," they cried, in the Report, " and you vote for morality,
and virtue, and religion!　Vote against them, and you vote for
disease, and misery, and crime!　Vote for them, and you vote
reason to the frantic brain, clearness to the bleared eye, steadiness to the trembling hand, joy to the heart of the forsaken
wife, and bread to the mouths of the famishing children!　Vote
against them, and you vote to fill our poor-houses and peniten-
tiaries—to tighten the diabolical hold of the rumseller on his
struggling victim—to lead our young men into temptation, and
bring ruin on our beloved land!　Yes, you would vote to fill
the drunkard's bottle; you would vote oaths and obscenity into
his speech; you would vote curses to his wife, blows to his
children, the shoes off their feet, the shirts off their backs,
the beds from under them, and the roofs from over their heads."

The Report was adopted with tremendous unanimity, and the faces of the members of the Committee beamed with satisfaction. The political movement might be considered as successfully inaugurated. This was the main object of the Convention, and the waiting orators now saw that they had a clear and pleasant field before them. Woodbury, who was leaning against a tree, near the end of a plank upon which his friends the Waldos were seated, listened with an involuntary sensation of pain and regret. The very character of the Report strengthened him in the conviction that the vice to be cured had its origin in a radical defect of the national temperament, which no legislation could reach.

Mrs. Waldo looked up at him, inquiringly. He shook his head. "It is a false movement," said he; "good works are not accomplished by violence."

"But sometimes by threatening it," she answered, with a meaning smile.

He was about to reply, when the President announced that Byron Baxter, of the Anacreon Seminary, would recite a poem, after which the meeting would be addressed by Mr. Abiram Stokes.

Byron Baxter, who was an overgrown, knock-kneed youth of nineteen, with long hair, parted in the middle, advanced to the front of the platform, bowed, and then suddenly started back, with both hands extended before him, in an attitude of horror. In a loud voice, he commenced to recite:

> "Oh, take the maddening bowl away!
>   Remove the poisonous cup!
> My soul is sick; its burning ray
>   Hath drunk my spirit up.
>
> "Take, take it from my loathing lip
>   Ere madness fires my brain:
> Oh, take it hence, nor let me sip
>   Its liquid death again!"

As the young man had evidently never tasted any thing

stronger than molasses-and-water, the expression of his abhorrence was somewhat artificial. Nevertheless, a shudder ran through the audience at the vehemence of his declamation, and he was greeted with a round of applause, at the close.

The orator of the day, Mr. Abiram Stokes, then made his appearance. He was a man of forty-five, with a large, handsome head, and an imposing presence. His hair and eyes were dark, and his complexion slightly tinted with olive. This trait, with his small hands and showy teeth, seemed to indicate a mixture of Spanish blood. He had a way of throwing his head forward, so as to let a large lock of his hair fall over his forehead with a picturesque effect, and then tossing it back to its place with a reverse motion. His voice was full and sonorous; although, to a practised ear, its pathos, in passages intended for effect, was more dramatic than real. Few of his present auditors, however, were able to discriminate in this respect; the young ladies, especially, were in raptures. It was rumored that his early life had been very wild and dissipated, and he was looked upon as one of the most conspicuous brands which had been snatched from the burning. This rumor preceded him wherever he went, created a personal interest for him, in advance, and added to the effect of his oratory.

His style of speaking, nevertheless, was showy and specious. He took no wide range, touched but slightly on the practical features of the subject, and indulged sparingly in anecdotes and illustrations. None of the latter professed to be drawn from his personal experience: his hearers might make whatever inference they pleased, he knew the value of mystery too well, to enlighten them further. He was greatest in apostrophes to Water, to Reform, to Woman, to any thing that permitted him, according to his own expression, "to soar." This feature of his orations was usually very effective, the first time he was heard. He was in the habit of introducing some of his favorite passages on every occasion. Woodbury, who was not aware of this trick, was agreeably surprised at the natural warmth and eloquence of the speaker's language.

His peroration ran something in this wise : " This, the purest and most beneficent of the Virtues, comes not to achieve her victory in battles and convulsions. Soft as the dews of heaven, her white feet are beautiful upon the mountains, bringing glad tidings of great joy ! Blessed are we that she has chosen her abode among us, and that she has selected us to do her work ! No other part of the world was fitted to receive her. She never could have been produced by the mouldering despotisms of Europe, where the instincts of Freedom are stifled by wine and debauchery; the Old World is too benighted to behold her face.   Here only—here on the virgin bosom of a new Continent—here, in the glorious effulgence of the setting sun— here only could she be born ! She is the child of the West— Temperance—and before her face the demon Alcohol flees to his caverns and hides himself among the bones of his victims, while Peace sits at her right hand and Plenty at her left !"

" Beautiful !" " splendid!" was whispered through the audience, as the speaker took his seat. Miss Carrie Dilworth wiped her eyes with a very small batiste handkerchief, and sighed as she reflected that this man, her beau-idèal (which she understood to mean an ideal beau), would never know what an appreciative helpmeet she would have made him.

" Oh, Hannah !" she whispered, leaning forward, to Miss Thurston, who was seated on the next plank, " did you ever hear any thing so beautiful ?"

" I thought it fine, the first time I heard it," Hannah replied, with a lack of enthusiasm which quite astounded the little sempstress. She began to fear she had made a mistake, when the sight of Miss Ruhaney Goodwin, equally in tears, (and no wonder, for her brother Elisha had been a miserable drunkard), somewhat revived her confidence.

" Flashy, but not bad of its kind," said Woodbury, in reply to Mrs. Waldo's question.

" Are you not ashamed ? It's magnificent. And he's such a handsome man !" she exclaimed. " But I see, you are determined not to admire any of them ; you've not forgotten

Grindle's attack. Or else you're a pess— what's the name of it? Mr. Waldo explained the word to me yesterday—pess "—

"Oh, a pessimist? Not at all, Mrs. Waldo. On the contrary, I am almost an optimist."

"Well, that's just as bad—though I am not sure I know what it is. Oh, there's Grindle going to speak. Now you'll catch it!"

She shook her hand menacingly, and Woodbury, much amused and not a little curious to hear the speaker, resumed his position against the tree.

Mr. Grindle, who carried on a moderate lumber business in Atauga City, neglected no opportunity of making himself heard in public. He was a man of shallow faculties, but profound conceit of himself, and would have preferred, at any time, to be abused rather than ignored. His naturally fluent speech had been cultivated by the practice of years, but as he was neither an earnest thinker nor a close reasoner, and, moreover, known to be unscrupulous in the statement of facts, the consideration which he enjoyed as a speaker would soon have become exhausted, but for the boldness and indecency of his personal attacks, whereby he replenished that element of hot water in which he rejoiced. Mr. Campbell, the landlord of the Ptolemy House, had several times threatened him with personal chastisement, and he only escaped by avoiding an encounter until the landlord's wrath had a little cooled. He was so accustomed to insulting epithets that they never produced the slightest impression upon him.

He had spoken nearly half an hour, airing a quantity of statistics, which he had mostly committed to memory—where that failed, he supplied the figures from his imagination— when he perceived that the audience, after having tasted the spiced meats of Mr. Abiram Stokes, seemed to find the plain food he offered them rather insipid. But he had still the resource of personality, which he knew, from long experience, is always entertaining, whether or not the hearers approve of it. The transition was easily made. "Looking at this terrible

11

array of facts," said he, "how can any man, who is worthy the
name of a human being, *dare* to oppose the doctrines of Temperance? How dare any man suppose that his own miserable
personal indulgences are of more consequence than the moral
salvation of his fellow-creatures? Yet there are such men—
not poor, ignorant, deluded creatures, who know no better,
and are entitled to some allowances—but men who are rich,
who appear to be educated, and who claim to be highly moral
and respectable. What are we to think of those men?"

Mrs. Waldo glanced up at Woodbury with a look which
said: "Now it's coming!"

"Let it come!" his look replied.

"They think, perhaps," the speaker continued, "that there
are different laws of morality for different climates—that they
can bring here among us the detestable practices of heathen
races, which we are trying to root out! I tell such, they had
better go back, and let their unhappy slaves hand them the
hookah, filled with its intoxicating draught, or steady their
tottering steps when the fumes of sherbet have mounted to
their brains!"

Many persons in the assembly knew who was meant, and
as Woodbury's position made him easily distinguished, they
watched him with curiosity as the speaker proceeded. He
leaned against the tree, with his arms folded, and an amused
half-smile on his face, until the foregoing climax was reached,
when, to the astonishment of the spectators, he burst into an
uncontrollable fit of laughter.

Mr. Grindle, too, had discovered his victim, and occasionally
darted a side look at him, calculating how far he might carry
the attack with safety to himself. Woodbury's sudden and
violent merriment encouraged while it disconcerted him: there
was, at least, nothing to be feared, and he might go on.

"Yes, I repeat it," he continued; "whatever name may be
given to the beverage, we are not to be cheated. Such men
may drink their sherbet, or their Heidsick; they may call their
drinks by *respectable* names, and the demon of Alcohol laughs

as he claims them for his own. St. Paul says 'the Prince of Darkness is a gentleman:' beware, beware, my friends, lest the accursed poison, which is harmless to you under its *vulgar* names, should beguile you with an *aristocratic* title!"

"Will the speaker allow me to make a remark?"

Woodbury, controlling his laughter with some difficulty, straightened himself from his leaning position against the tree, and, yielding to the impulse of the moment, spoke. His voice, not loud, but very clear, was distinctly heard all over the crowd, and there was a general rustling sound, as hundreds of heads turned towards him. Mr. Grindle involuntarily paused in his speech, but made no reply.

"I will only interrupt the proceedings for a moment," Woodbury resumed, in a cool, steady tone, amidst the perfect silence of the multitude—"in order to make an explanation. I will not wrong the speaker by supposing that his words have a personal application to myself; because that would be charging him with advocating truth by means of falsehood, and defending morality by the weapons of ignorance and insult. But I know the lands of which he speaks and the habits of their people. So far from drunkenness being a 'detestable heathen habit' of theirs, it is really we who should go to them to learn temperance. I must confess, also, my great surprise at hearing the speaker's violent denunciation of the use of sherbet, after seeing that it is openly sold, to-day, in this grove—after having, with my own eyes, observed the speaker, himself, drink a large glass of it with evident satisfaction."

There was a sudden movement, mixed here and there with laughter, among the audience. Mr. Grindle cried out, in a hoarse, excited voice: "The charge is false! I never use intoxicating beverages!"

"I made no such charge," said Woodbury, calmly, "but it may interest the audience to know that sherbet is simply the Arabic name for lemonade."

The laughter was universal, Mr. Grindle excepted.

"The speaker, also," he continued, "mentioned the intoxicating beverage of the hookah. As the hookah is a pipe, in which the smoke of the tobacco passes through water before reaching the mouth, it may be considered a less dangerous beverage than the clay-pipe of the Irish laborer. I beg pardon of the meeting for my interruption."

The laughter was renewed, more heartily than before, and for a minute after Woodbury ceased the tumult was so great that Mr. Grindle could not be heard. To add to the confusion, the leader of the Ptolemy band, taking the noise as a sign that the Convention had adjourned, struck up "Malbrook," which air, unfortunately, was known in the neighborhood by the less classical title of "We won't go home till morning."

The other members of the Committee, on the platform, privately begged Mr. Grindle to take his seat and allow them to introduce a new orator; but he persisted in speaking for another quarter of an hour, to show that he was not discomfited. The greater portion of the audience, nevertheless, secretly rejoiced at the lesson he had received, and the remainder of his speech was not heard with much attention. Woodbury, to escape the curious gaze of the multitude, took a narrow and uncomfortable seat on the end of the plank, beside Mrs. Waldo. He was thenceforth, very much against his will, an object of great respect to the rowdies of Ptolemy, who identified him with the opposite cause.

There was another song, commencing:

> " The wine that all are praising
> Is not the drink for me,
> But there's a spring in yonder glen,
> Whose waters flow for Temperance men," etc.,

which was likewise sung in chorus. Then succeeded other speakers, of less note, to a gradually diminishing circle of hearers. The farmers and their wives strayed off to gossip with acquaintances on the edges of the grove; baskets of provisions were opened and the contents shared, and the stalls of cake and sarsaparilla suds experienced a reflux of custom. As the

young men were not Lord Byrons, the young ladies did not
scruple to eat in their presence, and flirtations were carried on
with a chicken-bone in one hand and a piece of bread in the
other. The sun threw softer and slanter lights over the beautiful picture of the valley, and, gradually creeping below the
boughs, shot into the faces of those who were still seated in
front of the platform. It was time to close the performances
of the day, and they were accordingly terminated with a third
song, the refrain of which was :

> "Oh, for the cause is rolling on, rolling on, rolling on,
>   Over the darkened land."

Woodbury and the Waldos, to avoid the dust of the road,
walked back to Ptolemy by a pleasant path across the fields.
Ere long they overtook Hannah Thurston and Miss Dilworth.
Mr. Grindle was, of course, the theme of conversation.

"Wasn't he rightly served, Hannah?" Mrs. Waldo exclaimed, with enthusiasm. Woodbury was fast assuming
heroic proportions, in her mind.

"I think Mr. Woodbury was entirely justifiable in his interruption," Miss Thurston answered, "and yet I almost wish
that it had not occurred."

"So do I!" Woodbury exclaimed.

"Well—you two are queer people!" was Mrs. Waldo's
amazed remark.

CHAPTER XIX.

IN WHICH THERE IS BOTH ATTRACTION AND REPULSION.

HANNAH THURSTON's remark remained in Woodbury's ears long after it was uttered. His momentary triumph over, he began to regret having obeyed the impulse of the moment. Mr. Grindle's discomfiture had been too cheaply purchased; he was game of a sort too small and mean for a man of refined instincts to notice even by a look. His own interruption, cool and careless as he felt it to have been, nevertheless betrayed an acknowledgment that he had understood the speaker's insinuation; and, by a natural inference, that he was sufficiently sensitive to repel it. Mr. Grindle was acute enough to make this inference, and it was a great consolation to him, in his own overthrow, to think that he had stung his adversary.

Woodbury, however, forgot his self-blame in the grateful surprise of hearing its echo from Miss Thurston's lips. Her remark betrayed a delicacy of perception which he had not expected—more than this, indeed, it betrayed a consideration for his character as a gentleman, which she could not have felt, had she not, in imagination, placed herself in his stead. He knew that a refined nature must be born so; it can only be partially imitated by assiduous social study; and his previous intercourse with Miss Thurston had not prepared him to find her instincts so true. He looked at her, as she walked beside him, with a renewed feeling of interest. Her slender figure moved along the grassy path with a free, elastic step. She wore a dress of plain white muslin, with wide sleeves, and a knot of pearl-colored ribbon at the throat. Her parasol, and the trimming of her hat, were of the same quiet color; the only ornament she wore was a cluster of little pink flowers in the latter. The excitement of the occasion, or the act of walking, had brought a soft tinge to her usually pale cheek, and as her eyes dropped to avoid the level light of the sun, Woodbury noticed how long and dark were the lashes that fringed her lids. "At eighteen she must have been lovely," he said to himself, "but, even then, her expression could scarcely have been more virginly pure and sweet, than now."

He turned away, repressing a sigh. How one delusion could spoil a noble woman!

Before descending the last slope to the village, they paused, involuntarily, to contemplate the evening landscape. The sun was just dipping behind the western hill, and a portion of Ptolemy lay in shadow, while the light, streaming through th gap made by a lateral glen, poured its dusty gold over the distant elms of Roaring Brook, and caused the mansion of Lakeside to sparkle like a star against its background of firs Far down the lake flashed the sail of a pleasure-boat, and the sinking western shore melted into a vapory purple along the dim horizon. The strains of the band still reached them from the grove, but softened to the airy, fluctuating sweetness of an Æolian harp.

"Our lines are cast in pleasant places," said Mr. Waldo, looking from hill to hill with a cheerful content on his face.

"Every part of the earth has its moments of beauty, I think," Woodbury replied: "but Ptolemy is certainly a favored spot. If the people only knew it. I wonder whether happiness is not a faculty, or a peculiarity of temperament, quite independent of the conditions of one's life?"

"That depends on what you call happiness," Mrs. Waldo rejoined. "Come, now, let us each define it, and see how we shall agree. *My* idea is, it's in making the best of every thing."

"No, it's finding a congenial spirit!" cried Miss Carrie.

"You forget the assurance of Grace," said the clergyman.

"Fairly caught, Mrs. Waldo! You are no better than I:

you confess yourself an optimist!" Woodbury merrily exclaimed. "So far, you are right—but, unfortunately, there
are some things we cannot make the best of."

"We can always do our duty, for it is proportioned to our
power," said Hannah Thurston.

"If we know exactly what it is."

"Why should we not know?" she asked, turning quickly
towards him.

"Because the simple desire to know is not enough, although
I trust God gives us some credit for it. How much of Truth
is there, that we imperfectly grasp! How much is there, also,
that we shrink from knowing!"

"Shrink from Truth!"

"Yes, since we are human, and our nearest likeness to God
is a compassionate tenderness for our fellow-men. Does not
the knowledge of a vice in a dear friend give us pain? Do
we not cling, most desperately, to our own cherished opinions,
at the moment when we begin to suspect they are untenable?
No: we are not strong enough, nor stony-hearted enough, to
do without illusions."

"Yet you would convince me of mine!" Hannah Thurston
exclaimed, with a shade of bitterness in the tone of her voice.
The next moment she felt a pang of self-rebuke at having
spoken, and the color rose to her face. The application she
had made of his words was uncalled-for. He must not thus be
met. He was so impregnable in his calmness, and in the conclusions drawn from his ripe experience of life! Her own
faith tottered whenever their minds came in contact, yet if she
gave up it, how could she be certain, any longer, what was
Truth? He was not a hard materialist; he possessed fancy,
and feeling, and innate reverence; but his approach seemed to
chill her enthusiasm and benumb the free action of her mind.

"Oh, no!" he answered, with kindly seriousness, "I would
not consciously destroy a single innocent illusion. There are
even forms of Error which are only rendered worse by antagonism. I have no idea of assailing all views that do not har-

monize with my own. I am but one among many millions, and my aim is to understand Life, not forcibly change its character."

Walking a little in advance of the others, as they spoke, the conversation was interrupted by their arrival in Ptolemy. Woodbury declined an invitation to take tea with the Waldos, and drove home with Bute, in the splendor of sunset. The latter took advantage of the first opportunity to describe to Mrs. Fortitude Babb the confusion which his master had inflicted on Mr. Grindle.

"And sarved him right, too," said she, with a grim satisfaction. "To think o' *him* turnin' up his nose at *her* best Sherry, and callin' it pizon !"

She could not refrain from expressing her approbation to Woodbury, as she prepared his tea. Her manner, however, made it seem very much like a reproof. "I've heerd, Sir," she remarked, with a rigid face, "that you've been speakin'. I s'pose you'll be goin' to the Legislatur', next."

Woodbury smiled. "Ill news travels fast," he said.

"'T'a'n't ill, as I can see. *She* wouldn't ha' thought so, nuther. Though, to be sure, sich fellers didn't come here, in *her* time."

"He will not come again, Mrs. Babb."

"I'd like to see him try it !" With which words Mrs. Babb slapped down the lid of the teapot, into which she had been looking, with a sound like the discharge of a pocket-pistol.

Woodbury went into the library, wheeled his arm-chair to the open window, lighted a cigar, and watched the risen moon brighten against the yielding twilight. The figure of Hannah Thurston, in her white dress, with the pearl-colored ribbon at her throat, with the long lashes falling over her dark-gray eyes, the flush on her cheek, and the earnest sweetness of her lips, rose before him through the rings of smoke, in the luminous dusk of the evening. A persistent fate seemed to throw them together, only to show him how near they might have been, how far apart they really were. When he recalled her cour-

11*

age and self-possession during the scene in the grove above the cataract, and the still greater courage which led her to Tiberius, daring reproach in order to rescue a deluded creature from impending ruin, he confessed to himself that for no other living woman did he feel equal respect. He bowed down in reverence before that highest purity which is unconscious of what it ventures, and an anxious interest arose in his heart as he recognized the dangers into which it might lead her. He felt that she was capable of understanding him ; that she possessed the finer instincts which constituted what was best in his own nature ; that she yielded him, also, a certain respect : but it was equally evident that her mind was unnecessarily alert and suspicious in his presence. She assumed a constant attitude of defence, when no attack was intended. He seemed to exercise an unconscious repellant force towards her, the secret of which he suspected must be found in herself—in the tenacity with which she held to her peculiar views, and a feminine impatience of contrary opinions.

But, as he mused, his fancies still came back to that one picture—the pure Madonna face, with its downcast eyes, touched with the mellow glory of the sunset. A noiseless breath of the night brought to his window the creamy odor of the locust blossoms, and lured forth the Persian dreams of the roses. The moonlight silver on the leaves—the pearly obscurity of the sky—the uncertain murmurs of the air—combined to steep his senses in a sweet, semi-voluptuous trance. He was too truly and completely man not to know what was lacking to his life. He was accustomed to control passion because he had learned its symptoms, but this return of the fever of youth was now welcome, with all its pain.

Towards midnight, he started suddenly and closed the window. "My God!" he exclaimed, aloud ; "she in my arms ! her lips on mine ! What was I thinking of ? Pshaw—a strong-minded woman ! Well—the very strongest-minded of them all is still very far from being a man." With which consoling excuse for the absurdity of his thoughts, he went to bed.

The next morning he spent an hour in a careful inspection of the library, and, after hesitating between a ponderous translation of the "*Maha-bharata*" and Lane's "Arabian Nights," finally replaced them both, and took down Jean Paul's "Siebenkäs" and "Walt and Vult." After the early Sunday dinner, he put the volumes into his pockets, and, mounting his horse, rode to Ptolemy.

Hannah Thurston had brought a chair into the open air, and seated herself on the shady side of the cottage. The afternoon was semi-clouded and mildly breezy, and she evidently found the shifting play of sun and shade upon the eastern hill better reading than the book in her hand, for the latter was closed. She recognized Woodbury as he came into the street a little distance below, and watched the motion of his horse's legs under the boughs of the balsam-firs, which hid the rider from sight. To her surprise, the horse stopped, opposite the cottage-door: she rose, laid down her book, and went forward to meet her visitor, who, by this time, had entered the gate.

After a frank and unembarrassed greeting, she said : "My mother is asleep, and her health is so frail that I am very careful not to disturb her rest. Will you take a seat, here, in the shade?"

She then withdrew for a moment, in order to bring a second chair. In the mean time, Woodbury had picked up her book : it was Bettine's Correspondence with Günderode. "I am glad," said he, looking up at her approach, "that I was not wrong in my selection."

She answered his look with an expression of surprise.

"I am going away, in a few days, for a summer excursion," he added, by way of explanation, taking the books from his pockets, "and in looking over my library this morning I found two works, which, it occurred to me, you might like to read. The sight of this volume convinces me that I have judged correctly: they are also translations from the German."

Hannah Thurston's eyes brightened as she took the books, and looked at their title-pages. "Oh!" she exclaimed, "I thank you very much! I have long wished to see these works: Lydia Maria Child speaks very highly of them."

"Who is Lydia Maria Child?"

She looked at him, almost in dismay. "Have you never read her 'Letters from New York?'" she asked. "I do not suppose you are a subscriber to the *Slavery Annihilator*, which she edits, but these letters have been collected and published."

"Are they doctrinal?"

"Perhaps you would call them so. She has a generous sympathy with all Progress; yet her letters are mostly descriptive. I would offer them to you, if I were sure that you would read them willingly—not as a task thrust upon you."

"You would oblige me," said Woodbury, cordially. "I am not unwilling to hear new views, especially when they are eloquently presented. Anna Maria Child, I presume, is an advocate of Woman's Rights?"

"You will, at least, find very little of such advocacy in her letters."

"And if I should?" he asked. "Do not confound me, Miss Thurston, with the multitude who stand in hostile opposition to your theory. I am very willing that it should be freely discussed, because attention may thereby be drawn to many real wrongs. Besides, in the long run, the practice of the human race is sensible and just, and nothing can be permanently adopted which is not very near the truth."

"'*Real* wrongs!'" she repeated; "yes, I suppose our wrongs are generally considered imaginary. It is a convenient way of disposing of them."

"Is that charge entirely fair?"

She colored slightly. Is the man's nature flint or iron, she thought, that his mind is so equably clear and cold? Would not antagonism rouse him into warmth, imparting an answering warmth to her thoughts, which his unimpassioned manner chilled to death? Then she remembered his contagious gayety during the walk to Ptolemy, his terrible indignation in the inn at Tiberius, and felt that she had done him wrong.

"I ask your pardon," she answered, présently. "I did not mean to apply the charge to you, Mr. Woodbury. I was thinking of the prejudices we are obliged to encounter. We present what we feel to be serious truths in relation to our sex, and they are thrown aside with a contemptuous indifference, which wounds us more than the harshest opposition, because it implies a disbelief in our capacity to think for ourselves. You must know that the word 'feminine,' applied to a man, is the greatest reproach—that the phrase 'a woman's idea' is never uttered but as a condemnation."

"I have not looked at the subject from your point of view," said Woodbury, with an expressed respect in his manner, "but I am willing to believe that you have reason to feel aggrieved. You must remember, however, that the reproach is not all on one side. You women are just as ready to condemn masculine habits and ideas in your own sex. Among children a molly-coddle is no worse than a tomboy. The fact, after all, does not originate in any natural hostility or contempt, on either side, but simply from an instinctive knowledge of the distinctions of sex, in temperament, in habits, and in mind."

"In mind?" Hannah Thurston asked, with unusual calmness. "Then you think that minds, too, are male and female?"

"That there are general distinctions, certainly. The exact boundaries between them, however, are not so easily to be defined. But there is a radical difference in the texture, and hence in the action of the two. Do you not always instinctively feel, in reading a book, whether the author is a man or a woman? Can you name any important work which might have been written, indifferently, by either?"

Miss Thurston reflected a while, and then suggested: "Mrs. Somerville's 'Physical Geography?'"

"Fairly answered," said Woodbury, smiling. "I will not reject the instance. I will even admit that a woman might write a treatise on algebraic equations, in which there should be no sign of her sex. Still, this would not affect the main fact, which I think you will recognize upon reflection. I admit the greatness of the immortal women of History. Nay, more: I claim that men are not only willing, without the least touch of jealousy, to acknowledge genius in Woman, but are always the first to recognize and respect it. What female poet has selected for her subject that ' whitest lily on the shield of France,' the Maid of Orleans? But Schiller and Southey have not forgotten her. How rare it is, to see one of these famous women eulogized by a woman! The principal advocate of your cause—what is her name?—Bessie Stryker, would be treated with more fairness and consideration by men than by those of her own sex who are opposed to her views."

"Yes, that is it," she answered, sadly; "we are dependent on men, and fear to offend them."

"This much, at least, seems to be true," said he, "that a sense of reliance on the one hand and protection on the other constitutes a firmer and tenderer form of union than if the natures were evenly balanced. It is not a question of superiority, but of radical and necessary difference of nature. Woman is too finely organized for the hard, coarse business of the world, and it is for her own sake that man desires to save her from it. He stands between her and human nature in the rough."

"But could she not refine it by her presence?"

"Never—never!" exclaimed Woodbury. "On the contrary, it would drag her down to unutterable depths. If woman had the right of suffrage there would be less swearing among the rowdies at the polls, the first time they voted, but at the end of five years both sexes would swear together. That is"—he added, seeing the shocked expression of Hannah Thurston's face,—"supposing them to be equally implicated in the present machinery of politics. The first time a female candidate went into a bar-room to canvass for votes, she would see the inmates on their best behavior; but this could not last long. She would soon either be driven from the field, or brought down to the same level. Nay, she would go below it, for the rudest woman would be injured by associations through which the most refined man might pass unharmed."

The tone of grave conviction in his words produced a strong though painful impression upon his hearer. She had heard very nearly the same things said, in debate, but they were always met and apparently overcome by the millennial assurances of her friends—by their firm belief in the possible perfection of human nature, an illusion which she was too ready to accept. A share in all the special avocations of Man, she had believed, would result in *his* elevation, not in the debasement of Woman.

"I should not expect a sudden change," she said, at last, "but might not men be gradually redeemed from their low tastes and habits? Might not each sex learn from the other only what is best and noblest in it? It would be very sad if all hope for the future must be taken away from us."

"All hope? No!" said Woodbury, rising from his seat. "The human race is improving, and will continue to improve. Better hope too much than not at all. But between the natures of the sexes there is a gulf as wide as all time. The laws by which each is governed are not altogether arbitrary; they have grown, age after age, out of that difference in mental and moral development of which I spoke, and which—pardon me —you seem to overlook. Whatever is, is not always right, but you may be sure there is no permanent and universal relation founded on error. You would banish profanity, excesses, brute force from among men, would you not? Have you ever reflected that these things are distorted forms of that energy which has conquered the world? Mountains are not torn down, rivers bridged, wildernesses subdued, cities built, states founded, and eternal dikes raised against barbarism, by the eaters of vegetables and the drinkers of water! Every man who is worth the name possesses something of the coarse, original fibre of the race: he lacks, by a wise provision of Providence, that finer protecting instinct which holds woman back from the rude, material aspects of human nature. He knows and

recognizes as inevitable facts, many things, of which she does
not even suspect the existence. Therefore, Miss Thurston,
when you apply to men the aspirations of progress which you
have formed as a woman, you must expect to be disappointed.
Pardon me for speaking so plainly, in opposition to views
which I know you must cherish with some tenderness. I
have, at least, not been guilty of the offence which you
charged upon my sex."

"No," she answered, "you have been frank, Mr. Woodbury, and I know that you are sincere. But may not your
views be still somewhat colored by the old prejudice?"

She blushed, the moment after she spoke. She had endeavored to moderate her expressions, yet her words sounded
harsh and offensive.

But Woodbury smiled as he answered: "If it be so, why
should old prejudices be worse than new ones? A prejudice
is a weed that shoots up over night. It don't take two years
to blossom, like this foxglove."

He broke off one of the long purple bells, and stuck it in the
button-hole of his coat.

"I like what slowly matures, and lasts long," said he.

Hannah Thurston repeated some words of thanks for the
books, as he gave her his hand. From the shade of the fir she
watched him mount and ride into the village. "He will probably take tea with the Waldos," she thought: "I shall stay at
home."

She resumed her seat, mechanically taking up the volumes
he had left, but did not open them. His words still lingered
in her mind, with a strange, disturbing effect. She felt that
he exercised an influence over her which she was not able sat-
isfactorily to analyze. The calmness of his utterance, the ripeness of his opinions, the fairness of his judgment, attracted
her: she knew no man who compelled an equal respect: yet
there seemed to be very little in common between them. She
never met him without a painful doubt of herself being awakened, which lasted long after his departure. She determined

again and again, to avoid these mental encounters, but some secret force irresistibly led her to speak. She felt, in her inmost soul, the first lifting of a current, which, if it rose, would carry her, she knew not where. A weird, dangerous power in his nature seemed to strike at the very props on which her life rested. With a sensation, almost of despair, she whispered to herself: "I will see him no more."

Woodbury, riding down the street, shook his head, and thought, as he unnecessarily pricked his horse with the spur: "I fear she is incorrigible."

CHAPTER XX.

IN WHICH SETH WATTLES IS AGAIN DISAPPOINTED.

AFTER their return from Tiberius the life of the Merryfields was unusually quiet and subdued. The imprudent wife, released from the fatal influence which had enthralled her, gradually came to see her action in its proper light, and to understand the consequences she had so happily escaped. She comprehended, also, that there was a point beyond which her husband could not be forced, but within which she was secure of his indulgent love. Something of the tenderness of their early married life returned to her in those days; she forgot her habit of complaint; suspended, out of very shame, her jealous demand for her "rights;" and was almost the busy, contented, motherly creature she had been to James Merryfield before either of them learned that they were invested with important spiritual missions.

He, also, reflected much upon what had happened. He perceived the manner in which his wife's perverted views had grown out of the belief they had mutually accepted. The possible abuses of this belief became evident to him, yet his mind was unable to detect its inherent error. It rested on a few broad, specious propositions, which, having accepted, he was obliged to retain, with all their consequences. He had neither sufficient intellectual culture nor experience of life to understand that the discrepancy between the ideal reform and its practical realization arose, not so much from the truths asserted as from the truths omitted or concealed. Thus, the former serenity of his views became painfully clouded and disturbed, and there were times when he felt that he doubted what he knew must be true. It was better, he said to himself, that he should cease, for a while, to speculate on the subject; but his thoughts continually returned to it in spite of himself. He greatly felt the need of help in this extremity, yet an unconquerable shyness prevented him from applying to either of the two persons—Woodbury or Mr. Waldo—who were capable of giving it. Towards his wife he was entirely kind and considerate. After the first day or two, the subject of the journey to Tiberius was tacitly dropped, and even the question of Woman's Rights was avoided as much as possible.

While he read aloud the "*Annihilator*" in the evening, and Mrs. Merryfield knit or sewed as she listened, the servant-girl and the field-hand exchanged their opinions in the kitchen. They had detected, the first day, the change in the demeanor of the husband and wife. "They've been havin' a row, and no mistake," said Henry, "and I guess he's got the best of it."

"No sich a thing," replied Ann, indignantly. "Him, indeed! It's as plain as my hand that he's awfully cut up, and she's took pity on him."

"Why, she's as cowed as can be!"

"And he's like a dog with his tail between his legs."

There was a half-earnest courtship going on between the two, and each, of course, was interested in maintaining the honor of the sex. It was a prolonged battle, renewed from day to day with re-enforcements drawn from observations made at meal-times, or in the field or kitchen. Most persons who attempt to conceal any strong emotion are like ostriches with their heads in the sand: the dullest and stupidest of mankind will feel, if not see, that something is the matter. If, to a man who knows the world, the most finished result of hypocrisy often fails of its effect, the natural insight of those who do not think at all is scarcely less sure and true. The highest art that ever a Jesuit attained could not blind a ship's crew or a company of soldiers.

It was fortunate for the Merryfields, that, while their dependents felt the change, the truth was beyond their suspicions.

Towards the few who knew it, there was of course no necessity for disguise, and hence, after a solitude of ten days upon the farm, Mr. Merryfield experienced a sense of relief and satisfaction, as, gleaning the scattered wheat with a hay-rake in a field adjoining the road, he perceived Hannah Thurston approaching from Ptolemy. Hitching his horse to the fence, he climbed over into the road to meet her. It was a warm afternoon, and he was in his shirt-sleeves, with unbuttoned waistcoat; but, in the country, conventionalities have not reached the point of the ridiculous, and neither he nor his visitor was aware of the least impropriety. The farmers, in fact, would rather show their own brawny arms and bare breasts than see the bosoms of their daughters exposed to the public gaze by a fashionable ball-dress.

"I'm glad you've come, Hannah," said he, as he gave her his hard hand. "It seems a long time since I seen you before. We've been quite alone ever since then."

"I should have come to see you sooner, but for mother's illness," she replied. "I hope you are both well and—happy."

Her look asked more than her words.

"Yes," said he, understanding the question in her mind, "Sarah's got over her delusion, I guess. Not a hard word has passed between us. We don't talk of it any more. But, Hannah, I'm in trouble about the principle of the thing. I can't make it square in my mind, as it were. There seems to be a contradiction, somewhere, between principles and working them out. You've thought more about the matter than I have: can you make things straight?"

The struggle in Hannah Thurston's own mind enabled her to comprehend his incoherent questions. She scarcely knew how to answer him, yet would fain say something to soothe and comfort him in his perplexity. After a pause, she answered:

"I fear, James, that I have over-estimated my own wisdom—that we have all been too hasty in drawing conclusions from abstract reasoning. We have, perhaps, been presumptuous in taking it for granted that we, alone, possessed a truth which the world at large is too blind to see—or, admitting that all is true which we believe, that we are too hasty in endeavoring to fulfil it in our lives, before the needful preparation is made. You know that the field must be properly ploughed and har-rowed, before you sow the grain. It may be that we are so impatient as to commence sowing before we have ploughed."

This illustration, drawn from his own business, gave Merry-field great comfort. "That must be it!" he exclaimed. "I don't quite understand how, but I feel that what you say must be true, nevertheless."

"Then," she continued, encouraged by the effect of her words; "I have sometimes thought that we may be too strict in applying what we know to be absolute, eternal truths, to a life which is finite, probationary, and liable to be affected by a thousand influences over which we have no control. For in-stance, you may analyze your soil, and the stimulants you apply to it—measure your grain, and estimate the exact yield you ought to receive—but you cannot measure the heat and moisture, the wind and hail, and the destructive insects which the summer may bring; and, therefore, you who sow accord-ing to agricultural laws may lose your crop, while another, who disregards them, shall reap an abundant harvest. Yet the truth of the laws you observed remains the same."

"What would you do, then, to be sure that you are right?" the farmer asked, as he opened the gate leading into his lane.

"To continue the comparison, I should say, act as a prudent husbandman. Believe in the laws which govern the growth and increase of the seed, yet regulate your tillage according to the season. The crop is the main thing, and, though it sounds like heresy, the farmer may be right who prefers a good harvest secured in defiance of rules to a scanty one with the observance of them. But I had better drop the figure before I make a blunder."

"Not a bit of it!" he cried. "You've cheered me up mightily. There's sense in what you say; queer that it didnt come into my mind before. I'm not sure that I can work my own case so's to square with it—but I'll hold on to the idee."

As they reached the garden, Hannah Thurston plucked a white rosebud which had thrust itself through the paling, and fastened it to the bosom of her dress. Mr. Merryfield immediately gathered six of the largest and reddest cabbage-roses, and presented them with a friendly air.

"There," said he, "stick *them* on! That white thing don't show at all. It's a pity the pineys are all gone."

Mrs. Merryfield, sitting on the shaded portico, rose and met her visitor at the gate. The women kissed each other, as usual, though with a shade of constraint on the part of the former. The farmer, judging it best to leave them alone for a little while, went back to finish his gleaning.

After they were comfortably seated on the portico, and Hannah Thurston had laid aside her bonnet, there was an awkward pause. Mrs. Merryfield anticipated an attack, than which nothing was further from her visitor's thought.

"How quiet and pleasant it is here!" the latter finally said. "It is quite a relief to me to get away from the village."

"People are differently constituted," answered Mrs. Merryfield, with a slight defiance in her manner : "I like society, and there's not much life on a farm."

"You have enjoyed it so long, perhaps, that you now scarcely appreciate it properly. A few weeks in our little cottage would satisfy you which is best."

"I must be satisfied, as it is ;" Mrs. Merryfield replied. "We women have limited missions, I suppose."

She intended herewith to indicate that, although she had desisted from her purpose, she did not confess that it had been wrong. She had sacrificed her own desires, and the fact should be set down to her credit. With Mr. Waldo she would have been candidly penitent—more so, perhaps, than she had yet allowed her husband to perceive—but towards one of her own sex, especially a champion of social reform, her only feeling was a stubborn determination to vindicate her action as far as possible.   Hannah Thurston detected the under-current of her thought, and strove to avoid an encounter with it.

"Yes," said she; "I suspect there are few persons of average ambition who find a sphere broad enough to content them. But our merits, you know, are not measured by that.   You may be able to accomplish more good, here, in your quiet circle of neighbors, than in some more conspicuous place."

"*I* should be the judge of that," rejoined Mrs. Merryfield, tartly.   Then, feeling that she had been a little too quick, she added, with mournful meekness : " But I suppose some lights are meant to be hid, otherways there wouldn't be bushels."

As she spoke, a light which did not mean to be hid, whatever the accumulation of bushels, approached from the lane. It was Seth Wattles, gracefully attired in a baggy blouse of gray linen, over which, in front, hung the ends of a huge purple silk cravat.   He carried a roll of paper in one hand, and his head was elevated with a sense of more than usual importance.   The expression of his shapeless mouth became almost triumphant as he perceived Hannah Thurston.   She returned his greeting with a calmness and self-possession which he mistook for a returning interest in himself.

By the time the usual common-places had been exchanged, Merryfield had returned to the house.   Seth, therefore, hastened to communicate the nature of his errand.   "I have been working out an idea," said he, "which, I think, meets the wants of the world.   It can be improved, no doubt,—I don't say that it's perfect—but the fundamental basis is right, I'm sure."

"What is it?" asked Merryfield, not very eagerly.

"A Plan for the Reorganization of Society, by which we can lighten the burden of labor, and avoid the necessity of Governments, with all their abuses.   It is something like Fourier's plan of Phalansteries, only that don't seem adapted to this country. And it's too great a change, all at once.   My plan can be applied immediately, because it begins on a smaller scale.   I'm sure it will work, if I can only get it started.   A dozen persons are enough to begin with."

"Well, how would you begin?" asked the farmer.

"Take any farm of ordinary size—yours for instance—and make of it a small community, who shall represent all the necessary branches of labor. With the aid of machinery, it will be entirely independent of outside help. You want a small steam-engine, or even a horse-power, to thresh, grind, saw, churn, turn, and hammer. Then, one of the men must be a blacksmith and wheelwright, one a tailor, and another a shoe and harness maker. Flax and sheep will furnish the material for clothing, maple and Chinese cane will give sugar, and there will really be little or nothing to buy. I assume, of course, that we all discard an artificial diet, and live on the simplest substances. Any little illness can be cured by hydropathy, but that would only be necessary in the beginning, for diseases would soon vanish from such a community. The labor of the women must also be divided: one will have charge of the garden, another of the dairy, another of the kitchen, and so on. When any branch of work becomes monotonous, there can be changes made, so that, in the end, each one will understand all the different departments. Don't you see?"

"Yes, I see," said Merryfield.

"I was sure you would. Just consider what an advantage over the present system! There need not be a dollar of outlay: you can take the houses as they are. Nothing would be bought, and all the produce of the farm, beyond what the community required for its support, would be clear gain. In a few years, this would amount to a fund large enough to hire all the necessary labor, and the members could then devote the rest of their lives to intellectual cultivation. My plan is diplomatic—that's the word. It will reform men, in spite of themselves, by appealing to two of their strongest passions—acquisitiveness and love of ease. They would get into a higher moral atmosphere before they knew it."

"I dare say," Merryfield remarked, as he crossed one leg over the other, and then put it down again, restlessly. "And who is to have the general direction of affairs?"

" Oh, there I apply the republican principle !" Seth exclaimed. "It will be decided by vote, after discussion, in which all take part, women as well as men.   Here is my plan for the day. Each takes his or her turn, week about, to rise before sunrise, make the fires, and ring a bell to rouse the others.   After a cold plunge-bath, one hour's labor, and then breakfast, accompanied by cheerful conversation.   Then work until noon, when dinner is prepared.   An hour's rest, and labor again, when necessary.   I calculate, however, that six hours a day will generally be sufficient.   Supper at sunset, followed by discussion and settlement of plans for the next day.   Singing in chorus, half an hour ; dancing, one hour, and conversation on moral subjects until eleven o'clock, when the bell rings for rest. You see, the plan combines every thing; labor, recreation, society, and mental improvement.   As soon as we have established a few communities, we can send messengers between them, and will not be obliged to support the Government through the Post-Office.   Now, I want you to begin the reform."

" Me !" exclaimed Merryfield, with a start.

" Yes, it's the very thing.   You have two hundred acres, and a house big enough for a dozen.   I think we can raise the community in a little while.   We can call it ' Merryfield,' or, if you choose, in Latin—Tanner says it's Campus Gaudius, or something of the kind.   It will soon be known, far and wide, and we must have a name to distinguish it.   I have no doubt the Whitlows would be willing to join us ; Mrs. Whitlow could take the dairy, and Miss Thurston the garden.   He's been in the grocery-line : he could make sugar, until he got acquainted with other kinds of work."

" Dairy, indeed !" interrupted Mrs. Merryfield.   " Yes, she'd like to skim cream and drink it by the tumbler-full, no doubt. A delightful community it would be, with the cows in *her* charge, somebody else in the bedrooms, and me seeing to the kitchen !"

" Before I'd agree to it, I'd see all the communities——"

Mr. Merryfield's exclamation terminated with a stronger
12

word than his wife had heard him utter for years. He jumped
from his seat, as he spoke, and strode up and down the portico.
Hannah Thurston, in spite of a temporary shock at the unexpected profanity, felt that her respect for James Merryfield
had undergone a slight increase. She was a little surprised at
herself, that it should be so. As for Seth Wattles, he was
completely taken aback. He had surmised that his plan might
meet with some technical objections, but he was certain that
it would be received with sympathy, and that he should finally
persuade the farmer to accept it. Had the latter offered him
a glass of whiskey, or drawn a bowie-knife from his sleeve, he
could not have been more astounded. He sat, with open
mouth and staring eyes, not knowing what to say.

"Look here, Seth," said Merryfield, pausing in his walk;
"neither you nor me a'n't a-going to reform the world. A
good many things a'n't right, I know, and as far as talking
goes, we can speak our mind about 'em. But when it comes
to fixing them yourself, I reckon you want a little longer ap-
prenticeship first. I sha'n't try it at my age. Make as pretty
a machine as you like, on paper, but don't think you'll set it
up in my house. There's no inside works to it, and it won't go."

"Why—why," Seth stammered, "I always thought you
were in favor of Social Reform."

"So I am—but I want, first, to see how it's to be done.
I'll tell you what to do. Neither you nor Tanner are married,
and have no risk to run. Take a couple more with you, and
set up a household : do your cooking, washing, sweeping, and
bed-making, by turns, and if you hold together six months,
and say you're satisfied, I'll have some faith in your plan."

"And get Mrs. Whitlow to be one of your Community,"
added Mrs. Merryfield, "or the experiment won't be worth
much. Let her take care of your *dairy*, and Mary Wollstonecraft and Phillis Wheatley tend to your garden. Send me
word when you're ready, and I'll come and see how you get
on !"

"I don't need to work, as it is, more than's healthy for me," her husband continued, " and I don't want Sarah to, neither. I can manage my farm without any trouble, and I've no notion of taking ten green hands to bother me, and then have to divide my profits with them. Show me a plan that'll give me something more than I have, instead of taking away the most of it."

" Why, the society, the intellectual cultivation," Seth remarked, but in a hopeless voice.

"I don't know as I've much to learn from either you or Tanner. As for Whitlows, all I can say is, I've tried 'em. But what do you think of it, Hannah ?"

" Very much as you do. I, for one, am certainly not ready to try any such experiment," Miss Thurston replied. " I still think that the family relation is natural, true, and necessary, yet I do not wonder that those who have never known it should desire something better than the life of a boarding-house. I know what that is."

" Seth," said Merryfield, recovering from his excitement, which he now saw, was quite incomprehensible to the disappointed tailor, "there's one conclusion I've come to, and I'd advise you to turn it over in your own mind. You and me may be right in our idees of what's wrong and what ought to be changed, but we're not the men to set things right. I'm not Garrison, nor yet Wendell Phillips, nor you a— what's his name ?—that Frenchman ?—oh, Furrier, and neither of *them*'s done any thing yet but talk and write. We're only firemen on the train, as it were, and if we try to drive the engine, we may just run every thing to smash."

The trying experience through which Merryfield had passed, was not without its good results. There was a shade more of firmness in his manner, of directness in his speech. The mere *sentiment* of the reform, which had always hung about him awkwardly, and sometimes even ludicrously, seemed to have quite disappeared ; and though his views had not changed—at least, not consciously so—they passed through a layer of re-awakened practical sense somewhere between the organs of thought and speech, and thus assumed a different coloring. He was evidently recovering from that very prevalent disorder—an actual paralysis of the reasoning faculties, which the victim persists in considering as their highest state of activity.

Seth had no spirit to press any further advocacy of his sublime scheme. He merely heaved a sigh of coarse texture, and remarked, in a desponding tone: " There's not much satisfaction in seeing the Right, unless you can help to fulfil it. I may not have more than one talent, but I did not expect you to offer me a napkin to tie it up in."

This was the best thing Seth ever said. It surprised himself, and he repeated it so often afterwards, that the figure became as inevitable a part of his speeches, as the famous two horsemen, in a certain author's novels.

Merryfield, seeing how completely he was vanquished, became the kind host again and invited him to stay for tea. Then, harnessing one of his farm-horses, he drove into Ptolemy for his semi-weekly mail, taking Hannah Thurston with him. As they were about leaving, Mrs. Merryfield suddenly appeared at the gate, with a huge bunch of her garden flowers, and a basket of raspberries, for the Widow Thurston. She was, in reality, very grateful for the visit. It had dissipated a secret anxiety which had begun to trouble her during the previous two or three days.

" Who knows"—she said to herself, sitting on the portico in the twilight, while a breeze from the lake shook the woodbines on the lattice, and bathed her in their soothing balm—" who knows but there are Mrs. Whitlows, or worse, *there*, too !"

CHAPTER XXI.

WITH AN ENTIRE CHANGE OF SCENE.

AFTER leaving Lakeside, Maxwell Woodbury first directed his course to Niagara, to refresh himself with its inexhaustible beauty, before proceeding to the great lakes of the North-west. His intention was, to spend six or eight weeks amid the bracing atmosphere and inspiring scenery of the Northern frontier, both as a necessary change from his quiet life on the farm, and in order to avoid the occasional intense heat of the Atauga Valley. From Niagara he proceeded to Detroit and Mackinaw, where, enchanted by the bold shores, the wild woods, and the marvellous crystal of the water, he remained for ten days. A change of the weather to rain and cold obliged him to turn his back on the attractions of Lake Superior and retrace his steps to Niagara. Thence, loitering down the northern shore of Ontario, shooting the rapids of the Thousand Isles, or delaying at the picturesque French settlements on the Lower St. Lawrence, he reached Quebec in time to take one of the steamboats to the Saguenay.

At first, the superb panorama over which the queenly city is enthroned—the broad, undulating shores, dotted with the cottages of the *habitans*—the green and golden fields of the Isle d'Orleans, basking in the sun—the tremulous silver veil of the cataract of Montmorency, fluttering down the dark rocks, and the blue ranges of the distant Laurentian mountains—absorbed all the new keenness of his faculties. Standing on the prow of the hurricane-deck, he inhaled the life of a breeze at once resinous from interminable forests of larch and fir, and sharp with the salt of the ocean, as he watched the grander sweep of the slowly separating shores. Except a flock of Quebeckers on their way to Murray Bay and Rivière du Loup, there were but few passengers on board. A professor from a college in New Hampshire, rigid in his severe propriety, looked through his gold-rimmed spectacles, and meditated on the probable geology of the headland of Les Eboulemens; two Georgians, who smoked incessantly, and betrayed in their accent that of the negro children with whom they had played, commented, with unnecessary loudness, on the miserable appearance of the Canadian "peasants;" a newly-married pair from Cincinnati sat apart from the rest, dissolved in tender sentiment; and a tall, stately lady, of middle age, at the stern of the boat, acted at the same time as mother, guide, and companion to two very pretty children—a girl of fourteen and a boy of twelve.

As the steamboat halted at Murray Bay to land a number of passengers, Woodbury found time to bestow some notice on his fellow-travellers. His attention was at once drawn to the lady and children. The plain, practical manner in which they were dressed for the journey denoted refinement and cultivation. The Cincinnati bride swept the deck with a gorgeous purple silk; but this lady wore a coarse, serviceable gray cloak over her travelling-dress of brown linen, and a hat of gray straw, without ornament. Her head was turned towards the shore, and Woodbury could not see her face; but the sound of her voice, as she spoke to the children, took familiar hold of his ear. He had certainly heard that voice before; but where, and when? The boat at last backed away from the pier, and she turned her head. Her face was a long oval, with regular and noble features, the brow still smooth and serene, the dark eyes soft and bright, but the hair prematurely gray on the temples. Her look had that cheerful calmness which is the maturity of a gay, sparkling temperament of youth, and which simply reserves, not loses, its fire.

Woodbury involuntarily struck his hand upon his forehead, with a sudden effort of memory. Perhaps noticing this action, the lady looked towards him and their eyes met. Hers, too, betrayed surprise and semi-recognition. He stepped instantly forward.

"I beg pardon," said he, "if I am mistaken, but I feel sure that I have once known you as Miss Julia Remington. Am I not right?"

"That was my name fifteen years ago," she answered, slowly. "Why cannot I recall yours? I remember your face."

"Do you not remember having done me the honor to attend a soirée which I gave, at the corner of Bowery and —— street?"

"Mr. Woodbury!" she exclaimed, holding out both her hands: "how glad I am to see you again! Who could have dreamed that two old friends should come from Calcutta and St. Louis to meet at the mouth of the Saguenay?"

"St. Louis!"

"Yes, St. Louis has been my home for the last ten years. But you must know my present name—Blake: wife of Andrew Blake, and mother of Josephine and George, besides two younger ones, waiting for me at Saratoga. Come here, Josey; come, George—this is Mr. Woodbury, whom I used to know many, many years ago in New York. You must be good friends with him, and perhaps he will tell you of the wonderful ball he once gave."

Woodbury laughed, and cordially greeted the children, who came to him with modest respect, but without embarrassment. Long before the boat had reached Rivière du Loup, the old friendship was sweetly re-established, and two new members introduced into its circle.

Mrs. Blake had been spending some weeks at Saratoga, partly with her husband and partly alone, while he attended to some necessary business in New York and Philadelphia. This business had obliged him to give up his projected trip to the Saguenay, and it was arranged that his wife should make it in company with the two oldest children, the youngest being left, meanwhile, in the care of a faithful servant.

Woodbury had always held Miss Remington in grateful remembrance, and it was a great pleasure to him to meet her thus unexpectedly. He found her changed in outward appearance, but soon perceived that her admirable common sense, her faithful, sturdily independent womanhood, were still, as formerly, the basis of her nature. She was one of those rare women who are at the same time as clear and correct as possible in their perceptions, penetrating all the disguises and illusions of life, yet unerringly pure and true in instinct and feeling. Such are almost the only women with whom thoroughly developed and cultivated men can form those intimate and permanent friendships, in which both heart and brain find the sweetest repose, without the necessity of posting a single guard on any of the avenues which lead to danger. Few women, and still fewer men, understand a friendship of this kind, and those who possess it must brave suspicion and misunderstanding at every turn.

The relation between Woodbury and Miss Remington had never, of course, attained this intimacy, but they now instinctively recognized its possibility. Both had drunk of the cup of knowledge since their parting, and they met again on a more frank and confidential footing than they had previously known. Mrs. Blake was so unconsciously correct in her impulses that she never weighed and doubted, before obeying them. The wand of her spirit never bent except where the hidden stream was both pure and strong.

That evening, as the boat halted at Rivière du Loup for the night, they walked the hurricane-deck in the long Northern twilight, and talked of the Past. Many characters had faded away from the sight of both; others had either fallen from their early promise, or soared surprisingly far above it; but all, with their attendant loves, and jealousies, and hates, stood out sharp and clear in the memory of the speakers. Mrs. Blake, then, in answer to Woodbury's inquiries, gave him a rapid sketch of her own life.

"I am quite satisfied," she said at the close. "My husband

is not exactly the *preux chevalier* I used to imagine, as a girl, but he is a true gentleman"—

"You never could have married him, if he were not," Woodbury interrupted.

—"a true gentleman, and an excellent man of business, which is as necessary in this age as knighthood was in those famous Middle ones. Our married life has been entirely happy from the start, because we mutually put aside our illusions, and made charitable allowances for each other. We did not attempt to cushion the sharp angles, but courageously clashed them together until they were beaten into roundness."

She broke into a pleasant, quiet laugh, and then went on: "I want you to know my husband. You are very different, but there are points of contact which, I think, would attract both. You have in common, at least, a clear, intelligent faculty of judgment, which is a pretty sure sign of freemasonry between man and man. I don't like Carlyle as an author, yet I indorse, heart and soul, his denunciation of shams. But here I am at the end of my history: now tell me yours."

She listened with earnest, sympathetic interest to Woodbury's narrative, and the closing portion, which related to his life at Lakeside, evidently aroused her attention more than all the lazy, uneventful tropical years he had spent in Calcutta. When he had finished the outlines, she turned suddenly towards him and asked: "Is there nothing more?"

"What should there be?" he asked in return, with a smile which showed that he understood her question.

"What should be, is not, I know," said she; "I saw that much, at once. You will allow me to take a liberty which I am sure cannot *now* give pain: *she* is not the cause of it, I hope?"

She looked him full in the face, and felt relieved as she detected no trace of a pang which her words might have called up. The expression of his lips softened rather to pity as he answered: "She has long ceased to have any part in my life, and she has now very little in my thoughts. When I saw her

12*

again, last winter, there was not a single fibre of my heart disturbed. I will confess this much, however—another face, a more hopeless memory, long ago displaced hers. Both are gone, and I am now trying to find a third."

His tone was apparently light and indifferent, but to Mrs. Blake's true ear it betrayed both weariness and longing. "You cannot be deceived the third time," she said, consolingly.

"I was not deceived the second time," he answered, "but I will not tell you the story, just now. It is as completely at an end as if it had never happened. Can you help me to another trial?"

She shook her head. "It is strange that so few of the best men and women discover each other. Nature must be opposed to the concentration of qualities, and continually striving to reconcile the extremes; I cannot account for it in any other way. You are still young; but do not carelessly depend on your youth; you are not aware how rapidly a man's habits become ossified, at your age. Marriage involves certain mutual sacrifices, under the most favorable circumstances. Don't trust too long to your own strength."

"Ah, but where is the girl with your clear sense, Mrs. Blake?" asked Woodbury, pausing in his walk. "*My* wife must be strong enough to know her husband as he was and is. The deceits which so many men habitually practise, disgust me. Who would hear my confession, and then absolve me by love?"

"Who? Almost every woman that loves! No: I will make no exceptions, because the woman who would not do so, does not really love. Men are cowards, because they fancy that women are, and so each sex cheats itself through want of faith in the other. Is that a recent misgiving of yours?"

"You are a dangerous friend, Mrs. Blake. Your husband, I suspect, is forced to be candid, out of sheer despair at the possibility of concealing any thing from you. Yes, you have interpreted my thought correctly. I spoke with reference to one particular person, whom I am very far from loving, or even

desiring to love, but whose individuality somewhat interests
me. A woman's ideal of man, I am afraid, rises in proportion
to her intellectual culture. From the same cause, she is not so
dependent on her emotions, and therefore more calculating and
exacting. Is it not so?"

"No, it is not so!" replied Mrs. Blake, with energy. "Recollect, we are not speaking of the sham women."

"She does not belong to that class," said Woodbury. "She
is, in many respects, a rare and noble character; she possesses
natural qualities of mind which place her far above the average
of women; she is pure as a saint, bold and brave, and yet
thoroughly feminine in all respects save one—but that one
exceptional feature neutralizes all the others."

"What is it?"

"She is strong-minded."

"What!" exclaimed Mrs. Blake, "do you mean a second
Bessie Stryker?"

"Something of the kind—so far as I know. She is one of
the two or three really intelligent women in Ptolemy—but
with the most singularly exaggerated sense of duty. Some
persons would have censured me more considerately for for-
gery or murder than she did for smoking a cigar. I discussed
the subject of Women's Rights with her, the last thing before
leaving home, and found her as intolerant as the rankest Conservative. What a life such a woman would lead one! Yet,
I confess she provokes me, because, but for that one fault, she
would be worth winning. It is vexatious to see a fine creature
so spoiled."

"With all her fanaticism, she seems to have made a strong
impression on you."

"Yes, I do not deny it," Woodbury candidly replied.
"How could it be otherwise? In the first place, she is still
something of a phenomenon to me, and therefore stimulates
my curiosity. Secondly, she is far above all the other girls of
Ptolemy, both in intellect and in natural refinement. She
makes the others so tame that, while I could not possibly love

her, she prevents me from loving any of them. What am I to do?"

"A difficult case, upon my word. If I knew the characters, I might assist you to a solution. The only random suggestion I can make is this: if the strong-minded woman should come to love you, in spite of her strength, it will make short work of her theories of women's rights. Our instincts are stronger than our ideas, and the brains of some of us run wild only because our hearts are unsatisfied. I should probably have been making speeches through the country, in a Bloomer dress, by this time, if I had not met with my good Andrew. You need not laugh: I am quite serious. And I can give you one drop of comfort, before you leave the confessional: I see that your feelings are fresh and healthy, without a shade of cynicism: as we say in the West, the latch-string of your heart has not been pulled in, and I predict that somebody will yet open the door. Good-night!"

Giving his hand a hearty, honest pressure of sympathy, Mrs. Blake went to her state-room. Woodbury leaned over the stern-railing, and gazed upon the sprinkles of reflected starlight in the bosom of the St. Lawrence. The waves lapped on the stones of the wharf with a low, liquid murmur, and a boatman, floating upwards with the tide, sang at a distance: "*Jamais je ne t'oublierai.*" Woodbury mechanically caught the melody and sang the words after him, till boat and voice faded together out of sight and hearing. It refreshed rather than disturbed him that the eye of a true woman had looked upon his heart. "Whatever may be the end," he said to himself, "she shall know the whole truth, one day. When we suspect that a seed of passion may have been dropped in our natures, we must quietly wait until we feel that it has put forth roots. I did not tell her the whole truth. I am not sure but that I may love that girl, with all her mistaken views. Her face follows me, and calls me back. If each of us could but find the other's real self, then—why, then"——

He did not follow the thought further. The old pang arose,

the old hunger of the heart came over him, and brought with it those sacred yearnings for the tenderer ties which follow marriage, and which man, scarcely less than woman, craves. The red lights of two cigars came down the long pier, side by side : it was the Georgians, returning from a visit to the village. The New Hampshire Professor approached him, and politely remarked : " It is singular that the Old Red Sandstone reappears in this locality."

"Very singular," answered Woodbury. "Good-night, Sir !" and went to bed.

The next morning the steamer crossed to Tadoussac, and entered the pitch-brown waters of the savage, the sublime, the mysterious Saguenay. The wonderful scenery of this river, or rather fiord, made the deepest impression on the new-made friends. It completely banished from their minds the conversation of the previous evening. Who could speak or even think of love, or the tender sorrow that accompanies the memory of betrayed hopes, in the presence of this stern and tremendous reality. Out of water which seemed thick and sullen as the stagnant Styx, but broke into a myriad beads of dusky amber behind the steamer's paddles, leaped now and then a white porpoise, weird and solitary as the ghost of a murdered fish. On either side rose the headlands of naked granite, walls a thousand feet in height, cold, inaccessible, terrible; and even where, split apart by some fore-world convulsion, they revealed glimpses up into the wilderness behind, no cheating vapor, no haze of dreams, softened the distant picture, but the gloomy green of the fir-forests darkened into indigo blue, and stood hard and cold against the gray sky. After leaving L'Anse à l'Eau, all signs of human life ceased. No boat floated on the black glass ; no fisher's hut crouched in the sheltered coves; no settler's axe had cut away a single feather from the ragged plumage of the hills.

But as they reached the awful cliffs of Trinity and Eternity, rising straight as plummet falls from their bases, a thousand feet below the surface, to their crests, fifteen hundred feet in

the air, a wind blew out of the north, tearing and rolling
away the gray covering of the sky, and allowing sudden floods
of sunshine to rush down through the blue gaps. The hearts
of the travellers were lifted, as by the sound of trumpets.
Far back from between the two colossal portals of rock, like
the double propylæ of some Theban temple, ran a long, deep
gorge of the wilderness, down which the coming sunshine
rolled like a dazzling inundation, drowning the forests in
splendor, pouring in silent cataracts over the granite walls,
and painting the black bosom of the Saguenay with the blue
of heaven. It was a sudden opening of the Gates of the
North, and a greeting from the strong Genius who sat enthroned beyond the hills,—not in slumber and dreams, like his
languid sister of the South, cooling her dusky nakedness in the
deepest shade, but with the sun smiting his unflinching eyes,
with his broad, hairy breast open to the wind, with the best
blood of the world beating loud and strong in his heart, and
the seed of empires in his virile loins !

Woodbury was not one of your " gushing" characters, who
cry out "Splendid !" "Glorious !" on the slightest provocation.
When most deeply moved by the grander aspects of Nature,
he rarely spoke; but he had an involuntary habit of singing
softly to himself, at such times. So he did now, quite unconsciously, and had got as far as :

> "Thy heart is in the upper world,
>   And where the chamois bound;
> Thy heart is where the mountain fir
>   Shakes to the torrent's sound;"

—when he suddenly checked himself and turned away with
a laugh and a light blush of self-embarrassment. He had been
picturing to himself the intense delight which Hannah Thurs
ton would have felt in the scene before him.

Meanwhile the boat sped on, and soon reached the end of
the voyage at Ha-ha Bay. Mrs. Blake and her children were
delighted with their journey, to which the meeting with

Woodbury had given such an additional charm. As they descended the Saguenay in the afternoon, their eyes grew accustomed to the vast scale of the scenery; loftier and grander arose the walls of granite, and more wild and awful yawned the gorges behind them. The St. Lawrence now opened in front with the freedom of the sea, and in the crimson light of a superb sunset they returned to Rivière du Loup.

The companionship was not dropped after they had reached Quebec. Woodbury accompanied them to the Falls of the Montmorency and the Chaudière; to the Plains of Abraham and the quaint French villages on the shores; and their evenings were invariably spent on Durham Terrace, to enjoy, over and over again, the matchless view. It was arranged that they should return to Saratoga together, by way of Champlain and Lake George; and a few more days found them there, awaiting the arrival of Mr. Blake.

He came at last; and his wife had not incorrectly judged, in supposing that there were some points of mutual attraction between the two men. The Western merchant, though a shrewd and prudent man of business, was well educated, had a natural taste for art (he had just purchased two pictures by Church and Kensett), and was familiar with the literature of the day. He was one of those fortunate men who are capable of heartily enjoying such things, without the slightest ambition to produce them. He neither complained of his own vocation, nor did he lightly esteem it. He was not made for idle indulgence, and was sufficiently prosperous to allow himself proper recreation. His temperament, therefore, was healthy, cheerful, and stimulating to those with whom he came in contact. He was by no means handsome, and had a short, abrupt manner of speaking, which Woodbury's repose of manner threw into greater distinctness. His wife, however, knew his true value, as he knew hers, and their mutual confidence was absolute.

Woodbury strongly urged them to spend a few days with him at Lakeside, on their return journey to St. Louis. In ad-

dition to the pleasure he derived from their society, he had a
secret desire that Mrs. Blake should see Hannah Thurston—a
curiosity to know the impression which the two women would
make on each other. What deeper motive lurked behind this,
he did not question.

The discussion of the proposal reminded him that he had
not heard from Lakeside since his departure. He immediately
wrote to Arbutus Wilson, announcing his speedy return, and
asking for news of the farming operations. Six days afterwards an answer came, not from Arbutus, but from Mr.
Waldo—an answer of a nature so unexpected, that he left
Saratoga the same night.

CHAPTER XXII.

IN WHICH TROUBLE COMES TO LAKESIDE.

AFTER Woodbury had left Lakeside for his summer tour, Mrs. Fortitude Babb resumed her ancient authority. "Now," she said to Bute, as they sat down to supper on the day of his departure, "now we'll have a quiet time of it. A body'll know what to do without waitin' to be told whether it's jist to other people's likin's."

"Why, Mother Forty," said Bute, "Mr. Max. is as quiet a man as you'll find anywhere."

"Much you know about him, Bute. He lets you go on farmin' in y'r own way, pretty much; but look at my gard'n— tore all to pieces! The curran' bushes away at t'other end— half a mile off, if you want to git a few pies—and the kersan-thums stuck into the yard in big bunches, among the grass! What would *she* say, if she could see it? And the little room for bed-clo'es, all cleaned out, and a big bathin' tub in the corner, and to be filled up every night. Thank the Lord, he can't find nothin' to say ag'in my cookin'. If he was to come pokin' his nose into the kitchen every day, I dunno *what* I'd do!"

"It's his own garden," said Bute, sturdily. "He's paid for it, and he's got a right to do what he pleases with it. *I* would, if 't'was mine."

"Oh yes, *you!* You're gittin' mighty independent, seems to me. I 'xpect nothin' else but you'll go off some day with that reedic'lous thing with the curls."

"Mother Forty!" said Bute, rising suddenly from the

table, " don't you mention her name ag'in. I don't want to
see her any more, nor I don't want to hear of her !"

He strode out of the house with a fiery face. Mrs. Babb
sat, as if thunderstruck. Little by little, however, a presentiment of the truth crept through her stiff brain : she drew her
thin lips firmly together and nodded her head. The sense of
relief which she first felt, on Bute's account, was soon lost,
nevertheless, in an angry feeling toward Miss Carrie Dilworth.
Utterly unaware of her own inconsistency, she asked herself
what the little fool meant by turning up her nose at such a
fine young fellow as Arbutus—the very pick of the farmers
about Ptolemy, though she, Fortitude Babb, said it ! Where
would she find a man so well-built and sound, so honest and
good-hearted ? Everybody liked him ; there were plenty of
girls that would jump at the chance of having him for a husband—but no, he was not good enough for *her*. Ugh ! the
nasty, pert, stuck-up little hussy ! That comes o' wearin' your
hair like an Injun ! But Arbutus mustn't mind ; there's as good
fish in the sea as ever was ketched, and better too. 'Twas
reasonable, after all, that he should marry some time ; a man's
a man, though you brought him up yourself ; and the best
way is to take hold and help, when you can't hinder it.

Thereupon, she set her wits to work to discover the right
kind of a wife for her step-step-son. It was a perplexing subject : one girl was slatternly, another was unhealthy, a third
was too old, a fourth had disagreeable relatives, a fifth was as
poor as Job's turkey. Where was the compound of youth,
health, tidiness, thrift, and, most important of all, the proper
respect for Mrs. Babb's faculties ? " I'll find her yet !" she said
to herself, as she sat at her knitting, in the drowsy summer afternoons. Meanwhile, her manner towards Bute grew kinder
and more considerate—a change for which he was not in the
least grateful. He interpreted it as the expression of her
satisfaction with the disappointment under which he still
smarted. He became moody and silent, and before many days
had elapsed Mrs. Babb was forced to confess to herself that

Lakeside was lonely and uncomfortable without the presence of Mr. Woodbury.

As for Bute, though he felt that he was irritable and heavy, compared with his usual cheerful mood, there was more the matter with him than he supposed. The experience through which he had passed disturbed the quiet course of his blood. Like a mechanism, the action of which is even and perfectly balanced at a certain rate of speed, but tends to inevitable confusion when the speed is increased, his physical balance was sadly disarranged by the excitement of his emotional nature and the sudden shock which followed it. Days of feverish activity, during which he did the work of two men without finding the comfort of healthy fatigue, were followed by days of weariness and apathy, when the strength seemed to be gone from his arm, and the good-will to labor from his heart. His sleep was either restless and broken, or so unnaturally profound that he arose from it with a stunned, heavy head.

Among the summer's work which Mr. Woodbury had ordered, after wheat-harvest, was the draining of a swampy field which sloped towards Roaring Brook. An Irish ditcher had been engaged to work upon it, but Bute, finding that much more must be done than had been estimated, and restless almost to nervousness, assisted with his own hands. Day after day, with his legs bare to the thighs, he stood in the oozy muck, plying pick and shovel under the burning sun. Night after night, he went to bed with a curiously numb and deadened feeling, varied only by nervous starts and thrills, as if the bed were suddenly sinking under him.

One morning, he did not get up at the usual hour. Mrs. Babb went on with her labors for breakfast, expecting every moment to see him come down and wash his face at the pump outside the kitchen-door. The bacon was fried, the coffee was boiled, and still he did not appear. She opened the door of the kitchen staircase, and called in her shrillest tones, one, two, three times, until finally an answer reached her from the bedroom. Five minutes afterwards, Bute blundered

down the steps, and, seeing the table ready, took his accustomed seat.

"Well, Arbutus, you *have* slep', sure enough. I s'pose you
was tired from yesterday, though," said Mrs. Babb, as she
transferred the bacon from the frying-pan to a queensware
dish. Hearing no answer, she turned around. "Gracious
alive!" she exclaimed, "are you a-goin' to set down to breakfast without washin' or combin' your hair? I do believe
you're asleep yit."

Bute said nothing, but looked at her with a silly smile which
seemed to confirm her words.

"Arbutus!" she cried out, "wake up! You don't know
what you're about. Dash some water on your face, child; if
I ever saw the like!" and she took hold of his shoulder with
one of her bony hands.

He twisted it petulantly out of her grasp. "I'm tired,
Mike," he said: "if the swamp wasn't so wet, I'd like to lay
down and sleep a spell."

The rigid joints of Mrs. Babb's knees seemed to give way
suddenly. She dropped into the chair beside him, lifted his
face in both her trembling hands, and looked into his eyes.
There was no recognition in them, and their wild, wandering
glance froze her blood. His cheeks burned like fire, and his
head dropped heavily, the next moment, on his shoulder. "This
tussock'll do," he murmured, and relapsed into unconsciousness.

Mrs. Babb shoved her chair nearer, and allowed his head to
rest on her shoulder, while she recovered her strength. There
was no one else in the house. Patrick, the field-hand, was at
the barn, and was accustomed to be called to his breakfast.
Once she attempted to do this, hoping that her voice might
reach him, but it was such an unnatural, dismal croak, that she
gave up in despair. Bute started and flung one arm around
her neck with a convulsive strength which almost strangled her.
After that, she did not dare to move or speak. The coffee-pot
boiled over, and the scent of the scorched liquid filled the
kitchen; the fat in the frying-pan, which she had thought-

lessly set on the stove again, on seeing Bute, slowly dried to a crisp, and she knew that the bottom of the pan would be ruined. These minor troubles strangely thrust themselves athwart the one great, overwhelming trouble of her heart, and confused her thoughts. Bute was deathly sick, and stark, staring mad, was the only fact which she could realize; and with her left hand, which was free, she gradually and stealthily removed his knife, fork, and plate, and pushed back the table-cloth as far as she could reach. Then she sat rigidly as before, listening to the heavy, irregular breathing of the invalid, and scorched by his burning head.

Half an hour passed before Patrick's craving stomach obliged him to disregard the usual call. Perhaps, he finally thought, he had not heard it, and he then betook himself at once to the house. The noise he made in opening the kitchen-door, startled Bute, who clinched his right fist and brought it down on the table.

"Holy mother!" exclaimed Patrick, as he saw the singular group.

Mrs. Babb turned her head with difficulty, and shook it as a sign of caution, looking at him with wide, suffering eyes, from which the tears now first flowed, when she saw that help and sympathy had come to her at last.

"God preserve us! och, an' he isn't dead?" whispered Patrick, advancing a step nearer, and ready to burst into a loud wail.

"He's sick! he's crazy!" Mrs. Babb breathed hoarsely, in reply: "help me to git him to bed!"

The Irishman supported Bute by the shoulders, while Mrs. Babb gently and cautiously relieved herself from his choking arm. Without Pat's help it is difficult to say what she would have done. Tender as a woman, and gifted with all the whimsical cunning of his race, he humored Bute's delirious fancies to the utmost, soothing instead of resisting or irritating him, and with infinite patience and difficulty succeeded in getting him back into his bedroom. Here Mrs. Babb remade his bed, putting on fresh sheets and pillows, and the two undressed and laid him in it. The first thing she then did was to cut off his long yellow locks close to the head, and apply a wet cloth; beyond that, which she had heard was always used in such cases, she did not dare to go.

The next thing was, to procure medical assistance. There were no other persons about the house, and both of them together, it seemed probable, would scarcely be able to manage the patient, if a violent paroxysm should come on. Mrs. Babb insisted on remaining by him; but Patrick, who had seen similar attacks of fever, would not consent to this. He swore by all the saints that she would find Bute safely in bed on her return. She need not go farther than black Melinda's cabin, he said; it was not over three-quarters of a mile. She could send Melinda for the doctor, and for Misther Merryfield too—that 'ud be better; and then come directly back, herself.

Mrs. Babb gave way to these representations, and hurried forth on her errand. Her stiff old joints cracked with the violence of her motion; she was agitated by remorse as well as anxiety. She had been a little hard on the lad; what if he should die without forgiving her, and should go straight to heaven (as of course he would) and tell his own mother and Jason Babb, who was so fond of him? In that case, Jason would certainly be angry with her, and perhaps would not allow her to sit beside him on the steps of the Golden City, when her time came. Fortunately, she found old Melinda at home, and despatched her with the injunction to "go down to Merryfield's as hard as you can scoot, and tell him to ride for the doctor, and then you come directly back to the house." Melinda at once strode away, with her eyes fixed before her, muttering fragments of camp-meeting hymns.

When Mrs. Babb returned, she found Bute still in bed, panting from evident exhaustion. The wet cloth was on his head and the bed-clothes were straight. Patrick turned away his face from the light, and said: "Sure, an' he's been as quiet as a lamb"—an assertion which was disproved the next day by the multitude of indigo blotches, the marks of terrible blows, which appeared on his own face, breast, and arms. What happened while they were alone, Patrick always avoided telling, except to the priest. To his mind, there was a sanctity about delirium, the secrets of which it would be criminal to betray.

In two or three hours more the physician arrived, accompanied by Merryfield. The former pronounced Bute to be laboring under a very dangerous attack of congestive fever, of a typhoid character. He bled him sufficiently to reduce the excitement of the brain, prescribed the usual medicines, a little increased in quantity, and recommended great care and exactness in administering them. When he descended the stairs, the housekeeper stole after him, and grasped his arm as he entered the hall.

"Doctor," she asked, in her stern manner, "I jist want to know the truth. Is he goin' to git over it, or isn't he?"

"The chances are about even, Mrs. Babb," the physician replied. "I will not disguise from you the fact that it's a very serious case. If his constitution were not so fine, I should feel almost like giving him up. I will only say this: if we can keep him for a week, without growing much worse, we shall get the upper hand of the fever. It depends on his nurses, even more than on me."

"*I'll* nuss him!" Mrs. Babb exclaimed, defiantly. "A week, did you say? A week a'n't a life-time, and I can stand it. I stood more'n that, when Jason was sick. Don't be concerned about your orders, Sir: I'VE TOOK 'EM TO HEART, and that's enough said."

The housekeeper went back to the kitchen, clinching her fists and nodding her head—the meaning of which was, that there was to be a fair stand-up fight between Death and herself, for the possession of Arbutus Wilson, and that Death was not going to be the victor, no, not if he took herself instead, out of spite. Then and there she commenced her plan of defence. Those precautions which the physician had recommended were taken with a Draconian severity: what he had forbidden ceased to have a possibility of existence. Quiet, of course, was included in his orders, and never was a household conducted with so little noise. The sable Melinda, having let a pot-lid fall on the kitchen-floor, found her arm instantly grasped in a bony vice, while an awful voice whispered in her ear (Mrs. Babb had ceased to speak otherwise, even when she went to the garden)—"Don't you dare to do that ag'in!" She prepared and applied the blisters and poultices with her own hands; administered the medicines punctually to the second, whether by day or by night; and the invalid could not turn in his bed but she seemed to know it, by some sort of clairvoyance, in whatever part of the house she might be at the time. At night, although Patrick and Mr. Merryfield volunteered to watch by turns, and tried to induce her to sleep, she never undressed, but lay down on her bed in an adjoining chamber, and made her appearance in the sick-room, tall, dark, and rigid, every half-hour. She would listen with a fearful interest to Bute's ravings, whether profane or passionate, dreading to hear some accusation of herself, which, if he died, he would bear straight to Jason Babb. Her words, however, had made but the slightest surface-wounds on Bute's sturdy nature. No accusation or reproach directed towards her passed his lips; Miss Dilworth's name, it is true, was sometimes mentioned, but more in anger than in love; but his mind ran principally on farming matters, mixed with much incoherent talk, to which Patrick only appeared to have the clue. The latter, at least, was generally able to exercise a guidance over his hallucinations, and to lead them from the more violent to the gentler phases.

Half the week was gone, and no change could be detected in the invalid's condition. The powerful assault of disease had met as powerful a resisting nature, and the struggle continued, with no marked signs of weariness on either side. Much sympathy was felt by the neighbors, when the news became known, and there were kind offers of assistance. The physician, however, judged that the attendance was already sufficient, and as the fever was contagious in many cases, he recommended that there should be as few nurses as possible. The sympathy then took the form of recipes (every one of which was infallible), dried herbs, jellies, oranges, and the like. Mr. Jones, the miller, even sent a pair of trout, which he had caught in Roaring Brook. The housekeeper received all these articles with stern thanks, and then locked them up in her cupboard, saying to herself, "'Ta'n't time for sich messes yet: *I* can git all he wants, jist now."

Slowly the week drew to a close, and Mrs. Babb grew more anxious and excited. The unusual strain upon her old frame began to tell; she felt her strength going, and yet the agonizing suspense in regard to Bute's fate must be quieted before she could allow it to give way altogether. Her back kept its straightness from long habit, but her knees tottered under her every time she mounted the stairs, and the muscles around her mouth began to twitch and relax, in spite of herself. She no longer questioned the physician, but silently watched his face as he came from Bute's room, and waited for him to speak.

On the seventh day, what little information he voluntarily gave afforded no relief to her mind, and for the first time the iron will which had upheld her thus far began to waver. A weariness which, it seemed to her, no amount of sleep could ever heal, assailed her during the night. Slowly she struggled on until morning, and through the eighth day until late in the afternoon, when the physician came. *This* time, as he left the sick-room, she detected a slight change in his expression. Walking slowly towards him, striving to conceal her weakness and emotion, she said, brokenly:

"Can you tell me now?"

"I don't like to promise." he answered, "but there is a chance now that the fever will exhaust itself, before quite all the power of rallying afterwards has been spent. He is not out of danger, but the prospects of his recovery are better than they were, two to one. If he gets well, your nursing,

Mrs. Babb, will have saved him. I wish all my patients could have you."

The housekeeper dropped into the nearest chair, and gave vent to her feelings in a single hoarse, dry sob. When the doctor had gone, Melinda put the teapot on the table, arranged the cups and saucers, and said: "Come, now, Miss Forty, you take a cup. I sure you needs um; you jiss' killin' you'self, honey."

Mrs. Babb attempted to comply: she lifted the saucer to her lips, and then set it down again. She felt, suddenly, very faint and sick, and the next moment an icy chill seized her, and shook her from head to foot: her lips were blue, and her seven remaining teeth rattled violently together. Melinda, alarmed, flew to her assistance; but she pushed her back with her long, thin arm, saying, "I knowed it must come so. One of us had got to go. He'll git well, now."

"Oh, Missus!" cried Melinda, and threw her apron over her head.

"Where's the use, Melindy?" said the housekeeper, sternly. "I guess *she*'ll be glad of it: she'd kind o' got used to havin' me with her."

Even yet, she did not wholly succumb to the attack. Deliberately forcing herself to drink two cups of hot tea, in order to break the violence of the chill, she slowly crept up stairs to Bute's room, where Patrick was in attendance. Him she despatched at once to Ptolemy, with a message to the Rev. Mr. Waldo, whom she requested to come at as early an hour as possible. She sent no word to the physician, but the old Melinda had shrewdness enough to discover this omission and supply it.

Wrapped in a blanket, Mrs. Babb took her seat in the old-fashioned rocking-chair at Bute's bedside, and looked long and earnestly on his worn face, in the last light of day. What had become of the warm, red blood which had once painted his round cheeks, showing itself defiantly through the tan of all the suns of summer? Blood and tan seemed to have suddenly vanished together, leaving a waxen paleness and a sunken, pinched expression, so much like death, that his restless movements and mutterings comforted her, because they denoted life. "Yes, there's life in him still!" she whispered to herself. Presently he opened his eyes, and looked at her. The fierceness of his delirium had been broken, but his expression was still strange and troubled.

"I guess we'll begin the oats to-day, Pat," he said, in a weak voice.

"Arbutus!" she cried, "look at me! Don't you know Mother Forty no more?"

"Mother Forty's gittin' breakfast," said he, staring at her.

"Oh, Arbutus," she groaned, desperately; "do try to know me this once't! I'm mortal sick: I'm a-goin' to die. If there's anything on y'r mind ag'in me, can't you say you forgive me?" And the poor old creature began to cry in a noiseless way.

"I forgive you, Miss Carrie," answered Bute, catching at the word "forgive." "'Ta'n't worth mindin'. You're a little fool, and I'm a big one, that's all."

Mrs. Babb did not try again. She leaned back in the rocking-chair, folding the blanket more closely around her, to keep off the constantly recurring chills, and husbanding her failing strength to perform the slight occasional offices which the invalid required. Thus she sat until Patrick's return, when the negress helped her to bed.

In the morning the physician found her in a pitiable state of debility, but with a mind as clear and determined as ever. Her physical energies were completely broken, and the prospect of supporting them artificially until the fever should subside, seemed very slight. She understood the grave concern upon his face. "You needn't tell me, doctor," she said; "I know all about it. I'll take the medicines, to make *your* mind easy; but it's no use."

Mr. Waldo arriving about the same time, she begged the physician to wait until she had had an interview with the former. He had been summoned for no other purpose than to

draw up her will, the signing of which she wished both gentlemen to witness. The document was soon prepared. She bequeathed all she possessed to Arbutus Wilson, her adopted son,
after deducting the expenses of her funeral, and a tombstone
similar to that which she had erected to the memory of Jason
Babb.

Propped up in bed, she carefully went over the various
sums, obliging Mr. Waldo to repeat them after her and read
them aloud as he wrote them, in order that there might be no
mistake. "There's the four hundred dollars Jason left me,"
said she, " out at interest with David Van Horn ; then the mor-
gidge for a thousand dollars on Wilmot's store ; then the three
hundred *she* willed to me, two hundred lent to Backus, and
two hundred and fifty to Dan'el Stevens ;—let alone the int'rest
what I've saved. You'll find there'd ought to be twenty-seven
hundred and four dollars and six shillin's, altogether. The notes
is all in my tin box, and the int'rest tied up in my weddin'
stockins in the big trunk. I got it turned into gold : the banks is
breakin' all the time. It's enough to give Arbutus a good start
in the world—a heap better'n either me or Jason had. Put it
into the will that he's to be savin' and keerful, for 'twas got by
hard work. I know he won't spend it for hisself, but he's to
keep it out drawin' int'rest, and if he gits married, he mustn't
let his wife put it onto her back. And you may put down my
blessin', and that I've tried to bring him up in the right way
and hope he won't depart from it."

The will was finally completed. With a strong effort, she
signed it with a cramped, but steady hand. The physician
and clergyman affixed their signatures as witnesses. " Now
I'm ready," whispered Mrs. Babb, sinking down on the pillows, and almost instantly fell asleep.

As the two gentlemen issued from the house, the physician
said : " We must get somebody to take care of her."

" Of course," answered Mr. Waldo. " She cannot be intrusted to old Melinda. Leave it to me : I will see that there
is a good nurse in the house before night."

CHAPTER XXIII.

WHICH CONTAINS BOTH LOVE AND DEATH.

GOOD Mr. Waldo drove back to Ptolemy seriously troubled by the calamity which had come upon the household of Lakeside. Its helpless condition, now that the housekeeper was struck down, rendered immediate assistance necessary; but whence was the help to come? He could think of no woman at the same time willing and competent to render it— except his wife—and on her rested the entire care of his own house, as they were unable to afford a servant. The benevolent clergyman actually deliberated whether he should not let her go, and ask the hospitality of one of his parishioners during her absence, in case no other nurse could be found.

As he turned into the short private lane leading to his stable, a rapid little figure, in pink muslin, entered the front yard. It was Miss Caroline Dilworth, who had just returned from a farm-house on the road to Mulligansville, where she had been sewing for a fortnight past. She entered the plain little sitting-room at the same moment with Mr. Waldo. The clergyman's wife greeted her with astonishing brevity, and turned immediately to her husband.

"What was the matter?" she asked; "is Bute so much worse?"

"Bute worse!" ejaculated Miss Dilworth, opening her eyes in amazement.

"No," said Mr. Waldo, answering his wife, "the doctor thinks his chance is a little better, though he is still out of his head; but she has the fever now, and her case seems worse than his. I am distressed about them: there is nobody there

except the old negro woman, and Mrs. Babb needs a careful
nurse immediately."

"What is it? Do tell me what it is?" cried Miss Dilworth,
catching hold of the clergyman's arm with both hands.

He explained the case to her in a few words. To the astonishment of both, the little sempstress burst into a violent flood
of tears. For a minute or two the agitation was so great that
she was unable to speak.

"It's d-dreadful!" she sobbed at last. "Why—why didn't
you send w-word to me? But I'll g-go now: don't put out
your horse: take—take me there!"

"Carrie! do you really mean it?" said Mrs. Waldo.

Miss Caroline Dilworth actually stamped her foot. "Do
you think I'd make fun about it?" she cried. "Yes, I mean
to go, if I must go a-foot. He—they must have *somebody*, and
there's nobody can go so well as I can."

"I think she is right, wife," said the clergyman.

Mrs. Waldo hesitated a moment. "I know you would
be kind and careful, Carrie," she said at length, "and I could
come every day, and relieve you for a while. But are you sure
you are strong enough for the task?"

Miss Dilworth dried her eyes with her handkerchief and
answered: "If I'm not, you'll soon find it out. I'm going
over to Friend Thurston's to get some of my things to take
along."

"I'll call for you in a quarter of an hour, with the buggy,"
said Mr. Waldo.

The little sempstress was off without saying good-by. As
she went down the plank walk towards the Widow Thurston's
cottage, she pushed her tangled curls behind her ears, and then
held her hands clenched at her side, too much in earnest to
give her head a single toss or allow her feet a single mincing
step. All the latent firmness in her lithe figure was suddenly
developed. It spoke in her rapid, elastic gait, in the com-
pression of the short red lips, and the earnest forward glance
of her eyes, under their uplifted lids. During the spring and

summer she had been gradually coming to the conviction that she had treated Bute Wilson shamefully. The failure of the little arts which she had formerly employed with so much success had hastened this conviction. The softest drooping of her eyes, the gentlest drawl of her voice, ceased to move him from his cold, grave indifference. She began to feel that these charms only acquired their potency through the sentiments of those upon whom they were exercised. Had she not again and again cast them forth as nets, only to haul them in at last without having entrapped the smallest fish?

Besides, in another way, her ambition had suffered a severe check. The mistress of the school at Mulligansville having fallen sick, Miss Dilworth took her place for a fortnight. Her first sense of triumph in having attained what she considered to be her true mission, even as the proxy of another, did not last long. For a day or two, the novelty of her appearance kept the school quiet; but, one by one, the rude country children became familiar with her curls, with her soft green eyes, and her unauthoritative voice. They grinned in answer to her smile and met her frown with unconcealed derision; they ate green apples before her very face; pulled each other's hair or tickled each other under the arms; drew pictures on their slates and upset the inkstands over their copy-books. The bigger boys and girls threw saucy notes at each other across the whole breadth of the school-room. They came to her with "sums" which she found herself unable to solve; they read with loud, shrill voices and shocking pronunciation; and when the hour for dismissal came, instead of retiring quietly, they sprang from their benches with frightful whooping and rushed tumultuously out of the house. The "beautiful humanity" of the occupation, which she had heard so extolled, burst like a painted bubble, leaving no trace; the "moral suasion," on which she relied for maintaining discipline, failed her utterly; the "reciprocal love" between teacher and pupil, which she fancied she would develop in the highest degree, resolved itself into hideous contempt on the one side and repugnance on the other. She was finally indebted to one of the biggest and coarsest of the boys—a fellow who almost made her tremble every time he came near her—for sufficient help to prevent the school from falling into chaos before the fortnight came to an end. This boy, who was the bully of the school, and whose voice had a cracked hoarseness denoting the phase of development through which he was passing, was impressed with a vague respect for her curls and her complexion, and chivalrously threw his influence, including his fists, on her side. It was not pleasant, however, to hear the older girls giggle and whisper when he came: "There's the mistress's beau!"

Bute, also, increased in value in proportion as he became inaccessible. She confessed to herself that no masculine eyes had ever looked at her with such honest tenderness as his: and they were handsome eyes, whatever his nose might be. She had always liked to hear his voice, too, in the old time: now it was no longer the same. It was changed to *her*, and she had not imagined that the change could make her so restless and unhappy. Still, she did not admit to herself that she really loved him: their intercourse had had none of that sentimental poetic coloring—that atmosphere of sighs, murmurs, thrills, and silent raptures—which she fancied should accompany Love. He was even coarsely material enough to sneer at the idea of "kindred spirits!" Yet he loved her, for all that; she felt it in his altered manner, as she had never felt it before.

The unexpected shock of the news which Mr. Waldo communicated to her was a sudden betrayal of herself. Had she possessed the least power of introversion, she would have been amazed at it. But her nature was not broad enough to embrace more than a single sensation. The burst of tears and the impulse to offer her services came together, and all that she felt was: "If Bute dies, I shall be wretched." She continued to repeat this to herself, on her way to the Widow Thurston's, adding: "I'll do my best to save him and his stepmother, and I don't care who knows it, and I don't care what they say."

"Why, what's the matter, child?" exclaimed the widow, as Miss Dilworth walked into the sitting-room, erect, determined, and with a real expression on her usually vapid face.

The latter explained her purpose, not without additional tears. "Nobody else would be likely to go," she said: "they would be afraid of catching the fever. But I'm not afraid: I've seen the like before: I may be of use, and I ought to be there now."

The widow looked at her with a gentle scrutiny in her eyes, which made Miss Dilworth drop her lids for the first time and bring forward her curls from behind her ears. The glance changed to one of tender sympathy, and, checking a sigh which would have brought a memory with it, the old woman said:

"I think thee's right."

Thus encouraged, the necessary preparations were soon made, and in an hour from that time Miss Carrie Dilworth was at Lakeside.

The negress, who knew her, received her with a mixture of rejoicing and grief: "Bress de Lord, honey!" she exclaimed; "things is goin' bad. I'se mighty glad you come. Somebody's got to see to 'um, all de time, an' de cookin' *mus'* be 'tended to, ye knows."

Mrs. Babb, after a long sleep, was again awake, but in a state of physical prostration which prevented her from leaving her bed. Her anxiety lest Arbutus should not receive the proper care, aggravated her condition. She kept his medicines on a chair by her bedside, and demanded constant reports of him, which neither Patrick nor Melinda could give with sufficient exactness to satisfy her.

Miss Dilworth, somewhat nervously, ascended the kitchen stairs and entered the housekeeper's room. But the sight of the haggard, bony face, the wild restlessness in the sunken eyes, and the thin gray hair streaming loosely from the queer, old-fashioned night-cap, restored her courage through the inspiration of pity. She went forward with a quick, light step, and stooped down beside the bed.

13*

"I have come to help, Mrs. Babb," she said.

"Help, eh?" answered the housekeeper, in a weak, husky voice; "well—I've got to take any help that comes. Hard pushed, it seems. Thought *you* didn't keer about none of us. What are you good for, anyhow?"

"I've helped nurse before, Mrs. Babb. I'll do my best, if you'll let me try. Which medicine do you take?"

The housekeeper lay silent for a while, with her eyes on the sempstress's face. She was so weak that neither her first feeling of astonishment nor her second feeling of repugnance possessed a tithe of their usual force; the sense of her own helplessness overpowered them both. "That bottle with the red stuff," she said at last. "A tea-spoonful every two hours. Three o'clock, next. Take keer!" she gasped, as Miss Dilworth moved to the chair, "you'll knock every thing down with that hair o' yourn!"

The medicines were at last carefully arranged on a small table, the tea-spoonful administered, the pillows shaken up and smoothed, and, the invalid having declared herself comfortable, Miss Dilworth slipped out of the room. When she returned, ten minutes afterwards, her hair was drawn over her temples in masses as smooth as its former condition would allow, and fastened in a knot behind. The change was nevertheless an advantageous one; it gave her an air of sober womanhood which she had never before exhibited. The old woman noticed it at once, but said nothing. Her eyes continually wandered to the door, and she was growing restless.

"Shall I go and see how he is?" whispered Miss Carrie.

A strong expression of dislike passed over the housekeeper's face. For a few minutes she did not speak; then, as no one came, she finally groaned: "I can't go myself."

Miss Carrie opened the door of Bute's room with a beating heart. The curtains were down, to keep out the afternoon sun, and a dim yellow light filled the chamber. The air was close, and impregnated with a pungent etherous smell. In an old arm-chair, near the bed, sat Patrick, dozing. But that shorn head, that pale, thin face, and lean, hanging arm, did they really belong to Bute? She approached on tiptoe, holding her breath, and stood beside him. A rush of tenderness, such as she had never felt towards any man, came over her. She longed to lay the wasted head on her bosom, and bring back color into the cheeks from the warmth of her own heart. He turned and muttered, with half-closed eyes, as if neither asleep nor awake, and even when she gently took the hand that lay on the coverlet, the listless fingers did not acknowledge her touch. Once he looked full in her face, but vacantly, as if not even seeing her.

A horrible fear came over her. "Is he worse?" she whispered to the Irishman.

"No, he's no wurrse, Miss—maybe a bit better than he wur."

"When must he have his medicine?"

"I've jist guv' it to him. He'll be quieter now. Could ye stay here and laive me go to the barrn for an hour, jist?"

Miss Carrie reported to the housekeeper, and then relieved Patrick. She noiselessly moved the arm-chair nearer the bed, seated herself, and took Bute's feverish hand in her own. From time to time she moistened his parched lips and cooled his throbbing temples. His restless movements ceased and he lay still, though in a state of torpor, apparently, rather than sleep. It was pitiful to see him thus, stripped of his lusty strength, his red blood faded, the strong fibres of his frame weak and lax, and the light of human intelligence gone from his eye. His helplessness and unconsciousness now, brought into strong relief the sturdy, homely qualities of his mind and heart: the solemn gulf between the two conditions disclosed his real value. Miss Dilworth felt this without thinking it, as she sat beside him, yearning, with all the power of her limited nature, for one look of recognition, though it expressed no kindness for her; one rational word, though it might not belong to the dialect of love.

No such look, no such word, came. The hour slowly

dragged out its length; Patrick came back and she returned to the housekeeper's room. The physician paid a second visit in the evening, expressed his satisfaction with her nursing, thus far, and intrusted her with the entire care of administering the medicines. He advised her, however, not to be wasteful of her strength at the outset, as the patients would not soon be able to dispense with careful watching. It was arranged that the old negress should occasionally relieve her at night. In regard to the invalids, he confessed that he had some hope of Bute's recovery; in a day or two the crisis of the fever would be over; but Mrs. Babb, though her attack was much less violent, inspired him with solicitude. The apathetic condition of her system continued, in spite of all his efforts, and the strong will which might have upheld her, seemed to be suddenly broken.

Miss Dilworth fulfilled her duties with an astonishing patience and gentleness. Even the old housekeeper, no longer seeing the curls and drooping eyelids, or hearing the childish affectation of the voice, appeared to regard her as a different creature, and finally trusted the medicines implicitly to her care. On the day after her arrival, Bute, whose wan face and vacant eyes haunted her with a strange attraction, fell into a profound sleep. All that night he lay, apparently lifeless, but for the faint, noiseless breath that came from his parted lips. He could not be aroused to take his medicines. When this was reported to Mrs. Babb, she said, as sternly as her weakness would permit: "Let him alone! It's the turnin' p'int; he'll either die or git well, now."

This remark only increased Miss Dilworth's anxiety. Fifty times during the night she stole into his room, only to find him motionless, senseless as before. Patrick took advantage of the quiet to sleep, and snored loud and hard in his arm-chair. Once, moved by an impulse which she could not resist, she stooped down and kissed the sick man's forehead. The touch of her lips was light as a breath, but she rose, trembling and blushing at herself, and slipped out of the room.

"Quiet—nothing but quiet as long as he sleeps!" said the physician, next morning. Patrick was excluded from the room, because, although he pulled off his boots, there were two or three planks in the floor which creaked under his weight. Miss Dilworth silently laid a row of bed-room rugs from the door to the bedside, and went and came as if on down, over the enormous tufted roses. No sound entered the room but that of the summer wind in the boughs of the nearest elm. Hour after hour of the clouded August day went by, and still no change in the sleeper, unless an increased softness in his listless hand, as she cautiously touched it.

Towards sunset, after a restless day, Mrs. Babb fell asleep, and Miss Dilworth went into Bute's room and seated herself in the chair. The prolonged slumber frightened her. "Oh," she said to herself, "what would I do if he was to die. I've treated him badly, and he would never know that I'm sorry for it—never know that—that I love him! Yes, I know it now when it's too late. If he were well, he's done loving me as he used to—but he won't get well: he'll die and leave me wretched!"

As these words passed through her mind, while she leaned forward, with her face close to that of the invalid, she suddenly noticed a change in his breathing. Its faint, regular character was interrupted: it ceased a moment, and then his breast heaved with a deeper inspiration. "Oh, he's dying!" she whispered to herself in despair. Stooping down, she kissed his forehead passionately, while her tears dropped fast upon it. His arm moved; she rose, and met the glance of his open eyes—clear, tender, happy, wondering, but not with the blank wonder of delirium. It was Bute's self that looked at her —it was Bute's first, faithful love that first came to the surface from the very depth of his heart, before any later memory could thrust itself between. He had felt the kiss on his forehead: his eyes drew her, she knew not how, to his lips. His right arm lifted itself to her neck and held the kiss a moment fast: then it slid back again, and she sank into the chair, covering her face with her hands, and weeping.

After a while Bute's voice came to her—weak and gentle, but with its natural tone. "Carrie," said he, "what is it? What's happened?"

"Oh, Bute," she answered, "you've been very sick: you've been out of your head. And Mrs. Babb's sick too, and I've come to take care of you both. I thought you were going to die, Bute, and now you're going to get well, and I'm so glad— so happy!"

"Why are you glad, Carrie? Why did you come?" he asked, with an echo of the old reproach in his voice. The memory of his disappointment had already returned.

Nothing was further from Miss Dilworth's mind than a resort to her former arts. She was too profoundly and solemnly moved: she would tell the truth, as if it were her own dying hour. She took her hands from her face, lifted her head, and looked at him. "Because I have treated you badly, Bute," she said: "because I trifled with you wickedly. I wanted to make some atonement, and to hear you say you forgive me."

She paused. His eyes were fixed on hers, but he did not answer.

"Can you forgive me, Bute?" she faltered. "Try to do it, because I love you, though I don't expect you to love me any more."

"Carrie!" he cried. A new tint came to his face, a new light to his eye. His hand wandered towards her on the coverlet.

"Carrie," he repeated, feebly grasping her hand with his fingers and drawing her towards him, "once't more, now!" In the kiss that followed there was forgiveness, answering love, and a mutual compact for the future.

"You've brought me back ag'in to life," he murmured, closing his eyes, while two bright tears crept out from under the lids. She sat beside him, holding his hand. He seemed too weak to say more, and thus ten minutes silently passed away.

"Tell me how it happened," said Bute, finally. "Where's Mother Forty?"

"I must go to her at once!" cried Miss Dilworth, starting up. "She's worrying herself to death on your account. And the doctor said if you got awake you were to keep quiet, and not talk. I must go, Bute: do lie still and try to sleep till I come back. Oh, we oughtn't to have said any thing!"

"What we've said won't do me no harm," he murmured, with a patient, happy sigh. "Go, then, Carrie: I'll keep quiet."

Miss Dilworth went into the housekeeper's room so much more swiftly than usual that the latter was awakened by the rustling of her dress. She started and turned her head with a look of terror in her eyes.

"Oh, Mrs. Babb!" cried the sempstress: "Bute's awake at last. And his mind's come back to him! And he says he'll get well!"

The old woman trembled visibly. Her bony hands were clasped under the bed-clothes and her lips moved, but no audible words came from them. Then, fixing her eyes on the face of the kneeling girl, she asked: "What have you been a-sayin' to him?"

Miss Dilworth involuntarily drooped her lids and a deep color came into her face. "I asked him," she answered, "to forgive me for my bad behavior towards him."

"Nothin' else?"

"Yes, Mrs. Babb, I said he could do it now, because I love him."

"You do, do ye?"

"Yes, and he has forgiven me."

"Hnh!"

With this, her customary snort, when she was not prepared to express a decided opinion, the housekeeper closed her eyes and seemed to meditate. Presently, however, she turned her

head, and said, rather sternly, though without any signs of
bitterness:

"Go 'way now, gal! I want to be alone a spell."

Miss Dilworth obeyed. When she returned, at the time
appointed for administering the medicine, Mrs. Babb had resumed her state of passive patience. She made no further
inquiries about the conversation which had taken place, nor
about any which took place afterwards. A change had come
over her whole nature. She lay for hours, with her eyes open,
without speaking, evidently without suffering, yet keenly
alive to every thing that took place. She took her medicines
mechanically, with an air of listless obedience to the orders of
the physician, and without any apparent result. Stimulants
and sedatives alike failed to produce their customary effect.
From day to day she grew weaker, and the physician finally
declared that, unless she could be roused and stirred in some
way, to arrest the increasing prostration, he could do nothing
for her. As the knowledge of the favorable change in Bute's
case had left her as before, there was little hope that any
further source of excitement remained.

As for Bute, he rallied with a rapidity which amazed the
physician, who ascribed to an unusual vitality of his own the
life which the invalid had really drawn from another. The
only difficulty now was, to retard his impatient convalescence,
and Miss Dilworth was obliged to anticipate her conjugal authority and enjoin silence when he had still a thousand happy
questions left unasked and unanswered. When that authority
failed, she was forced to absent herself from the room, on the
plea of watching Mrs. Babb. His impatience, in such case,
was almost as detrimental as his loquacity, and the little
sempstress was never at ease except when he slept.

After passing a certain stage in the fever, the housekeeper
began to sink rapidly. Her mind, nevertheless, made feeble
efforts to retain its ascendency—efforts which reacted on her
body and completed the ruin of its faculties. One day she astonished Miss Dilworth by rising in her bed with a violent effort.

"I must go and see him!" she said: "help me into his room!"

"Oh, you cannot!" cried Miss Dilworth, supporting her with one arm around her waist. "Lie down: you are not strong enough. He will be able to come to you in a day or two."

"No, no! to-day!" gasped the housekeeper. "I a'n't certain o' knowin' him to-morrow, or o' bein' able to say to him what I've got to say." Thereupon her temporary strength gave way, and she sank down on the bed in a fainting state.

After she had somewhat revived, Miss Dilworth took counsel with herself, and soon came to a decision. She went down stairs and summoned Patrick, who carefully wrapped up Bute and placed him in the arm-chair. She herself then assisted in carrying him into the housekeeper's room, and placing him by the bedside. A look of unspeakable fondness came over Mrs. Babb's haggard face; the tears silently flowed from her eyes and rolled down the wrinkles in her hollow cheeks.

"Cheer up, Mother Forty," said Bute, who was the first to speak. "I'm gittin' on famous' and 'll soon be round again."

"It's as it should be, Arbutus," she whispered, hoarsely, catching her breath between the words; "the old 'un 'll go and the young 'un 'll stay. 'T had to be one of us."

"Don't say that; we'll take care of you—Carrie and me. Won't we, Carrie?"

"Yes, Bute," said Carrie, with her handkerchief to her eyes.

Mrs. Babb looked from one to another, but without any sign of reproof. She feebly shook her head. "What must be must," said she; "my time's come. P'raps I sha'n't see you no more, Arbutus. Maybe I ha'n't done my duty by you always; maybe I've seemed hard, once't and a while, but I meant it for your good, and I don't want you to have any hard thoughts ag'in me when I'm gone."

"Mother Forty!" cried Bute, his eyes filling and overflowing, "God knows I ha'n't nothin' ag'in you! You've been as good to me as you knowed how; it's me that's been rough, and forgitful o' how you took care o' me when I was a little boy. Don't talk that a-way now, don't!"

"Do you really mean it, Arbutus? Do you forgive me my trespasses, as I forgive them that trespass agi'n me? Can I go to Jason and say I've done my duty by you?"

Bute could not answer: he was crying like a child. He slid forward in the chair. Miss Dilworth put her arm around his waist to steady him, and they sank down together on their knees beside the bed. Bute's head fell forward on the coverlet. The housekeeper placed both her hands upon it.

"Take my blessin', child!" she said, in a feebler voice. "You've been a good boy, Arbutus. I'll tell _her_, and I'll tell your mother. Maybe I'll have a seat betwixt her and Jason. All I have'll be yourn. But you mustn't stay here: say good-by to me and go."

"Will you bless me, with him?" faltered Miss Carrie.

The left hand slowly moved to her head, and rested there. "Be a good wife to him when the time comes, and I'll bless you always. There a'n't many like him, and I hope you know it."

"I do know it," she sobbed; "there's _nobody_ like him."

"I want you to leave the money where it is," said the housekeeper, "and only draw the interest. You'll have an easier time of it in your old days than what I've had; but I don't begrudge it to you. It's time you were goin'—say good-by, child!"

The sempstress, small as she was, lifted Bute until his foster-mother could catch and hold his head to her bosom. Then, for the first time in his remembrance, she kissed him, once, twice, not with any violent outburst of feeling, but with a tender gravity as if it were a necessary duty, the omission of which would not be agreeable to Jason Babb. Then she turned over on the pillow, saying "Amen!" and was silent. Patrick was summoned and Bute was speedily replaced in his own bed, where Miss Dilworth left him to resume her place by the housekeeper's side.

But that same night, about midnight, Mrs. Babb died. She scarcely spoke again after her interview with Bute, except to ask, two hours later, whether he seemed to be any the worse on account of it. On being told that he was sleeping quietly, she nodded her head, straightened her gaunt form as well as she was able, and clasped her fingers together over her breast. Thus she lay, as if already dead, her strong eyebrows, her hooked nose, and her sharp chin marking themselves with ghastly distinctness as the cheeks grew more hollow and the closed eyes sank deeper in their sockets. Towards midnight a change in her breathing alarmed Miss Dilworth. She hastily called the old negress, who was sleeping on the kitchen settee.

"Honey," said the latter, in an awe-struck whisper, as she stood by the bedside, "she's a-goin' fast. She soon see de glory. Don't you wish fur her to stay, 'case dat'll interfere wid her goin'."

Her breath grew fainter, and came at longer intervals, but the moment when it ceased passed unnoticed by either of the watchers. Melinda first recognized the presence of Death. "You go an' lay down," she said to Miss Carrie. "You can't do no good now. I'll stay wid her till mornin'."

The sempstress obeyed, for she was, in truth, wretchedly weary. For the remainder of the night Melinda sat on a low chair beside the corpse, swinging her body backwards and forwards as she crooned, in a low voice:

> "De streets is paved wid gold,
>   Ober on de udder shore."

CHAPTER XXIV.

VARIOUS CHANGES, BUT LITTLE PROGRESS IN THE STORY.

As soon as the news of Mrs. Babb's death became known, the neighbors hastened to Lakeside to offer their help. The necessary arrangements for the funeral were quietly and speedily made, and, on the second day afterwards, the body of the housekeeper was laid beside that of Jason Babb, in the Presbyterian churchyard at Ptolemy, where he had been slumbering for the last twenty-three years. The attendance was very large, for all the farmers' wives in the valley had known Mrs. Babb, and still held her receipts for cakes, preserves, and pickles in high esteem. The Reverends Styles and Waldo made appropriate remarks and prayers at the grave, so that no token of respect was wanting. All the neighbors said, as they drove homewards, "The funeral was a credit to her." Her spirit must have smiled in stern satisfaction, even from its place by Jason's side, and at the feet of Mrs. Dennison, as it looked down and saw that her last unconscious appearance among mortals was a success.

Miss Dilworth took counsel of her friends, Hannah Thurston and Mrs. Waldo, on the day of the funeral. She confessed to them, with returning misgivings, what had taken place between Bute Wilson and herself, and was a little surprised at the hearty gratification which they both expressed.

"How glad I am!" cried Mrs. Waldo; "it is the very thing!"

"Yes," said Hannah Thurston, in her grave, deliberate manner, "I think you have made a good choice, Carrie."

If any spark of Miss Caroline Dilworth's old ambition still burned among the ashes of her dreams, it was extinguished at that moment. The prophets of reform were thenceforth dead to her. She even took a consolation in thinking that if her wish had been fulfilled, her future position might have had its embarrassments. She might have been expected to sympathize with ideas which she did not comprehend—to make use of new shibboleths before she had learned to pronounce them —to counterfeit an intelligent appreciation when most conscious of her own incompetency. Now, she would be at ease. Bute would never discover any deficiency in her. She spoke better English and used finer words than he did, and if she made a mistake now and then, he wouldn't even notice it. With the disappearance of her curls her whole manner had become more simple and natural. Her little affectations broke out now and then, it is true, but they had already ceased to be used as baits to secure a sentimental interest. There was even hope that her attachment to Bute would be the means of developing her somewhat slender stock of common-sense.

"Bute says we must be married as soon as he gets well," she said: "he won't wait any longer. Is there any harm in my staying here and taking care of him until he's entirely out of danger?"

Mrs. Waldo reflected a moment. "Certainly none until Mr. Woodbury returns," she said. "Mr. Waldo has answered his letter to Bute, which came this morning. If he leaves Saratoga at once, he will be here in three or four days. The doctor says you are an admirable nurse, and that is reason enough why you should not leave at present."

"The other reason *ought* to be enough," said Hannah Thurston. "She owes a wife's duty towards him now, when he needs help which she can give. I am sure Mr. Woodbury will see it in the same light. He is noble and honorable."

"Why, Hannah!" cried Mrs. Waldo, "I thought you and he were as far apart as the opposite poles!"

"Perhaps we are, in our views of certain subjects," was the

quiet reply. "I can, nevertheless, properly estimate his char acter as a man."

Mrs. Waldo suppressed a sigh. "If you could only estimate your own true character as a woman!" she thought.

Miss Dilworth's duties were now materially lightened. The danger of further contagion had passed, and some one of the neighbors came every day to assist her. Bute only required stimulating medicines, and the usual care to prevent a relapse, of which there seemed to be no danger. He began to recover his healthful sleep at night, and his nurse was thus enabled to keep up her strength by regular periods of rest. Once or twice a day she allowed him to talk, so long as there was no appearance of excitement or fatigue. These half-hours were the happiest Bute had ever known. To the delicious languor and peace of convalescence, was added the active, ever-renewed bliss of his restored love, and the promises which it whispered. He delighted to call Miss Carrie, in anticipation, "Little wife!" pausing, each time he did so, to look for the blush which was sure to come, and the smile on the short red lips, which was the sweetest that ever visited a woman's face. Of course it was.

One day, nevertheless, as he lay looking at her, and thinking how much more steady and sensible she seemed since her curls were gathered up—how much more beautiful the ripples of light brown hair upon her temples—a cloud came over his face. "Carrie," he said, "there's one thought worries me, and I want you to put it straight, if you can. S'pose I hadn't got sick,—s'pose I hadn't lost my senses, would you ever ha' come to your'n?"

She was visibly embarrassed, but presently a flitting roguish expression passed over her face, and she answered: "Would you have given me a chance to do it, Bute?"

"Likely not," said he. "You spoke plain enough last winter, and 'twasn't for me to say the first word, after that. When a man's burnt his fingers once't, he keeps away from the fire. But I want to know why you come to take keer o' me and Mother Forty. Was it only because you were sorry, and wanted to pay me for my disapp'intment in that way? Can you lay your hand on your heart and say there was any thing more?"

Miss Carrie immediately laid her hand on her heart. "Yes, Bute," she said, "there *was* something more. I was beginning to find it out, before, but when I heard you were so bad, it came all at once."

"Look here, Carrie," said Bute, still very earnestly, although the cloud was beginning to pass away, "some men have hearts like shuttlecocks, banged back and forth from one gal to another, and none the wuss of it. But I a'n't one of 'em. Whenever I talk serious, I 'xpect to be answered serious. I believe what you say to me. I believed it a'ready, but I wanted to be double sure. You and me have got to live together as man and wife. 'Twon't be all skylarkin': we've got to work, and help one another, and take keer o' others besides, if things goes right. What'll pass in a gal, won't pass in a married woman: you must get shut o' your coquettin' ways. I see you've took the trap out o' your hair, and now you must take it out o' your eyes. 'Ta'n't that it'll mean any thing any more—if I thought it did, I'd feel like killin' you—but it won't look right."

"You mustn't mind my foolishness, Bute," she answered, penitently, "and you mustn't think of Seth Wattles!"

"Seth be—*con-sarn'd!*" Bute exclaimed. "When I see you pickin' up dead frogs, I'll believe you like to shake hands with Seth! I've got agreeabler thoughts than to have him in my head. Well—I don't bear no grudge ag'in him now; but I a'n't like him."

"I don't like him either. Fancy such a fellow as he thinking himself good enough for Hannah Thurston! There's no man good enough for her!"

"Like enough *she* thinks herself too good for any man,' Bute remarked. "But them a'n't the women, Carrie, that a man wants to marry. It'll be a lucky woman that gits Mr. Max."

"Oh, I must go and see to Mr. Woodbury's room!" cried Miss Dilworth, starting up. "Perhaps he'll come this very day. Then I suppose I must go away, Bute."

"I hope not, Carrie. I wouldn't mind bein' a bit sicker for a day or two, o' purpose to keep you here. What! are you goin' away in that fashion, Little Wife?"

Miss Dilworth darted back to the bedside, stooped down, like a humming-bird presenting its bill to a rather large flower, and was about to shoot off again, when Bute caught her by the neck and substituted a broad, firm kiss, full of consistency and flavor, for the little sip she had given him.

"That's comfortin'," said he. "I thank the Lord my mouth a'n't as little as your'n."

Before night, Mr. Woodbury arrived, having taken a carriage at Tiberius and driven rapidly over the hills. Mr. Waldo's letter, announcing Bute's dangerous condition and Mrs. Babb's death, had greatly startled and shocked him. His summer tour was nearly at an end, and he at once determined to return to Lakeside for the autumn and winter. He was not surprised to find his household in charge of Miss Dilworth, for the news had already been communicated to him. She met him at the door, blushing and slightly embarrassed, for she scarcely felt herself entitled to be ranked among his acquaintances, and the calm reserve of his usual manner had always overawed her.

"I am very glad to find you still here, Miss Dilworth," he said, pressing her hand warmly; "how can I repay you for your courage and kindness? Bute—?"

"He is much better, Sir. He is expecting you: will you walk up and see him?"

"Immediately. I suppose I ought not to carry all this dust with me. I will go to my room first."

"It is ready, Sir," said Miss Dilworth. "Let me have your coat."

Before Woodbury had finished washing his face and hands and brushing the white dust of the highway out of his hair there was a light tap on the door. He opened it and beheld his coat, neatly dusted and folded, confronting him on the back of a chair. Bute's room he found in the most perfect order. The weather had been warm, dry, and still, and the window furthest from the bed was open. The invalid lay, propped up with two extra pillows, awaiting him. Woodbury was at first shocked by his pale, wasted face, to which the close-cut hair gave a strange, ascetic character. His eyes were sunken, but still bright and cheerful, and two pale-blue sparks danced in them as he turned his head towards the door.

"Bute, my poor fellow, how are you? I did not dream this would have happened," said Woodbury, taking the large, spare hand stretched towards him.

"Oh, I'm doin' well now, Mr. Max. 'Twas queer how it come—all 't once't, without any warnin'. I knowed nothin' about it till I was past the danger."

"And Mrs. Babb—was she sick long? Did she suffer much?"

"I don't think she suffered at all: she was never out of her head. She seemed to give up at the start, I'm told, and all the medicines she took was no use. She jist made up her mind to die, and she always had a strong will, you know, Mr. Max." Bute said this quietly and seriously, without the least thought of treating the memory of his foster-mother lightly.

"She had a good nurse, at least," said Woodbury, "and you seem to be equally fortunate."

"Well, I guess I am," answered Bute, his face on a broad grin, and with more color in it than he had shown for many days. "I've had the best o' nussin', Mr. Max. Not but what Pat and Mr. Merryfield was as kind as they could be— 'twasn't the same thing. And I may as well out with it plump: there's no nuss quite ek'l to a man's own wife."

"Wife!" exclaimed Woodbury, in amazement.

"Well—no—not jist yit," stammered Bute; "but she will be as soon as I git well enough to marry. I'd been hankerin' after her for these two years, Mr. Max., but it mightn't ha' come to nothin' if I hadn't got sick."

14

" You mean Miss Dilworth, of course ?"

Bute nodded his head.

" You astonish me, Bute. I scarcely know her at all, but I think you have too much good sense to make a mistake. I wish you joy, with all my heart ; and yet"—he continued in a graver tone, taking Bute's hand, " I shall be almost sorry for it, if this marriage should deprive me of your services on the farm."

"How ?" cried Bute, instantly recovering his former paleness, " do you mean, Mr. Max., that you wouldn't want me afterwards ?"

" No, no, Bute ! On the contrary, I should be glad to see you settled and contented. But it is natural, now, that you should wish to have a farm of your own, and as Mrs. Babb's legacy will enable you to buy a small one, I thought——"

"Bless you, Mr. Max.!" interrupted Bute, "it *would* be a small one. What's a few hundred dollars ? I've no notion o' goin' into farmin' on a ten-acre lot."

"Mr. Waldo tells me that her property amounts to about twenty-seven hundred dollars."

" *Twenty—seven—hundred !* " and Bute feebly tried to whistle. " Well—Mother Forty always was a cute 'un—who'd ha' thought it ? And she's left it all to me—she keered a mighty sight more for me than she let on." Here something rose in his throat and stopped his voice for a moment. " I'll do her biddin' by it, that I will !" he resumed. " I shall leave it out at interest, and not touch a cent of the capital. Time enough for my children to draw that. Oh, Mr. Max., now the Lord may jist send as many youngsters to me and Carrie, as He pleases !"

A dim sensation, like the memory of a conquered sorrow, weighed upon Woodbury's heart for an instant, and passed away.

" I know when I'm well off," Bute went on. " I'm content-ed to stay as I am : every thing on the farm—the horses, th' oxen, the pigs, the fences, the apple-trees, the timber-land—

seems to me as much mine as it is your'n. If I had a farm o' my own, it'd seem strange like, as if it belonged to somebody else. I've got the hang of every field here, and know jist what it'll bring. I want to make a good livin': I don't deny that; but if I hold on to what I've got now, and don't run no resks, and put out th' interest ag'in every year, it'll roll up jist about as fast and a darned sight surer, than if I was to set up for my-self. If you're willin', Mr. Max., we can fix it somehow. If the tenant-house on the 'Nacreon road was patched up a little, it'd do for the beginnin'."

"We can arrange it together, Bute," said Woodbury, rising. "Now you have talked long enough, and must rest. I will see you again before I go to bed."

As Miss Dilworth, at his request, took her seat at the table and poured out the tea, Woodbury looked at her with a new interest. He had scarcely noticed her on previous occasions, and hence there was no first impression to be removed. It seemed to him, indeed, as if he saw her for the first time now. The ripples in her hair caught the light; her complexion was un-usually fair and fresh; the soft green of her eyes became almost brown under the long lashes, and the mouth was infan-tine in shape and color. A trifle of affectation in her manner did not disharmonize with such a face; it was natural to her, and would have been all the same, had she been eighty years old instead of twenty-six. With this affectation, however, were combined two very useful qualities—a most scrupulous neatness and an active sense of order. "Upon my soul, it is Lisette herself," said Woodbury to himself, as he furtively watched her airs and movements. Who would have expected to find so many characteristics of the Parisian grisette in one of our staid American communities? And how astonishing, could he have known it, her ambitious assumption of Hannah Thurston's views! It was a helmet of Pallas, which not only covered her brow, but fell forward over her saucy retroussé nose, and weighed her slender body half-way to the earth.

She felt his scrutiny, and performed her tea-table duties with two spots of bright color in her cheeks. Woodbury knew that she suspected what Bute's principal communication to him had been, and, with his usual straightforward way of meeting a delicate subject, decided to speak to her at once. She gave a little start of confusion—not entirely natural—as he commenced, but his manner was so serious, frank, and respectful, that she soon felt ashamed of herself and was drawn, to her own surprise, to answer him candidly and naturally.

"Bute has told me, Miss Dilworth," said he, "of your mutual understanding. I am very glad of it, for his sake. He is an honest and faithful fellow, and deserves to be happy. I think he is right, also, in not unnecessarily postponing the time, though perhaps I should not think so, if his marriage were to deprive me of his services. But he prefers to continue to take charge of Lakeside, rather than buy or lease a farm for himself. I hope you are satisfied with his decision?"

"Yes, Mr. Woodbury," she answered: "I should not like to leave this neighborhood. I have no relatives in the country, except an aunt in Tiberius. My brother went to Iowa five years ago."

"Bute must have a home," Woodbury continued. "He spoke of my tenant-house, but besides being old and ruinous, it is not well situated, either for its inmates, or for the needs of the farm. I had already thought of tearing it down, and building a cottage on the knoll, near the end of the lane. But that would take time, and——"

"Oh, we can wait, Mr. Woodbury!"

He smiled. "I doubt whether Bute would be as ready to wait as you, Miss Dilworth. I am afraid if I were to propose it, he would leave me at once. No, we must make some other arrangement in the mean time. I have been turning the matter over in my mind and have a proposition to make to you."

"To me!"

"Yes. Mrs. Babb's death leaves me without a housekeeper. My habits are very simple, the household is small, and I see already that you are capable of doing all that will be required. Of course you will have whatever help you need; I ask nothing more than a general superintendence of my domestic affairs until your new home is ready. If you have no objection of your own to make, will you please mention it to Bute?"

"Bute will be *so* pleased!" she cried. "Only, Mr. Woodbury, if it isn't more than I am capable of doing? If I'm able to give you satisfaction!"

"I shall be sure of your wish to do so, Miss Dilworth," said Woodbury, rising from the table; "and I have the further guarantee that you will have Bute to please, as well as myself."

He went into the library and lighted a cigar. "Lucky fellow!" he said to himself, with a sigh. "He makes no intellectual requirements from his wife, and he has no trouble in picking up a nice little creature who is no doubt perfection in his eyes, and who will be faithful to him all his days. If she doesn't know major from minor; if she confuses tenses and doubles negatives; if she eats peas with her knife, and trims her bonnet with colors at open war with each other; if she never heard of Shakespeare, and takes Petrarch to be the name of a mineral—what does he care? She makes him a tidy home; she understands and soothes his simple troubles; she warms his lonely bed, and suckles the vigorous infants that spring from his loins; she gives an object to his labor, a contented basis to his life, and a prospect of familiar society in the world beyond the grave. Simple as this relation of the sexes is for him, he feels its sanctity no less than I. His espousals are no less chaste; his wedded honor is as dear, his paternal joys as pure. My nature claims all this from woman, but, alas! it claims more. The cultivated intelligence comes in to question and criticize the movements of the heart. Here, on one side, is goodness, tenderness, fidelity; on the other, grace, beauty, refinement, intellect—both needs must be fulfilled. How shall I ever reach this double marriage, except through a blind chance? Yet here is one woman in whom it would be nearly fulfilled, and a strange delusion into which she has fallen warns me to think of her no more!"

The conscious thread of his thoughts broke off, and they loosened themselves into formless reverie. As he rose to revisit Bute's chamber, he paused a moment, thinking: "That I can analyze her nature thus deliberately, is a proof that I do not love her."

Bute was delighted with the new arrangement which Woodbury had proposed to Miss Dilworth. The latter would leave in a few days, he said, and spend the subsequent two or three weeks before the wedding could take place, at the Widow Thurston's.

"After it's all over, Mr. Max.," said Bute, "she shall stay here and tend to the house jist as long as you want; but—you won't mind my sayin' it, will you?—there's only one right kind of a housekeeper for *you*, and I hope you won't be too long a-findin' her."

CHAPTER XXV.

IN WHICH HANNAH THURSTON MAKES A NEW ACQUAINTANCE.

In another week, Bute was able to dispense with the grateful nursing which had more than reconciled him to the confinement of his sick-room. He required no attendance at night, and was able to sit, comfortably pillowed, for a great part of the day. He consumed enormous quantities of chicken-broth, and drank immoderately of Old Port and Albany Ale. Miss Dilworth, therefore, made preparations to leave : she was now obliged to sew for herself, and a proper obedience to custom required that she should not remain at Lakeside during the last fortnight of her betrothal.

On the morning of her departure, Woodbury called her into the library. "You have done me a great service, Miss Dilworth," said he, "and I hope you will allow me to acknowledge it by furnishing you with one article which I know will have to be provided." With these words he opened a paper parcel and displayed a folded silk, of the most charming tint of silver-gray.

The little sempstress looked at it in speechless ecstasy. "It's heavenly !" she at last cried, clasping her hands. "I'm obliged to you a thousand times, Mr. Woodbury. It's too much, indeed it is !"

"Bute won't think so," he suggested.

She snatched the parcel, and darted up-stairs in three bounds. "Oh, Bute !" she cried, bursting into his room, "only look at this ! It's my wedding-dress ! And he's just given it to me !"

"It's the prettiest thing I ever laid my eyes on," said Bute, looking at the silk reverently but not daring to touch it. "That's jist like Mr. Max.—what did I always tell you about him ?"

After Miss Dilworth's departure, the housekeeping was conducted, somewhat indifferently, by the old negress. She had, however, the one merit of being an admirable cook, and Woodbury might have managed to live with her assistance, for a fortnight, but for one awkward circumstance. He received a letter from Mrs. Blake, saying that her husband had completed his business in the East and they were preparing to leave Saratoga. Would it be still convenient for him to entertain them for a few days at Lakeside, on their return to St. Louis? If the illness in his household, which had called him home so suddenly, still continued, they would, of course, forego the expected pleasure; but if not, they would be the more delighted to visit him, as it was probable they would not come to the East the following summer. Would he answer the letter at once, as they were nearly ready to leave ?

Woodbury was uncertain what to do in this emergency. There was no longer the slightest fear of contagion, and he particularly desired the offered visit; but how could he entertain his friends without a housekeeper? He finally decided that it must be arranged, somehow; wrote an affirmative answer, and rode into Ptolemy to post it without delay, first calling at the Cimmerian Parsonage to ask the advice of a sensible female friend.

"You see," said he, after stating the dilemma to Mrs. Waldo, "now that my tyrant has gone, I wish her back again. A despotism is better than no government at all."

"Ah, but a republic is better than a despotism!" she replied. "Do you take my meaning? I'm not certain, after all, that the figure is quite correct. But the thing is to find a temporary housekeeper. I know of no single disengaged woman in Ptolemy, unless it is Miss Ruhaney Goodwin, and her mournful countenance and habit of sighing, would be very discouraging to your guests, even if she were willing to go. Mrs. Bue is a complete intelligence office for Ptolemy servants. Your only chance is to see her."

"And if that fails?"

"Then there is no hope. I shall be vexed, for I want to see this Mrs. Blake. If it were not for taking care of my good husband, I should myself be willing to act as mistress of Lakeside for a few days."

"I knew you would be able to help me!" cried Woodbury, joyfully. "Let me add Mr. Waldo to the number of my guests. I shall be delighted to have him, and the change may be refreshing to him. Besides, you will have us all at the Cimmerian Church, if the Blakes remain over a Sunday."

"You are mistaken, if you supposed that any thing of the kind was in my thoughts," said Mrs. Waldo. "But the proposal sounds very pleasantly. I am sure we both should enjoy it very much, but I cannot accept, you know, before consulting with my husband."

"Leave Mr. Waldo to me."

The matter was very easily arranged. The clergyman, faithful to the promise of his teeth, appreciated a generous diet. His own table was oftentimes sparely supplied, and he was conscious of a gastric craving which gave him discouraging views of life. There was no likelihood of any immediate birth or death in his congregation, and it was not the season of the year when members were usually assailed by doubts and given to backsliding. More fortunate clergymen went to the watering places, or even to Europe, to rest their exhausted lungs; why should he not go to Lakeside for a week? They had no servant, and could shut up the parsonage during their absence: but the old horse?

"Wife, we must get somebody to look after Dobbin," he said, thoughtfully.

"Bring Dobbin along," Woodbury laughed, "my old Dick will be glad to see him."

Although neither he nor the Waldos were aware that they

4*

had spoken to any one on the subject, the arrangement that had been made was whispered to everybody in Ptolemy before twenty-four hours were over. Nothing was known of the Blakes, except that they were "fashionable," and those who would have been delighted to be in the place of the poor clergyman and his wife, expressed their astonishment at the conduct of the latter.

"It's what I call *very* open communion," said the Rev. Mr. Pinchman, of the Campbellite Church.

Miss Ruhaney Goodwin heaved three of her most mournful sighs, in succession, but said nothing.

"Merry-makings so soon after a death in the house," remarked Mrs. Hamilton Bue: "it's quite shocking to think of."

"Our friend is getting *very* select," said the Hon. Zeno Harder, in his most pompous manner, thereby implying that *he* should not have been overlooked.

Mr. Grindle, of course, improved the opportunity on every possible occasion, and before the Blakes had been two days at Lakeside, it was reported, in temperance circles, that they had already consumed one hundred dollars' worth of wine.

Had these rumors been known to the pleasant little community of Lakeside, they would have added an additional hilarity to the genial atmosphere which pervaded the house. But it was quite removed from the clatter of the village gossip, and by the time such news had gone its rounds, and been conveyed to the victim by sympathizing friends, the occasion which gave rise to it had entirely passed away. In our small country communities, nothing is so much resented as an indirect assumption of social independence. A deviation from the prevailing habits of domestic life—a disregard for prevailing prejudices, however temporary and absurd they may be—a visit from strangers who excite curiosity and are not made common social property: each of these circumstances is felt as an act of injustice, and constitutes a legitimate excuse for assault. Since the railroad had reached Tiberius, and the steamer on Atauga Lake began to bring summer visitors to Ptolemy, this species of despotism had somewhat relaxed, but it now and then flamed up with the old intensity, and Woodbury was too cosmopolitan in his nature not to provoke its exercise.

Mr. and Mrs. Waldo reached Lakeside the day before the arrival of the Blakes, and the latter took immediate and easy possession of her temporary authority. In addition to Melinda, than whom no better cook, in a limited sphere of dishes, could have been desired, Woodbury had hit upon the singular expedient of borrowing a chamber-maid from the Ptolemy House. Mrs. Waldo's task was thus rendered light and agreeable—no more, in fact, than she would have voluntarily assumed in any household rather than be idle. It was more than a capacity—it was almost a necessity of her nature, to manage something or direct somebody. In the minor details her sense of order may have been deficient; but in regulating departments and in general duties she was never at fault. Her subordinates instantly felt the bounds she had drawn for them, and moved instinctively therein.

The Blakes were charmed with Lakeside and the scenery of the Atauga Valley. Between the boy George and Bute, who was now able to sit on the shaded veranda on still, dry days, there grew up an immediate friendship. Miss Josephine was beginning to develop an interest in poetry and romances, and took almost exclusive possession of the library. Mr. Blake walked over the farm with Woodbury in the forenoons, each developing theories of agriculture equally original and impracticable, while the Mesdames Waldo and Blake improved their acquaintance in house and garden. The two ladies understood each other from the start, and while there were some points, in regard to which—as between any two women that may be selected—each commiserated the other's mistaken views, they soon discovered many reasons for mutual sympathy and mutual appreciation. Mrs. Blake had the greater courage, Mrs. Waldo the greater tact. The latter had more natural grace and pliancy, the former more acquired refinement of

manner.   They were alike in the correctness of their instincts,
but in Mrs. Blake the faculty had been more exquisitely developed, through her greater social experience. It was the
same air, in the same key, but played an octave higher. Mrs.
Waldo was more inclined to receive her enjoyment of life
through impulse and immediate sensation ; Mrs. Blake through
a philosophic discrimination.   Both, perhaps, would have
borne misfortune with like calmness ; but the resignation of
one would have sprung from her temperament, and of the
other from her reason. The fact that the resemblances in their
matured womanhood were developed from different bases of
character, increased the interest and respect which they
mutually felt.

On one point, at least, they were heartily in accord ; namely,
their friendship for Woodbury. Mrs. Blake was familiar,
as we have already described, with his early manhood in New
York, and furnished Mrs. Waldo many interesting particulars
in return for the description which the latter gave of his life
at Lakeside.   They were also agreed that there was too much
masculine sweetness in him to be wasted on the desert air, and
that the place, beautiful as it was, could never be an actual
home until he had brought a mistress to it.

"He was already chafing under Mrs. Babb's rule," said Mrs.
Waldo, as they walked up and down the broad garden-alley,
"and he will be less satisfied with the new housekeeper.
Bute's wife—as she will be—is a much more agreeable person, and will no doubt try to do her best, but he will get very
tired of her face and her silly talk.   It will be all the worse
because she has not a single characteristic strong enough for
him to seize upon and say: This offends me! You know what
I mean ?"

"Perfectly ; and your remark is quite correct.   Mr. Woodbury is one of those men who demand positive character, of
some kind, in the persons with whom they associate. He likes
fast colors, and this new housekeeper, from your description,
must be a piece that will fade the longer it is used.   In that

case, she will become intolerable to him, though she may not possess one serious fault."

"That characteristic of his," said Mrs. Waldo, "is the very reason, I think, why it will be difficult for him to find a wife."

"By the by," asked Mrs. Blake, pausing in her walk, "he spoke to me, when we met on the Saguenay, of one woman, here, in your neighborhood, who seems to have made a strong impression upon his mind."

"It was certainly Hannah Thurston!"

"He did not give me her name. He seemed to admire her sincerely, except in one fatal particular—she is strong-minded."

"Yes, it is Hannah!" exclaimed Mrs. Waldo. "She is a noble girl, and every way worthy of such a man as he—that is, if she were not prejudiced against all men."

"You quite interest me about her. I heard Bessie Stryker once, when she lectured in St. Louis, and must confess that, while she did not convince me, I could see very well how she had convinced herself. Since then, I have been rather tolerant towards the strong-minded class. The principal mistakes they make arise from the fact of their not being married, or of having moral and intellectual milksops for husbands. In either case, no woman can understand our sex, or the opposite."

"I have said almost the same thing to Hannah Thurston," Mrs. Waldo remarked. "If she would only take one step, the true knowledge would come. But she won't."

"I suspect she has not yet found her Fate," said Mrs. Blake. "Was she ever in love, do you think?"

"No, I am sure of it. She has refused two good offers of marriage to my knowledge, and one of them was from a man who believed in the doctrine of Women's Rights. I can't understand her, though I love her dearly, and we have been intimate for years."

"Can you not contrive a way for me to make her acquaintance?"

"Whenever you please. I have no doubt she remembers the story Mr. Woodbury told us last winter. I am hostess, now, you know, and I can invite her to dinner to-morrow, only I must ask somebody else. I have it! Mr. Woodbury must invite Mr. and Mrs. Styles. It will not do for him to show too much partiality to our little sect, and that will keep up the balance of civility."

Woodbury accepted the proposition with more satisfaction than he judged proper to express. It was the very object he desired to accomplish, yet which he could not himself mention without exciting suspicions in the minds of both the ladies. He had not seen Hannah Thurston since his return, and felt a strange curiosity to test his own sensations when they should meet again. Under the circumstances, the invitation could be given and accepted without in the least violating the social propriety of Ptolemy.

The disturbing emotion which had followed her last interview with Woodbury had entirely passed away from Hannah Thurston's mind. Her momentary resolution to avoid seeing him again, presented itself to her as a confession of weakness. A studied avoidance of his society would be interpreted as springing from a hostility which she did not feel. On the contrary, his culture attracted her: his bearing towards her was gratefully kind and respectful, and she acknowledged a certain intellectual pleasure in his conversation, even when it assailed her dearest convictions. Her mother's health, always fluctuating with the season and the weather, had somewhat improved in the last calm, warm days of August, and she could safely leave her for a few hours in Miss Dilworth's charge. The latter, indeed, begged her to go, that she might bring back a minute account of Bute's grade of convalescence. In short, there was no plausible excuse for declining the invitation, had she been disposed to seek one.

It was a quiet but very agreeable dinner-party. Mr. and Mrs. Styles were both amiable and pleasantly receptive persons, and Mrs. Waldo took care that they should not be overlooked in the lively flow of talk. Hannah Thurston, who was seated beside Mr. Blake and opposite his wife, soon overcame her first timidity, and conversed freely and naturally with her new acquaintances. Woodbury's reception of her had been frank and kind, but he had said less to her than on former occasions. Nevertheless, she occasionally had a presentiment that his eyes were upon her—that he listened to her, aside, when he was engaged in conversing with his other guests. It was an absurd fancy, of course, but it constantly returned.

After dinner, the company passed out upon the veranda, or seated themselves under the old oaks, to enjoy the last mellow sunshine of the afternoon. Mrs. Blake and Hannah Thurston found themselves a little apart from the others—an opportunity which the former had sought. Each was attracted towards the other by an interest which directed their thoughts to the same person, and at the same time restrained their tongues from uttering his name. Hannah Thurston had immediately recognized in her new acquaintance the same mental poise and self-possession, which, in Woodbury, had extorted her unwilling respect, while it so often disconcerted her. She knew that the two were natives of the same social climate, and was curious to ascertain whether they shared the same views of life—whether, in fact, those views were part of a conventional creed adopted by the class to which they belonged, or, in each case, the mature conclusions of an honest and truth-seeking nature. With one of her own sex she felt stronger and better armed to defend herself. Mrs. Blake was not a woman of unusual intellect, but what she did possess was awake and active, to its smallest fibre. What she lacked in depth, she made up in quickness and clearness of vision. She did not attempt to follow abstract theories, or combat them, but would let fall, as if by accident, one of the sharp, positive truths, with which both instinct and experience had stored her mind, and which never failed to prick and let the wind out of every bubble blown towards her. This faculty, added to the advantage of sex, made her the most dangerous antagonist Hannah Thurston could have met. But the latter, unsuspecting, courted her fate.

The conversation, commencing with the beauties of the

landscape, branching thence to Ptolemy and its inhabitants, to
their character, their degree of literary cultivation, and the
means of enlightenment which they enjoyed, rapidly and
naturally approached the one important topic. Hannah Thurston mentioned, among other things, the meetings which were
held in the interest of Temperance, Anti-Slavery, Non-Resistance, and Women's Rights ; Mrs. Blake gave her impressions
of Bessie Stryker's lecture : Hannah Thurston grasped the
whole gauntlet where only the tip of a finger had been presented, and both women were soon in the very centre of the
debatable ground.

"What I most object to," said Mrs. Blake, "is that women
should demand a sphere of action for which they are incapaci-
tated—understand me, not by want of intellect, but by sex."

"Do you overlook all the examples which History fur-
nishes ?" cried Hannah Thurston. "What is there that Woman has not done ?"

"Commanded an army."

"Zenobia !"

"And was brought in chains to Rome. Founded an empire ?"

"She has *ruled* empires !"

"After they were already made, and with the help of men.
Established a religion ? Originated a system of philosophy ?
Created an order of architecture ? Developed a science ? In-
vented a machine ?"

"I am sure I could find examples of her having distinguished herself in all these departments of intellect," Hannah
Thurston persisted.

"Distinguished herself! Ah! yes, I grant it. After the
raw material of knowledge has been dug up and quarried out,
and smelted, and hewn into blocks, she steps in with her fine
hand and her delicate tools, and assists man in elaborating the
nicer details. But she has never yet done the rough work,
and I don't believe she ever will."

"But with the same education—the same preparation—the

same advantages, from birth, which man possesses? She is taught to anticipate a contracted sphere—she is told that these pursuits were not meant for her sex, and the determination to devote herself to them comes late, when it comes at all. Those intellectual muscles which might have had the same vigor as man's, receive no early training. She is thus cheated out of the very basis of her natural strength: if she has done so much, fettered, what might she not do if her limbs were free?" Hannah Thurston's face glowed: her eyes kindled, and her voice came sweet and strong with the intensity of a faith that *would* not allow itself to be shaken. She was wholly lost in her subject.

After a pause, Mrs. Blake quietly said: "Yes, if we had broad shoulders, and narrow hips, we could no doubt wield sledge-hammers, and quarry stone, and reef sails in a storm."

Again the same chill as Woodbury's conversation had sometimes invoked, came over Hannah Thurston's feelings. Here was the same dogged adherence to existing facts, she thought, the same lack of aspiration for a better order of things! The assertion, which she would have felt inclined to resent in a man, saddened her in a woman. The light faded from her face, and she said, mournfully: "Yes, the physical superiority of man gives him an advantage, by which our sex is overawed and held in subjection. But the rule of force cannot last forever. If woman would but assert her equality of intellect, and claim her share of the rights belonging to human intelligence, she would soon transform the world."

Mrs. Blake instantly interpreted the change in countenance and tone; it went far towards giving her the key to Hannah Thurston's nature. Dropping the particular question which had been started, she commenced anew. "When I lived in New York," said she, "I had many acquaintances among the artists, and what I learned of them and their lives taught me this lesson—that there can be no sadder mistake than to miscalculate one's powers. There is very little of the ideal and imaginative element in me, as you see, but I have learned its

nature from observation. I have never met any man who inspired me with so much pity as a painter whom I knew, who
might have produced admirable tavern-signs, but who persisted in giving to the world large historical pictures, which
were shocking to behold. No recognition came to the man,
for there was nothing to be recognized. If he had moderated
his ambition, he might at least have gained a living, but he
was ruined before he could be brought to perceive the truth,
and then died, I am sure, of a broken heart."

"And you mean," said Miss Thurston, slowly, " that I—
that we who advocate the just claims of our sex, are making
the same mistake."

"I mean," Mrs. Blake answered, "that you should be very
careful not to over-estimate the capacity of our sex by your
own, as an individual woman. *You* may be capable—under
certain conditions—of performing any of the special intellectual employments of Man, but to do so you must sacrifice
your destiny as a woman—you must seal up the wells from
which a woman draws her purest happiness."

"Why ?"

"Ah, my dear," said Mrs. Blake, tenderly, "if your hair
were as gray as mine, and you had two such creatures about
you as Josey and George yonder, you would not ask. There
are times when a woman has no independent life of her own
—when her judgment is wavering and obscured—when her
impulses are beyond her control. The business of the world
must go on, in its fixed order, whether she has her share in it
or not. Congresses cannot be adjourned nor trials postponed,
nor suffering patients neglected, to await her necessities. The
prime of a man's activity is the period of her subjection. She
must then begin her political career in the decline of her
faculties, when she will never be able to compete successfully
with man, in any occupation which he has followed from
youth."

Hannah Thurston felt that there must be truth in these
words. At least it was not for her, in her maiden ignorance,

to contradict them. But she was sure, nevertheless, that Mrs. Blake's statement was not sufficient to overthrow her theory of woman's equality. She reflected a moment before she spoke again, and her tone was less earnest and confident than usual.

"The statesmen and jurists, the clergymen, physicians, and men of science," she said, "comprise but a small number of the men. Could not our sex spare an equal number? Would not some of us sacrifice a part of our lives, if it were necessary?"

"And lose the peace and repose of domestic life, which consoles and supports the public life of man!" exclaimed Mrs. Blake. "It is not in *his* nature to make this sacrifice—still less is it in ours. You do not think what you are saying. There is no true woman but feels at her bosom the yearning for a baby's lips. The milk that is never sucked dries into a crust around her heart. There is no true woman but longs, in her secret soul, for a man's breast to lay her head on, a man's eyes to give her the one look which he gives to nobody else in the world!"

Hannah Thurston's eyes fell before those of Mrs. Blake. She painfully felt the warm flush that crept over neck, and cheek, and brow, betraying her secret, but betraying it, fortunately, to a noble and earnest-hearted woman. A silence ensued, which neither knew how to break.

"What are you plotting so seriously?" broke in Woodbury's voice, close behind them. "I must interrupt this *tête-à-tête*, Mrs. Blake. See what you are losing?"

They both rose and turned, in obedience to the movement of his hand. The sun had sunk so low that the shade of the western hill filled all the bed of the valley, and began to creep up the eastern side. A light blue film was gathering over the marsh at the head of the lake, where it divided into two lines, pointing up the creeks. But the patches of woodland on the East Atauga hill, the steep fields of tawny oat-stubble, and the fronts of white farm-houses and barns in the distance, were drowned in a bath of airy gold, slowly deepening into flame color as its tide-mark rose higher on the hills. Over Ptolemy a mountain of fire divided the forking valleys, which receded on either hand, southward, into dim depths of amethyst. Higher and higher crept the splendor, until it blazed like a fringe on the topmost forests and fields: then it suddenly went out and was transferred to a rack of broken cloud, overhead.

Mrs. Styles presently made her appearance, bonneted for the return to Ptolemy. Hannah Thurston was to accompany her. But as they drove homewards through the cool evening air, through the ripe odors of late-flowering grasses, and the golden-rods on the road-banks and the eupatoriums in the meadows, it was the passionate yearning of the woman, not the ambition of the man, which had entire possession of her heart.

CHAPTER XXVI.

IN WHICH A WEDDING TAKES PLACE.

"Do you know, Mr. Woodbury," said Mrs. Blake, the same evening, as they were all gathered together in the library, "that I have taken an immense liking to your strong-minded woman?"

"Indeed!" he remarked, with assumed indifference.

"Yes. I had a serious talk with her. I employed a moral probe, and what do you think I found?"

"What?" he repeated, turning towards her with an expression of keen interest.

"No, it would not be fair," tantalizingly answered Mrs. Blake, in her most deliberate tones. "I shall not betray any discoveries I have accidentally made. She is too earnest and genuine a nature to be disposed of with a pleasantry. I will only say this—as far as she is wrong—which, of course, is admitting that she is partly right, I, woman as I am, would undertake to convince her of it. A man, therefore, ought to be able to restore her to the true faith more easily. Yet you have been living at Lakeside nearly a year and have not succeeded."

"I have never tried, my friend," said Woodbury.

"Really?"

"Of course not. Why should I? She is relentless in her prejudices, even in those which spring from her limited knowledge of life. The only cure for such is in a wider experience. She cannot understand that a humane and liberal tolerance of all varieties of habit and opinion is compatible with sincerity of character. She would make every stream turn some kind of a mill, while I am willing to see one now and then dash

itself to pieces over the rocks, for the sake of the spray and
the rainbows. I confess, though, that I do not think this
moral rigidity is entirely natural to her; but the very fact that
she has slowly reasoned herself into it, and so intrenched and
defended herself against attack from all quarters, makes it so
much the more difficult for her to strike her flag. If you
were to approach her position disarmed and propose a truce,
she would look upon it as the stratagem of an enemy."

"No, no!" cried Mrs. Blake, shaking her head, with a mis-
chievous sparkle in her eyes; "that is not the way at all!
Don't you know that a strong woman can only be overcome
by superior strength? No white flags—no proposals of
truce—but go, armed to the teeth, and fire a train to the
mine which shall blow her fortress to atoms in a moment!"

"Bravo! What a commander is lost to the world in you!
But suppose I don't see any train to the mine?"

"Pshaw!" exclaimed Mrs. Blake, turning away in mock
contempt. "You know very well that there is but *one* kind
of moral gunpowder to be used in such cases. I am going to
drive into Ptolemy this afternoon with Mrs. Waldo, and I
shall make a call at the Thurston cottage. Will you go with
us?"

"Thank you, not to-day. Mr. Blake and I have arranged
to take a boat on the Lake and fish for pickerel. It is better
sport than firing trains of moral gunpowder."

The two ladies drove into Ptolemy as they had proposed.
Mrs. Blake made herself quite at home at the Cimmerian
Parsonage, where she recognized the Christus Consolator as
an old friend out of her own bedroom, and went into raptures
over Hannah Thurston's bouquet of grasses. She mentally
determined to procure from the donor a similar ornament for
her boudoir in St. Louis, and managed the matter, indeed,
with such skill that Miss Thurston innocently supposed the
offer to make and forward the bouquet came spontaneously
from herself.

To the Widow Thurston's cottage Mrs. Blake came like a

strong, refreshing breeze. In other households, her sharp, clear, detective nature might have uncomfortably blown away the drapery from many concealed infirmities, but here it encountered only naked truthfulness, and was welcome. She bowed down at once before the expression of past trials in the old woman's face, and her manner assumed a tenderness all the sweeter and more fascinating that it rarely came to the surface. She took Miss Dilworth's measure at a single glance, and the result, as she afterwards expressed it to Mrs. Waldo, was much more favorable than that lady had anticipated.

"He could not have a better housekeeper than she, just at present."

"Why, you astonish me!" Mrs. Waldo exclaimed; "why do you think so?"

"I have no particular reason for thinking so," Mrs. Blake answered; "it's a presentiment."

Mrs. Waldo turned away her eyes from Dobbin's ears (which she always watched with some anxiety, although the poor old beast had long since forgotten how to shy them back), and inspected her companion's face. It was entirely grave and serious. "Oh," she said at last, in a puzzled tone, "that's all?"

"Yes, and therefore you won't think it worth much. But my presentiments are generally correct: wait and see."

The Blakes remained over a Sunday, and went, as it was generally surmised they would, to the Cimmerian Church. The attendance was unusually large on that day, embracing, to the surprise of Mrs. Waldo, the Hamilton Bues and Miss Ruhaney Goodwin. On the entrance of the strangers into the church, a subdued rustling sound ran along the benches (pews were not allowed by the Cimmerians), and most of the heads turned stealthily towards the door. The immediate silence that followed had something of disappointment in it. There was nothing remarkable in the tall, keen-eyed lady in plain black silk, or the stout, shrewd-faced, gray-whiskered man who followed her. Miss Josephine's flat straw

hat and blue silk mantilla attracted much more attention
among the younger members of the congregation. After the
hymn had been given out, however, and the first bars of the
triumphant choral of "Wilmot" (according to the music-
books, but Carl Maria von Weber in the world of Art) were
heard, a new voice gradually took its place in the midst of
the accustomed and imperfectly according sounds, and very
soon assumed the right of a ruler, forcing the others to keep
step with it in the majestic movement of the choral. Not
remarkably sweet, but of astonishing strength and metal-
lic sonority, it pealed like a trumpet at the head of the ill-
disciplined four battalions of singers, and elevated them to a
new confidence in themselves.

The voice was Mrs. Blake's. She professed to be no singer,
for she knew her own deficiencies so well, that she never attempted to conceal them; but her voice had the one rare
element, in a woman, of power, and was therefore admirably
effective in a certain range of subjects. In society she rarely
sang any except Scotch songs, and of these especially such as
dated from the rebellion of 1745—those gloriously defiant
lays, breathing of the Highlands and the heather and bonnie
Prince Charlie, which cast an immortal poetic gleam over the
impotent attempt to restore a superannuated dynasty. Had
she lived in those days Mrs. Blake might have sung the slogan
to the gathering clans: as it was, these songs were the only
expression of the fine heroic capacity which was latent in her
nature. She enjoyed the singing fully as much as her auditors
the hearing, and, if the truth could be distinctly known, it is
quite probable that she had prompted Mr. Waldo in his selection of the hymn. Her participation in it threw the whole
Cimmerian congregation on her side, and the Hamilton Bues
privately expressed their belief that the clergyman had taken
an undue advantage of his opportunities as a guest at Lakeside, to instil his heretical ideas of baptism into the minds of
Mr. and Mrs. Blake. It transpired afterwards, however, that
the latter were Episcopalian, both by faith and inheritance.

The day at last arrived for the breaking up of the new household, to the great regret of all its members. Miss Josephine tore herself with difficulty from the library, only partially consoled by the present of "Undine" and "Sintraim." George wanted to stay with Bute and learn to trap musk-rats and snare rabbits. Mr. Waldo half sheathed his teeth with his insufficient lips and went back to his plain fare with a sigh of resignation. The ladies kissed each other, and Woodbury would assuredly have kissed them both if he had known how charitably they would have received the transgression. Bute was embarrassed beyond all his previous experience by the present of half a dozen silver tea-spoons which Mrs. Blake had bought in Ptolemy and presented to him through her boy George.

"You are going to begin housekeeping, I hear," said she, "and you must let George help you with the outfit."

Bute colored like a young girl. "They're wuth more'n the silver, comin' to us that-a-way," he said at last. "I'll tell Carrie, and we sha'n't never use 'em, without thinkin' o' you and George."

The farewells were said, and Lakeside relapsed into its accustomed quiet. The borrowed chambermaid was returned to the Ptolemy House, and the old Melinda alone remained in the kitchen, to prepare her incomparable corn-cake and broiled chicken. Bute was now able, with proper precautions, to walk about the farm and direct the necessary labor, without taking part in it. Woodbury resumed his former habit of horseback exercise, and visited some of his acquaintances in Ptolemy and the neighborhood, but the departure of his pleasant guests left a very perceptible void in his life. He had sufficient resources within himself to endure solitude, but he was made, like every healthily-constituted man, for society.

Thus a few days passed away, and Bute's convalescence began to take the hue of absolute health. He now visited Ptolemy every day or two, to watch the progress made in a

15

certain silver-gray dress, and to enjoy the exquisite novelty of
consulting Miss Dilworth about their future household ar
rangements. The latter sometimes, from long habit, reassumed
her former air of coquetry, but it was no longer tantalizing.
and an earnest word or look sufficed to check her. A charming humility took the place of her affected superiority, and
became her vastly better, as she had sense enough to discern.
Her ringlets had disappeared forever, and her eyelids gradually recovered strength for an open and steady glance. In
fact, her eyes were prettier than she had supposed. Their
pale beryl-tint deepened into brown at the edges, and when
the pupil expanded in a subdued light, they might almost have
been called hazel. In Spain they would have been sung as
" *ojos verdes*" by the poets. On the whole, Bute had chosen
more sensibly than we supposed, when we first made Miss
Dilworth's acquaintance.

The arrangements for the wedding were necessarily few and
simple. Woodbury first proposed that it should be solemnized
at Lakeside, but Mrs. Waldo urged, that, since her husband
was to officiate on the occasion, it would be better for many
reasons—one of which was Mrs. Babb's recent death—that it
should take place at the parsonage. Miss Dilworth was secretly bent on having a bridesmaid, who should, of course, be
Hannah Thurston, but was obliged to relinquish her project,
through the unexpected resistance which it encountered on
the part of Bute. "None of the fellows that I could ask to
stand up with me would do for *her*," said he.

" Why not Mr. Woodbury?" suggested Miss Carrie.

" He! Well—he'd do it in a minute if I was to ask him, but
I won't. Between you and me, Carrie, they can't bear each
other ; they're like cats and dogs."

" Bute! a'n't you ashamed?"

" What? O' tellin' the truth? No, nor a'n't likely to be.
See here, Carrie, why can't we let it alone? Mr. Waldo'll tie
us jist as tight, all the same, and when it's over you won't
know the difference."

"But—Bute," Miss Carrie persisted, "I think she expects it of me."

"She ha'n't set her heart on it, I'll be bound. I'll ask her. Miss Hannah!"

The two were in the open air, at the corner of the cottage nearest the garden. The window of the little sitting-room was open, and Bute's call brought Miss Thurston to it.

"Oh, Bute, don't!" pleaded Miss Dilworth, ready to cry, but he had already gone too far to stop. "Miss Hannah," said he, "we're talkin' about the weddin'. I'm thinkin' it'll be jist as well without waiters. Carrie'd like to have you for bridesmaid, and I'm sure I'd be glad of it, only, you know, you'd have to stand up with somebody on my side, and there's nobody I could ask but Mr. Max, and—and I'm afraid *that* wouldn't be agreeable, like, for either o' you."

"Bute!" cried Carrie, in real distress.

Bute, however, was too sure of the truth of what he had said to suspect that he could possibly give pain by uttering it. The first rude shock of his words over, Hannah Thurston felt greatly relieved. "You were right to tell me, Arbutus," said she; "for, although I should be quite willing, at another time, to do as Carrie wishes, no matter whom *you* might choose as your nearest friend, I think it best, at present, that there should be as little ceremony as possible. I will talk with you about it afterwards, Carrie." And she moved away from the window.

At length the important day arrived. Bute woke when the cocks crowed three o'clock, and found it impossible to get to sleep again. His new clothes (not made by Seth Wattles) were in the top drawer of the old bureau, and Melinda had laid some sprigs of lavender among them. He tried to imagine how he would look in them, how he would feel during the ceremony and afterwards, how curious it must be to have a wife of your own, and everybody know it. He pictured to himself his friends on the neighboring farms, saying: "How's your wife, Bute?" when they met, and then he thought of

Mother Forty, and what a pity that she had not lived long
enough to know Carrie Wilson—who, of course, would be a
very different creature from Carrie Dilworth; but he always
came back to the new clothes in the top bureau-drawer, and
the duty of the day that was beginning to dawn.   Then, he
heard Pat.'s voice among the cattle at the barn; then, a stirring in the kitchen under him, and presently the noise of the
coffee-mill—and still it was not light enough to shave!   More
slowly than ever before the sun rose; his toilet, which usually
lasted five minutes, took half an hour; he combed his hair in
three different ways, none of which was successful; and finally
went down to breakfast, feeling more awkward and uncomfortable than ever before in his life.

Woodbury shook hands with him and complimented him on
his appearance, after which he felt more composed.   The
preparations for the ride to Ptolemy, nevertheless, impressed
him with a certain solemnity, as if he were a culprit awaiting
execution or a corpse awaiting burial.   A feeling of helplessness came over him: the occasion seemed to have been
brought about, not so much by his own will as by an omnipo-
tent fate which had taken him at his word.   Presently Pat.
came up grinning, dressed in his Sunday suit, and announced:
"The hosses is ready, Misther Bute, and it'll be time we're
off."   After the ceremony Pat. was to drive the happy pair to
Tiberius, where they proposed spending a honeymoon of two
days with the bride's old aunt.   He wore a bright blue coat
with brass buttons, and Melinda had insisted on pinning a
piece of white ribbon on the left lappel, "Kase," as she remarked, "down Souf ole Missus always had 'um so."

Woodbury mounted his horse and rode off, in advance,
through the soft September morning.   At the parsonage he
found every thing in readiness.   Mrs. Waldo, sparkling with
satisfaction, rustled about in a dark-green silk (turned, and
with the spots carefully erased by camphene), vibrating incessantly between the little parlor where the ceremony was to
take place, and the bedroom up-stairs, where the bride was

being arrayed under the direction of Hannah Thurston.
Nothing, as she candidly confessed, enlisted her sympathies so
completely as a wedding, and it was the great inconvenience
of a small congregation that her husband had so few occasions
to officiate.

"Promise me, Mr. Woodbury," she said, as she finally
paused in her movements, from the impossibility of finding
any thing else to do, " that you will be married by nobody but
Mr. Waldo."

"I can safely promise that," he answered : " but pray don't
ask me to fix the time when it shall take place."

"If it depended on me, I would say to-morrow. Ah, there
is Bute ! How nicely he looks !" With these words she went
to the door and admitted him.

Bute's illness had bleached the tan and subdued the defiant
ruddiness of his skin.   In black broadcloth and the white silk
gloves (white kids, of the proper number, were not to be
found in Ptolemy) into which he had been unwillingly persuaded
to force his large hands, an air of semi-refinement overspread
the strong masculine expression of his face and body. His
hair, thinned by fever and closely cut, revealed the shape
of his well-balanced head, and the tender blue gleam in his
honest eyes made them positively beautiful.   Mrs. Waldo
expressed her approval of his appearance, without the least
reserve.

Soon afterwards, a rustling was heard on the stairs ; the
door opened, and Miss Carrie Dilworth entered the parlor with
blushing cheeks and downcast eyes, followed by Hannah
Thurston, in the white muslin dress and pearl-colored ribbons
which Woodbury so well remembered.   The bride was really
charming in her gray, silvery silk, and a light-green wreath
crowning her rippled hair.   Orange-blossoms were not to be
had in Ptolemy, and there were no white garden-flowers in
bloom except larkspurs, which of course were not to be
thought of.   Hannah Thurston, therefore, persuaded her to
content herself with a wreath of the myrtle-leaved box, as the

nearest approach to the conventional bridal diadem, and the
effect was simple and becoming.

Each of the parties was agreeably surprised at the other's
appearance. Bute, not a little embarrassed as to how he
should act, took Miss Dilworth's hand, and held it in his own,
deliberating whether or not it was expected that he should
kiss her then and there. Miss Dilworth, finding that he did
not let it go, boldly answered the pressure and clung to him
with a natural and touching air of dependence and reliance.
Nothing could have been more charming than the appearance
of the two, as they stood together in the centre of the little
room, he all man, she all woman, in the most sacred moment
of life. They expressed the sweetest relation of the sexes, he
yielding in his tenderness, she confiding in her trust. No
declaration of mutual rights, no suspicious measurement of
the words of the compact, no comparison of powers granted
with powers received, but a blind, unthinking, blissful, reciprocal self-bestowal. This expression in their attitude and their
faces did not escape Hannah Thurston's eye. It forced upon
her mind doubts which she would willingly have avoided, but
which she was only strong enough to postpone.

Pat. had already slipped into the room, and stood awkwardly
in a corner, holding his hat in both hands. The only other
stranger present was Miss Sophia Stevenson, who had kindly
assisted the bride in the preparation of her wardrobe, and who
differed from her sister spinster, Miss Ruhaney Goodwin, in
the fact that she was always more ready to smile than sigh.
All being assembled, Mr. Waldo came forward and performed
the simple but impressive ceremony, following it with an
earnest prayer. Miss Carrie lifted up her head and pronounced
the "I will" with courage, but during the prayer she bent it
again so that it partly rested against Bute's shoulder. When
the final "Amen!" was said, Bute very gently and solemnly
kissed his wife, and both were then heartily congratulated by
the clergyman, who succeeded in closing his lips sufficiently
to achieve the salute which an old friend might take without

blame. Then there were hearty greetings all round : the certificate of marriage was signed and given to the wife for safe-
keeping, as if its existence were more important to her than
to the husband; and finally Mrs. Waldo prepared what the
Hon. Zeno Harder would have called a " coe-lation." Woodbury had been thoughtful enough to send to the parsonage a
bottle or two of the old Dennison Madeira, rightly judging
that if Mrs. Babb had been alive, she would have desired it
for the reason that " *she*" would have done the same thing.
On this occasion all partook of the pernicious beverage except
Hannah Thurston, and even she was surprised to find but a
very mild condemnation in her feelings. The newly-wedded
couple beamed with a mixture of relief and contentment;
Carrie was delighted at hearing herself addressed as "Mrs.
Wilson," and even Bute found the words "your wife," after
the first ten minutes, not the least strange or embarrassing.

Presently, however, the wife slipped away to reappear in a
pink gingham and a plaid shawl. The horses were ready at the
door, and Pat. was grinning, whip in hand, as he stowed away
a small carpet-bag, containing mingled male and female articles,
under the seat. A few curious spectators waited on the plank
side-walk, opposite, but Bute, having gone through the grand
ordeal, now felt courage to face the world. As they took
their seats, and Pat. gave a preliminary flourish of his whip,
Mrs. Waldo produced an ancient slipper of her own, ready to
hurl it at the right moment. The horses started; the slipper
flew, whizzed between their heads and dropped into the bottom of the carriage.

" Don't look back !" she cried ; but there was no danger of
that. The road must have been very rough, for Bute was
obliged to put his arm around his wife's waist, and the dust
must have been very dense, for she had raised her handkerchief to her eyes.

" Will you take care of me to-day ?" said Woodbury to the
Waldos. " I shall not go back to Lakeside until evening."

CHAPTER XXVII.

DESCRIBING CERTAIN TROUBLES OF MR. WOODBURY.

WHEN they returned to Mrs. Waldo's parlor, the conversation naturally ran upon the ceremony which had just been solemnized and the two chief actors in it. There was but one judgment in regard to Bute, and his wife, also, had gained steadily in the good opinion of all ever since her betrothal beside the sick-bed.

"I had scarcely noticed her at all, before it happened," said Woodbury, "for she impressed me as a shallow, ridiculous, little creature—one of those unimportant persons who seem to have no other use than to fill up the cracks of society. But one little spark of affection gives light and color to the most insipid character. Who could have suspected the courage and earnestness of purpose which took her to Lakeside, when the fever had possession of the house? Since then I have heartily respected her. I have almost come to the conclusion that no amount of triumphant intellect is worth so much reverence as we spontaneously pay to any simple and genuine emotion, common to all human beings."

"I am glad to hear you say so!" exclaimed Mrs. Waldo. "Because then you will never fail in a proper respect to our sex. Hannah, do you remember, when you lent me Longfellow's Poems, how much I liked that line about 'affection?' I don't often quote, Mr. Woodbury, because I'm never sure of getting it exactly right; but it's this:

> "'What I esteem in woman
> Is her affection, not her intellect,'

"And I believe all men of sense do."

"I cannot indorse the sentiment, precisely in those words," Woodbury answered. "I esteem *both* affection and intellect in woman, but the first quality must be predominant. Its absence in man may now and then be tolerated, but to woman it is indispensable."

"Might not woman make the same requirement of man?" Hannah Thurston suddenly asked.

"Certainly," he answered, "and with full justice. That is one point wherein no one can dispute the equal rights of the sexes. But the capacity to love is a natural quality, and there is no true affection where the parties are continually measuring their feelings to see which loves the most. Bute and his wife will be perfectly happy so long as they are satisfied with the simple knowledge of giving and receiving."

"That's exactly my idea!" cried Mrs. Waldo, in great delight. "Husband, do you recollect the promises we made to each other on our wedding-day? There's never a wedding happens but I live it all over again. We wore Navarino bonnets then, and sleeves puffed out with bags of down, and you *would* lay your head on one of them, as we drove along, just like Bute and Carrie to-day, on our way to Father Waldo's. I said then that I'd never doubt you, never take back an atom of my trust in you—and I've kept my word from that day to this, and I'll keep it in this world and the next!"

Here Mrs. Waldo actually burst into tears, but smiled through them, like the sudden rush of a stream from which spray and rainbow are born at the same instant. "I am a silly old creature," she said: "don't mind me. Half of my heart has been in Carrie's breast all morning, and I knew I should make a fool of myself before the day was out."

"You're a good wife," said Mr. Waldo, patting her on the head as if she had been a little girl.

Hannah Thurston rose, with a wild, desperate feeling in her heart. A pitiless hand seemed to clutch and crush it in her bosom. So, she thought, some half-drowned sailor, floating on the plank of a wreck, must feel when the sail that promised

15*

him deliverance, tacks with the wind and slides out of his
horizon. The waves of life, which had hitherto only stirred
for her with the grand tidal pulse which moves in their depths,
now heaved threateningly and dashed their bitter salt in her
face at every turn. Whence came these ominous disturb-
ances? What was there in the happy marriage of two
ignorant and contented souls, to impress her with such vague,
intolerable foreboding? With the consciousness of her inability to suppress it came a feeling of angry shame at the
deceitfulness of her own strength. But perhaps—and this
was a gleam of hope—what she experienced was the disappointed protest of an instinct common to every human being, and which must therefore be felt and conquered by others
as well.

She stole a glance at Woodbury. His face was abstracted
but it expressed no signs of a struggle akin to her own. The
large brown eyes were veiled with the softness of a tender,
subdued longing; the full, regular lips, usually closed with all
the firmness and decision of his character in their line of
junction, were slightly parted, and the corners drooped with
an expression unutterably sad. Even over cheeks and brow,
a soft, warm breath seemed to have blown. He appeared to
her, suddenly, under a new aspect. She saw the misty shadow
which the passion of a man's heart casts before it, and turned
away her eyes in dread of a deeper revelation.

As she took leave of the Waldos, he also rose and gave her
his hand. The tender cloud of sadness had not entirely passed
from his face, and she avoided meeting his gaze. Whether it
was the memory of a lost, or the yearning for an absent love,
which had thus betrayed itself, she felt that it gave him the
temporary power to discern something of the emotion which
had mastered her. Had he done so, she never could have
met him again. To this man, of all men, she would continue
to assert her equality. Whatever weaknesses others might
discover, he at least should only know her in her strength.

The rest of the day passed rather tamely to Woodbury, and

as he rode down the valley during the sweet and solemn coming-on of the twilight, he was conscious of a sensation which he had not experienced since the days of his early trials in New York. He well remembered the melancholy Sabbath evenings, when he walked along the deserted North River piers, watching the purple hills of Staten Island deepen into gray as the sunset faded—when all that he saw, the quiet vessels, the cold bosom of the bay, the dull red houses on the shores and even the dusky heaven overhead, was hollow and unreal—when there was no joy in the Present and no promise in the Future. The same hopeless chill came over him now. All the life had gone out of the landscape; its colors were cold and raw, the balmy tonic odor of the golden-rods and meadow marigolds seemed only designed to conceal some rank odor of decay, and the white front of Lakeside greeted him with the threat of a prison rather than the welcome of a home.

On the evening of the second day Bute returned, as delighted to get back as if he had made a long journey. The light of his new life still lay upon him and gave its human transfiguration to his face. Woodbury studied the change, unconsciously to its subject, with a curiosity which he had never before acknowledged in similar cases. He saw the man's supreme content in the healthy clearness of his eye, in the light, elastic movement of his limbs, and in the lively satisfaction with which he projected plans of labor, in which he was to perform the principal part. He had taken a fresh interest in life, and was all courage and activity. In Carrie, on the other hand, the trustful reliance she had exhibited appeared now to have assumed the form of a willing and happy submission. She recognized the ascendency of sex, in her husband, without being able to discern its nature. Thus Bute's plain common-sense suddenly took the form of rough native intellect in her eyes, and confessing (to herself, only) her own deficiency, her affection was supported by the pride of her respect. Her old aunt had whispered to her, before they left Tiberius:

" *Carr*line, you're a lucky gal. Y'r husband's a proper nice
man as ever I see, and so well set-up, too. You'll both be
well to do, afore you die, if you take keer o' what you've got,
and lay up what it brings in. I shouldn't wonder if you was
able to send your boys to Collidge."

This suggestion opened a new field for her ambition. The
thought seemed still a scarcely permitted liberty, and she did
not dare to look at her face in the glass when it passed
through her mind ; but the mother's instinct, which lurks, unsuspected, in every maiden's breast, boldly asserted its existence to the young wife, and she began to dream of the
future reformers or legislators whom it might be her fortunate lot to cradle. Her nature, as we have already more
than once explained, was so shallow that it could not contain
more than one set of ideas at a time. The acquired affectations by which she had hitherto been swayed, being driven
from the field, her new faith in Bute possessed her wholly,
and she became natural by the easiest transition in the world.
Characters like hers rarely have justice done to them. Generally, they are passed over as too trivial for serious inspec·
tion : their follies and vanities are so evident and transparent,
that the *petit verre* is supposed to be empty, when at the
bottom may lie as potent a drop of the honey of human love,
as one can find in a whole huge ox-horn of mead.

Now began for Woodbury a life very different from what
he had anticipated. Bute took possession of his old steward-
ship with the joyous alacrity of a man doubly restored to the
world, and Mrs. Carrie Wilson fidgeted about from morning
until night, fearful lest some neglected duty in her department
might be seen. The careful respect which Woodbury exercised towards her gave her both courage and content in her
new position, while it preserved a certain distance between
them. She soon learned, not only to understand but to share
Bute's exalted opinion of his master. In this respect, Woodbury's natural tact was unerring. Without their knowledge,
he guided those who lived about him to the exact places,

which he desired them to fill. In any European household such matters would have settled themselves without trouble; but in America, where the vote of the hired neutralizes that of the hirer, and both have an equal chance of reaching the Presidential chair—where the cook and chambermaid may happen to wear more costly bonnets than their mistress, and to have a livelier interest in the current fashions, it requires no little skill to harmonize the opposite features of absolute equality and actual subjection. Too great a familiarity, according to the old proverb, breeds contempt; too strict an assertion of the relative positions, breeds rebellion.

The man of true cultivation, who may fraternize at will with the humblest and rudest of the human race, reserves, nevertheless, the liberty of selecting his domestic associates. Woodbury insisted on retaining his independence to this extent, not from an assumption of superiority, but from a resistance to the dictation of the uncultivated in every thing that concerned his habits of life. He would not have hesitated to partake of a meal in old Melinda's cottage, but it was always a repugnant sensation to him, on visiting the Merryfields, when an Irish laborer from the field came in his shirt-sleeves, or a strapping mulatto woman, sweating from the kitchen fire, to take their places at the tea-table. Bute's position was above that of a common laborer, and Woodbury, whose long Indian life had not accustomed him to prefer lonely to social meals, was glad to have the company of his wedded assistants at breakfast and dinner, and this became the ordinary habit; but he was careful to preserve a margin sufficient for his own freedom and convenience. Carrie, though making occasional mistakes, brought so much good-will to the work, that the housekeeping went on smoothly enough to a bachelor's eyes. If Mrs. Blake's favorable judgment had reference to this aspect of the case, she was sufficiently near the truth, but in another respect she certainly made a great mistake.

It was some days before Woodbury would confess to himself the disturbance which the new household, though so conveniently regulated, occasioned him. The sight of Bute's clear morning face, the stealthy glance of delight with which he followed the movements of his beaming little wife, as she prepared the breakfast-table, the eager and absurd manœuvres which she perpetrated to meet him for just *one* second (long enough for the purpose), outside the kitchen-door as he returned from the field—all these things singularly annoyed Woodbury. The two were not openly demonstrative in their nuptial content, but it was constantly around them like an atmosphere. A thousand tokens, so minute that alone they meant nothing, combined to express the eternal joy which man possesses in woman, and woman in man. It pervaded the mansion of Lakeside from top to bottom, like one of those powerful scents which cling to the very walls and cannot be washed out. When he endeavored to avoid seeing it or surmising its existence, in one way, it presented itself to him in another. When, as it sometimes happened, either of the parties became conscious that he or she had betrayed a little too much tenderness, the simulated indifference, the unnatural gravity which followed, made the bright features of their new world all the more painfully distinct by the visible wall which it built up, temporarily, between him and them. He was isolated in a way which left him no power of protest. They were happy, and his human sympathy forbade him to resent it; they were ignorant and uncultivated, in comparison to himself, and his pride could give him no support; they were sincere, and his own sincerity of character was called upon to recognize it; their bond was sacred, and demanded his reverence. Why, then, should he be disturbed by that which enlisted all his better qualities, and peremptorily checked the exercise of the opposite? Why, against all common-sense, all gentle instincts, all recognition of the loftiest human duty, should he in this new Paradise of Love, be the envious serpent rather than the protecting angel?

The feeling was clearly there, whatever might be its explanation. There were times when he sought to reason it away as the imaginary jealousy of a new landed proprietor, who presents to himself the idea of ownership in every possible form in order to enjoy it the more thoroughly. Lakeside was his, to the smallest stone inside his boundary fence, and the mossiest shingle on the barn-roof; but the old house —the vital heart of the property—now belonged more to others than to himself. The dead had signed away their interest in its warmth and shelter, but it was haunted in every chamber by the ghosts of the living. The new-made husband and wife filled it with a feeling of home, in which he had no part. They had usurped his right, and stolen the comfort which ought to belong to him alone. It was *their* house, and he the tenant. As he rode down the valley, in the evenings, and from the bridge over Roaring Brook glanced across the meadows to the sunny knoll, the love, which was not his own, looked at him from the windows glimmering in the sunset and seemed to say: "You would not ask me to be your guest, but I am here in spite of you!"

Woodbury, however, though his nature was softened by the charm of a healthy sentiment, was not usually imaginative. He was not the man to endure, for any length of time, a mental or moral unrest, without attempting to solve it. His natural powers of perception, his correct instincts, his calm judgment, and his acquired knowledge of life, enabled him to interpret himself as well as others. He never shrank from any revelation which his own heart might make to him. If a wound smarted, he thrust the probe to the bottom with a steady hand. The pain was none the less, afterwards, perhaps, but he could estimate when it would heal. He possessed, moreover, the virtue, so often mistaken for egotism, of revering in himself the aspirations, the sacrifices, and the sanctities which he revered in other men. Understanding, correctly, his nature as a man, his perceptions were not easily confused. There are persons whose moral nature is permanently unhinged by the least license: there are others who may be led, by circumstance, into far graver aberrations, and then swing back, without effort, to their former integrity. He belonged to the latter class.

It was not long, therefore, before he had surveyed the whole ground of his disturbance. Sitting, late into the night, in his library, he would lay down his book beside the joss-stick, which smouldered away into a rod of white ashes in its boat, and quietly deliberate upon his position. He recalled every sensation of annoyance or impatience, not disguising its injustice or concealing from himself its inherent selfishness, while on the other hand he admitted the powerful source from which it sprang. He laid no particular blame to his nature, from the fact that it obeyed a universal law, and deceived himself by no promise of resistance. Half the distress of the race is caused by their fighting battles which can never be decided. Woodbury's knowledge simply taught him how to conceal his trouble, and that was all he desired. He knew that the ghost which had entered Lakeside must stay there until he should bring another ghost to dislodge it.

Where was the sweet phantom to be found? If, in some impatient moment, he almost envied Bute the possession of the attached, confiding, insipid creature, in whom the former was so unspeakably content, his good sense told him, the next, that the mere capacity to love was not enough for the needs of a life. That which is the consecration of marriage does not alone constitute marriage. Of all the women whom he knew, but one could offer him the true reciprocal gifts. Towards her, he acknowledged himself to be drawn by an interest much stronger than that of intellect—an interest which might grow, if he allowed it, into love. The more he saw or learned of this woman, the more admirably pure and noble his heart acknowledged her to be. He had come to look upon her errors with a gentle pity, which taught him to avoid assailing them, whenever the assault might give her pain. Was the hard, exacting manner in which she claimed delusive rights—not indeed, specially for herself, but for all her sex—the result of her position as a champion of those rights, or was it an inte gral part of herself? This was the one important question which it behooved him to solve. To what extent was the false nature superimposed upon the true woman beneath it?

Supposing, even, that he should come to love her, and, improbable as it might seem, should awaken an answering love in her heart, would she unite her fate, *unconditionally*, to his? Would she not demand, in advance, security for some unheard-of domestic liberty, as a partial compensation for the legal rights which were still withheld? One of her fellow-championesses had recently married, and had insisted on retaining her maiden name. He had read, in the newspapers, a contract drawn up and signed by the two, which had disgusted him by its cold business character. He shuddered as the idea of Hannah Thurston presenting a similar contract for his signature, crossed his mind. "No!" he cried, starting up: "it is incredible!" Nothing in all his intercourse with her suggested such a suspicion. Even in the grave dignity of her manner she was entirely woman. The occasional harshness of judgment or strength of prejudice which repelled him, were faults, indeed, but faults that would melt away in the light of a better knowledge of herself. She was at present in a position of fancied antagonism, perhaps not wholly by her own action. The few men who agreed with her gave her false ideas of their own sex: the others whom she knew misunderstood and misrepresented her. She thus stood alone, bearing the burden of aspirations, which, however extravagant, were splendidly earnest and unselfish.

Mrs. Blake's words came back to Woodbury's memory and awakened a vague confidence in his own hopes. She was too clear-eyed a woman to be easily mistaken in regard to one of her sex. Her bantering proposition might have been intended to convey a serious counsel. "A strong woman can only be overcome by superior strength." But how should this strength (supposing he possessed it) be exercised? Should he crush her masculine claims under a weight of argument? Impossible: if she were to be convinced at all, it must be by the knowledge that comes through love. There was another form of strength, he thought—a conquering magnetism of presence, a force of longing which supplants will, a warmth of passion which disarms resistance—but such strength, again, is simply Love, and *he* must love before he could exercise it. The question, therefore, was at last narrowed to this : should he cherish the interest he already felt until it grew to the passion he prefigured, and leave to fate its return, free as became a woman or fettered with suspicious provisions?

This, however, was a question not so easy to decide. Were he sure of exciting a reciprocal interest, the venture, he felt, would be justified to his own heart; but nothing in her manner led him to suspect that she more than tolerated him—in distinction to her former hostile attitude—and there is no man of gentle nature but shrinks from the possibility of a failure. "Ah," said he, "I am not so young as I thought. A young man would not stop to consider, and doubt, and weigh probabilities. If I fail, my secret is in sacred keeping; if I win, I must win every thing. Am I not trying to keep up a youthful faculty of self-illusion which is lost forever, by demanding an ideal perfection in woman? No, no! I must cease to cheat myself: I must not demand a warmer flame than I can give."

Sometimes he attempted to thrust the subject from his mind. The deliberations in which he had indulged seemed to him cold, material, and unworthy the sanction of love. They had the effect, however, of making Hannah Thurston's image an abiding guest in his thoughts, and the very familiarity with his own doubts rendered them less formidable than at first. A life crowned with the bliss he passionately desired, might reward the trial. If it failed, his future could not be more barren and lonely than it now loomed before him : how barren, how lonely, every sight of Bute's face constantly resuggested.

The end of it all was a determination to seek Hannah Thurston's society—to court a friendly intimacy, in which he should not allow his heart to be compromised. So far he might go with safety to himself, and in no case, according to his views, could there be danger to her. His acquaintance with the widow, which had been kept up by an occasional brief visit, and the present condition of the latter's health, gave him all the opportunity he needed. The Catawba grapes were already ripening on the trellises at Lakeside, and he would take the earliest bunches to the widow's cottage.

The impression, in Ptolemy society, of a strong antagonism between himself and Hannah Thurston, was very general. Even Mrs. Waldo, whose opportunities of seeing both were best of all, fancied that their more cordial demeanor towards each other, in their later interviews, was only a tacitly understood armistice. Woodbury was aware of this impression, and determined not to contradict it for the present.

Thus, tormented from without and within, impelled by an outcry of his nature that would not be silenced, without consciousness of love, he took the first step, knowing that it might lead him to love a woman whose ideas were repugnant to all his dreams of marriage and of domestic peace.

CHAPTER XXVIII.

IN WHICH HANNAH THURSTON, ALSO, HAS HER TROUBLES.

WHEN Woodbury made his first appearance at the cottage, the Widow Thurston, who had not seen him since his return from the Lakes, frankly expressed her pleasure in his society. It was one of her favorable days, and she was sitting in her well-cushioned rocking-chair, with her feet upon a stool. She had grown frightfully thin and pale during the summer, but the lines of physical pain had almost entirely passed away from her face. Her expression denoted great weakness and languor. The calm, resigned spirit which reigned in her eyes was only troubled, at times, when they rested on her daughter. She had concealed from the latter, as much as possible, the swiftness with which her vital force was diminishing, lest she should increase the care and anxiety which was beginning to tell upon her health. She knew that the end was not far off: she could measure its approach, and she acknowledged in her heart how welcome it would be, but for her daughter's sake.

"It's very kind of thee to come, Friend Woodbury," said she. "I've been expecting thee before."

"I ought to have come sooner," said he, "but there have been changes at Lakeside."

"Yes, I know. The two guests that will not be kept out have come to thy home, as they come to the homes of others. We must be ready for either. The Lord sends them both."

"Yes," said Woodbury, with a sigh, "but one of them is long in coming to me." The sweet serenity and truth of the old woman's words evoked a true reply. All that she said came from a heart too sincere for disguise, and spoke to his undisguised self. There would have been something approaching to sacrilege in an equivocal answer.

She looked at him with a sad, serious inquiry in her glance. "I see thee's not hasty to open thy doors," she said, at last, "and it's well. There's always a blessing in store for them that wait. I pray that it may come to thee in the Lord's good time."

"Amen!" he exclaimed, earnestly. An irresistible impulse, the next moment, led him to look at Hannah Thurston. She was setting in order the plants on the little flower-stand before the window, and her face was turned away from him, but there was an indefinable intentness in her attitude which told him that no word had escaped her ears.

Presently she seated herself, and took part in the conversation, which turned mainly upon Bute and his wife. The light from the south window fell upon her face, and Woodbury noticed that it had grown somewhat thinner and wore a weary, anxious expression. A pale violet shade had settled under the dark-gray eyes and the long lashes drooped their fringes. No latent defiance lurked in her features: her manner was grave, almost to sadness, and in her voice there was a gentle languor, like that which follows mental exhaustion.

In all their previous interviews, Woodbury had never been able entirely to banish from his mind the consciousness of her exceptional position, as a woman. It had tinged, without his having suspected the fact, his demeanor towards her. Something of the asserted independence of man to man had modified the deferential gentleness of man to woman. She had, perhaps, felt this without being able to define it, for, though he had extorted her profound respect he had awakened in her a disposition scarcely warmer than she gave to abstract qualities. Now, however, she presented herself to him under a different aspect. He forgot her masculine aspirations, seeing in her only the faithful, anxious daughter, over whom the shadow of her approaching loss deepened from day to day. The former chill of his presence did not return, but in its place a subtle warmth seemed to radiate from him. Before, his words had excited her intellect: now, they addressed themselves to her feelings. As the conversation advanced, she recovered her usual animation, yet still preserved the purely feminine character which he had addressed in her. The positions which they had previously occupied were temporarily forgotten, and at parting each vaguely felt the existence of unsuspected qualities in the other.

During this first visit, Hannah Thurston indulged without reserve, in the satisfaction which it gave to her. She always found it far more agreeable to like than to dislike. Woodbury's lack of that enthusiasm which in her soul was an ever burning and mounting fire—his cold, dispassionate power of judgment—his tolerance of what she considered perverted habits of the most reprehensible character, and his indifference to those wants and wrongs of the race which continually appealed to the Reformer's aid, had at first given her the impression that the basis of his character was hard and selfish. She had since modified this view, granting him the high attributes of truth and charity; she had witnessed the manifestation of his physical and moral courage; but his individuality still preserved a cold, statuesque beauty. His mastery over himself, she supposed, extended to his intellectual passions and his affections. He would only be swayed by them so far as seemed to him rational and convenient.

His words to her mother recalled to her mind, she knew not why, the description of her own father's death. It was possible that an equal capacity for passion might here again be hidden under a cold, immovable manner. She had sounded, tolerably well, the natures of the men of whom she had seen most, during the past six or eight years, and had found that their own unreserved protestations of feeling were the measure of their capacity to feel. There was no necessity, indeed, to throw a plummet into their streams, for they had egotistically set up their own Nilometers, and the depth of the current was indicated at the surface. She began to suspect, now, that she had been mistaken in judging Woodbury by the same test. The thought, welcome as it was from a broad, humane point of view, nevertheless almost involved a personal humiliation. Her strong sense of justice commanded her to rectify the mistake, while her recognition of it weakened her faith in herself.

In a few days Woodbury came again, and as before, on an errand of kindness to her mother. She saw that his visits gave pleasure to the latter, and for that reason alone it was her duty to desire them, but on this occasion she detected an independent pleasure of her own at his appearance. A certain friendly familiarity seemed to be already established between them. She had been drawn into it, she scarcely knew how, and could not now withdraw, yet the consciousness of it began to agitate her in a singular way. A new power came from Woodbury's presence, surrounded and assailed her. It was not the chill of his unexcitable intellect, stinging her into a half-indignant resistance. It was a warm, seductive, indefinable magnetism, which inspired her with a feeling very much like terror. Its weight lay upon her for hours after he had gone. Whatever it was, its source, she feared, must lie in herself; he seemed utterly unconscious of any design to produce a particular impression upon her. His manner was as frank and natural as ever : he conversed about the books which he or she had recently read, or on subjects of general interest, addressing much of his discourse to her mother rather than herself. She noticed, indeed, that he made no reference to the one question on which they differed so radically ; but a little reflection showed her that he had in no former case commenced the discussion, nor had he ever been inclined to prolong it when started.

Their talk turned for a while on the poets. Hannah Thurston had but slight acquaintance with Tennyson, who was Woodbury's favorite among living English authors, and he promised to bring her the book. He repeated the stanzas descriptive of Jephtha's Daughter, in the "Dream of Fair

Women," the majestic rhythm and superb Hebrew spirit of which not only charmed her, but her mother also. The old woman had a natural, though very uncultivated taste for poetry. She enjoyed nothing which was purely imaginative : verse, for her, must have a devotional, or at least an ethical character. In rhythm, also her appreciation was limited. She delighted most in the stately march of the heroic measure, and next to that, in the impetuous rush of the dactylic. In youth her favorite poems had been the " Davidis" of Thomas Elwood, Pope's " Essay on Man," and the lamenting sing-song of Refine Weeks, a Nantucket poet, whom history has forgotten. The greater part of these works she knew by heart, and would often repeat in a monotonous chant, resembling that in which she had formerly preached. Hannah, however, had of late years somewhat improved her mother's taste by the careful selection of poetry of a better character, especially Milton's " Christmas Hymn," and the works of Thomson and Cowper.

Woodbury returned the very next day, bringing the promised volumes. He was about to leave immediately, but the widow insisted on his remaining.

" Do sit down a while, won't thee ?" said she. " I wish thee would read me something else : I like to hear thy voice."

Woodbury could not refuse to comply. He sat down, turned over the leaves of the first volume, and finally selected the lovely idyll of " Dora," which he read with a pure, distinct enunciation. Hannah Thurston, busy with her sewing at a little stand near the eastern window, listened intently. At the close she turned towards him with softened eyes, and exclaimed : " How simple ! how beautiful !"

" I'm greatly obliged to thee, Maxwell," said the widow, addressing Woodbury for the first time by his familiar name. " It is always pleasant," she added, smiling, " to an old woman, to receive a kindness from a young man."

" But it ought to be the young man's pleasure, as it is his duty, to give it," he answered. " I am glad that you like my favorite author. I have brought along 'The Princess,' also, Miss Thurston : you have certainly heard of it ?"

"Oh yes," said she, "I saw several critical notices of it when it was first published, and have always wished to read it."

"It gives a poetical view of a subject we have sometimes discussed," he added playfully, "and I am not quite sure that you will be satisfied with the close. It should not be read, however, as a serious argument on either side. Tennyson, I suspect, chose the subject for its picturesque effects, rather than from any intentional moral purpose. I confess I think he is right. We may find sermons in poems as we find them in stones, but one should be as unconscious of the fact as the other. It seems to me that all poetry which the author designs, in advance, to be excessively moral or pious, is more or less a failure."

"Mr. Woodbury! Do you really think so?" exclaimed Hannah Thurston, in surprise.

"Yes; but the idea is not original with me. I picked it up somewhere, and finding it true, adopted it as my own. There was a fanciful illustration, if I recollect rightly—that poetry is the blossom of Literature, not the fruit; therefore that while it suggests the fruit—while its very odor foretells the future flavor—it must be content to be a blossom and nothing more. The meaning was this: that a moral may *breathe* through a poem from beginning to end, but must not be plumply expressed. I don't know the laws which govern the minds of poets, but I know when they give me most pleasure. Apply the test to yourself: I shall be interested to know the result. Here, for instance, is 'The Princess,' which, if it has a particular moral, has one which you may possibly reject, but I am sure your enjoyment of pure poetry will not thereby be lessened."

"I shall certainly read the book with all the more interest from what you have said," she frankly replied. "You have very much more literary cultivation than I, and perhaps it is

16

presumptuous in me to dispute your opinion; but my nature leads me to honor an earnest feeling for truth and humanity, even when its expression is not in accordance with literary laws."

"I honor such a feeling also, whenever it is genuine, however expressed," Woodbury answered, "but I make a distinction between the feeling and the expression. In other words, the cook may have an admirable character, and yet the roast may be spoiled. Pollok is considered orthodox and Byron heretical, but I am sure you prefer the 'Hebrew Melodies' to the "Course of Time.'"

"Hannah, I guess thee'd better read the book first," said the widow, who did not perceive how the conversation had drifted away from its subject. "It is all the better, perhaps, if our friend differs a little from thee. When we agree in every thing, we don't learn much from one another."

"You are quite right, Friend Thurston," said Woodbury, rising. "I should be mistaken in your daughter if she accepted any opinion of mine, without first satisfying her own mind of its truth. Good-by!"

He took the widow's hand with a courteous respect, and then extended his own to Hannah. Hers he held gently for a moment while he said: "Remember, I shall want to know what impression the poem makes on your mind. Will you tell me?"

"Thank you. I will tell you," she said.

Strange to say, the boldest eulogiums which had ever reached Hannah Thurston's ears, never came to them with so sweet a welcome as Woodbury's parting compliment. Nay, it was scarcely a compliment at all; it was a simple recognition of that earnest seeking for truth which she never hesitated to claim for herself. Perhaps it was his supposed hostile attitude which gave the words their value, for our enemies always have us at a disadvantage when they begin to praise us. Politicians go into obscurity, and statesmen fall from their high places, ruined, not by the assaults but by the flatteries of the opposite party.

She could no longer consider Woodbury in the light of an enemy. His presence, his words, his self-possessed manner failed to excite the old antagonism, which always marred her intellectual pleasure in his society. One by one the discordant elements in her own nature seemed to be withdrawn, or rather, she feared, were *benumbed* by some new power which he was beginning to manifest. She found, with dismay, that instead of seeking, as formerly, for weapons to combat his views, her mind rather inclined to the discovery of reasons for agreeing with them. It mattered little, perhaps, which course she adopted, so long as the result was Truth; but the fact that she recognized the change as agreeable gave her uneasiness. It might be the commencement of a process of mental subjection—the first meshes of a net of crafty reasoning, designed to ensnare her judgment and lead her away from the high aims she prized. Then, on the other hand, she reflected that such a process presupposed intention on Woodbury's part, and how could she reconcile it with his manly honesty, his open integrity of character? Thus, the more enjoyment his visits gave her while they lasted, the greater the disturbance which they left behind.

That new and indescribable effluence which his presence gave forth not only continued, but seemed to increase in power. Sometimes it affected her with a singular mixture of fascination and terror, creating a physical restlessness which it was almost impossible to subdue. An oppressive weight lay upon her breast; her hands burned, and the nerves in every limb trembled with a strange impulse to start up and fly. When, at night, in the seclusion of her chamber, she recalled this condition, her cheeks grew hot with angry shame of herself, and she clenched her hands with the determination to resist the return of such weakness. But even as she did so, she felt that her power of will had undergone a change. An insidious, corrosive doubt seemed to have crept over the foundations of her mental life: the forms of faith, once firm and fair as Ionic pillars under the cloudless heaven, rocked and tottered as if with the first me

nacing throes of an earthquake. When she recalled her past
labors for the sacred cause of Woman, a mocking demon now
and then whispered to her that even in good there were the
seeds of harm, and that she had estimated, in vanity, the fruits
of her ministry. "God give me strength!" she whispered—
"strength to conquer doubt, strength to keep the truth for
which I have lived and which must soon be my only life,
strength to rise out of a shameful weakness which I cannot
understand!"

Then, ere she slept, a hope to which she desperately clung,
came to smooth her uneasy pillow. Her own future life must
differ from her present. The hour was not far off, she knew,
when her quiet years in the cottage must come to an end.
She could not shut her eyes to the fact that her mother's time
on earth was short; and short as it was, she would not cloud
it by anxiety for the lonely existence beyond it. She resolutely thrust her own future from her mind, but it was nevertheless
always present in a vague, hovering form. The uncertainty of
her fate, she now thought,—the dread anticipation of coming
sorrow—had shaken and unnerved her. No doubt her old,
steadfast self-reliance and self-confidence would assert themselves, after the period of trial had been passed. She must only
have patience, for the doubts which she could not now answer
would then surely be solved. With this consolation at her
heart—with a determination to possess *patience*, which she
found much more easy than the attempt to possess herself of
will, she would close her aching eyes and court the refreshing
oblivion of sleep.

But sleep did not always come at her call. That idea of
the sad, solitary future, so near at hand, would not be exor-
cised. If she repelled it, it came back again in company with
a still more terrible ghost of the Past—her early but now
hopeless dream of love. When she tried to call that dream a
delusion, all the forces of her nature gave her the lie—all the
fibres of her heart, trembling in divinest harmony under the
ouch of the tormenting angel, betrayed her, despairingly, to

her own self. The crown of independence which she had won bruised her brows; the throne which she claimed was carved of ice; the hands of her sister women, toiling in the same path, were grateful in their help, but no positive pulse of strength throbbed from them to her heart. The arm which alone could stay her must have firmer muscle than a woman's; it must uphold as well as clasp. Why did Heaven give her the dream when it must be forever vain? Where was the man at the same time tender enough to love, strong enough to protect and assist, and just enough to acknowledge the equal rights of woman? Alas! nowhere in the world. She could not figure to herself his features; he was a far-off unattainable idea, only; but a secret whisper, deep in the sacredest shrine of her soul, told her that if he indeed existed, if he should find his way to her, if the pillow under her cheek were his breast, if his arms held her fast in the happy subjection of love—but no, the picture was not to be endured. It was a bliss, more terrible in its hopelessness, than the most awful . grief in its certainty. She shuddered and clasped her hands crushingly together, as with the strength of desperation, she drove it from her bosom.

Had her life been less secluded, the traces of her internal struggles must have been detected by others. Her mother, indeed, noticed an unusual restlessness in her manner, but attributed it to care for her own condition. With the exception of Mrs. Waldo, they saw but few persons habitually. Miss Sophia Stevenson or even Mrs. Lemuel Styles occasionally called, and the widow always made use of these occasions to persuade Hannah to restore herself by a walk in the open air. When the former found that their visits were thus put to good service, they benevolently agreed to come regularly. The relief she thus obtained, in a double sense, cheered and invigorated Hannah Thurston. Her favorite walk, out the Mulligansville road, to the meadows of East Atauga Creek, took her in a quarter of an hour from the primly fenced lots and stiff houses of the village to the blossoming banks of the winding stream, to the sweet breath of the scented grass, and the tangled thickets of alder, over which bittersweet and clematis ran riot and strove for the monopoly of support. Here, all her vague mental troubles died away like the memory of an oppressive dream; she drew resignation from every aspect of Nature, and confidence in herself from the crowding associations of the Past which the landscape inspired.

Mrs. Waldo, of course, soon became aware of Woodbury's frequent visits. He had made no secret of them, as he always called at the Parsonage at the same time, and she had shared equally in the ripening vintage of Lakeside. But he had spoken much more of the Widow Thurston than of her daughter, and the former had been equally free in expressing her pleasure at his visits, so that Mrs. Waldo never doubted the continuance of the old antagonism between Hannah and Woodbury. Their reciprocal silence in relation to each other confirmed her in this supposition. She was sincerely vexed at a dislike which seemed not only unreasonable, but unnatural, and grew so impatient at the delayed conciliation that she finally spoke her mind on the subject.

"Well, Hannah," she said, one day, when Woodbury's name had been incidentally mentioned, "I really think it is time that you and he should practise a little charity towards each other. I've been waiting, and waiting, to see your prejudices begin to wear away, now that you know him better. You can't think how it worries me that two of my best friends, who are so right and sensible in all other acts of their lives, should be so stubbornly set against each other."

"Prejudices? Does _he_ think I am stubbornly set against him?" Hannah Thurston cried, the warm color mounting into her face.

"Not he! He says nothing about you, and that's the worst of it. You say nothing about him, either. But anybody can see it. There, I've vexed you, and I suppose I ought not to have opened my mouth, but I love you so dearly, Hannah—I love him, too, as a dear friend—and I can't for the life of me see why you are blind to the truth and goodness in each other that I see in both of you."

Here Mrs. Waldo bent over her and kissed her cheek as a mother might have done. The color faded from Hannah Thurston's face, as she answered: "I know you are a dear, good friend, and as such you cannot vex me. I do not know whether you have mistaken Mr. Woodbury's feelings: you certainly have mistaken mine. I did his character, at first, injustice, I will confess. Perhaps I may have had a prejudice against him, but I am not aware that I have one now. I honor him as a noble-minded, just, and unselfish man. We have different views of life, but in this respect he has taught me, by his tolerance towards me, to be at least equally tolerant towards him."

"You make me happy!" cried Mrs. Waldo, in unfeigned delight; but the next instant she added, with a sigh: "But, in spite of all, you don't seem to me like friends."

This explanation added another trouble to Hannah Thurston's mind. It was very possible that Woodbury suspected her of cherishing an unfriendly prejudice against him. She had assuredly given him cause for such a suspicion, and if the one woman in Ptolemy, who, after her mother, knew her best, had received this impression, it would not be strange if he shared it. In such case, what gentle consideration, what forgiving kindness had he not exhibited towards her? What other man of her acquaintance would have acted with the same magnanimity? Was it not her duty to undeceive him—not by words, but by meeting him frankly and gratefully—by exhibiting to him, in some indirect way, her confidence in his nobility of character?

Thus, every thing conspired to make him the centre of her thoughts, and the more she struggled to regain her freedom, the more helplessly she entangled herself in the web which his presence had spun around her.

CHAPTER XXIX.

IN WHICH A CRISIS APPROACHES.

ONE cannot play with fire without burning one's fingers. Woodbury supposed that he was pursuing an experiment, which might at any moment be relinquished, long after a deep and irresistible interest in its object had taken full possession of him.   Seeing Hannah Thurston only as a daughter—conversing with her only as a woman—her other character ceased to be habitually present to his mind.   After a few visits, the question which he asked himself was not: " Will I be able to love her ?" but: " Will I be able to make her love me ?"   Of his own ability to answer the former question he was entirely satisfied, though he steadily denied to himself the present existence of passion.   He acknowledged that her attraction for him had greatly strengthened—that he detected a new pleasure in her society—that she was not unfemininely cold and hard, as he had feared, but at least gentle and tender: yet, with all this knowledge, there came no passionate, perturbing thrill to his heart, such as once had heralded the approach of love. She had now a permanent place in his thoughts, it is true: he could scarcely have shut her out, if he had wished : and all the new knowledge which he had acquired prompted him to stake his rising hopes upon one courageous throw, and trust the future, if he gained it, to the deeper and truer development of her nature which would follow.

At the next visit which he paid to the cottage after Mrs. Waldo's half-reproachful complaint, the friendly warmth with which Hannah Thurston received him sent a delicious throb of sweetness to his heart. Poor Hannah ! In her anxiety to be just, she had totally forgotten what her treatment of Seth Wattles, from a similar impulse, had brought upon her. She only saw, in Woodbury's face, the grateful recognition of her manner towards him, and her conscience became quiet at once. The key-note struck at greeting gave its character to the interview, which Woodbury prolonged much beyond his usual habit. He had never been so attractive, but at the same time, his presence had never before caused her such vague alarm. All the cold indifference, which she had once imagined to be his predominant characteristic, had melted like a snow-wreath in the sunshine: a soft, warm, pliant grace diffused itself over his features and form, and a happy under-current of feeling made itself heard in his lightest words. He drew her genuine self to the light, before she suspected how much she had allowed him to see: she, who had resolved that he should only know her in her strength, had made a voluntary confession of her weakness!

Hannah Thurston was proud as she was pure, and this weird and dangerous power in the man, wounded as well as disturbed her. She felt sure that he exercised it unconsciously, and therefore he was not to be blamed; but it assailed her individual freedom—her coveted independence of other minds—none the less. It was weakness to shrink from the encounter: it was humiliation to acknowledge, as she must, that her powers of resistance diminished with each attack.

Woodbury rode home that evening very slowly. For the first time since Bute's marriage, as he looked across the meadows to a dusky white speck that glimmered from the knoll in the darkening twilight, there was no pang at his heart. "I foresee," he said to himself, "that if I do not take care, I shall love this girl madly and passionately. I know her now in her true tenderness and purity; I see what a wealth of womanhood is hidden under her mistaken aims. But is she not too loftily pure—too ideal in her aspirations—for my winning? Can she bear the knowledge of my life? I cannot spare her the test. If she comes to me at last, it must be with eveey

16*

veil of the Past lifted. There dare be no mystery between
us—no skeleton in our cupboard. If she were less true, less
noble—but no, there can be no real sacrament of marriage,
without previous confession. I am laying the basis of relations
that stretch beyond this life. It would be a greater wrong to
shrink, for her sake, than for my own. It must come to this,
and God give her strength of heart equal to her strength of
mind!"

Woodbury felt that her relation to him had changed, and
he could estimate, very nearly, the character which it had now
assumed. Of her struggles with herself—of the painful impression which his visits left behind—he had, of course, not
the slightest presentiment. He knew, however, that no suspicion of his feelings had entered her breast, and he had
reasons of his own for desiring that she should remain innocent of their existence, for the present. His plans, here, came
to an end, for the change in himself interposed an anxiety
which obscured his thoughts. He had reached the point where
all calculation fails, and where the strongest man, if his passion be genuine, must place his destiny in the hands of
Chance.

But there is, fortunately, a special chance provided for cases
of this kind. All the moods of Nature, all the little accidents
of life, become the allies of love. When the lover, looking
back from his post of assured fortune over the steps by which
he attained it, thinks: "Had it not been for such or such a
circumstance, I might have wholly missed my happiness," he
does not recognize that all the powers of the earth and air
were really in league with him—that his success was not the
miracle he supposed, but that his failure would have been. It
is well, however, that this delusion should come to silence the
voice of pride, and temper his heart with a grateful humility:
for him it is necessary that "fear and sorrow fan the fire of
joy."

Woodbury had no sooner intrusted to Chance the further
development of his fate, than Chance generously requited the

trust. It was certainly a wonderful coincidence that, as he walked into Ptolemy on a golden afternoon in late September, quite uncertain whether he should this time call at the widow's cottage, he should meet Hannah Thurston on foot, just at the junction of the Anacreon and Mulligansville highways. It was Miss Sophia Stevenson's day for relieving her, and she had gone out for her accustomed walk up the banks of the stream.

As Woodbury lifted his hat to greet her, his face brightened with a pleasure which he did not now care to conceal. There was a hearty, confiding warmth in the grasp of his hand, as he stood face to face, looking into her clear, dark-gray eyes with an expression as frank and unembarrassed as a boy's. It was this transparent warmth and frankness which swept away her cautious resolves at a touch. In spite of herself, she felt that an intimate friendship was fast growing up between them, and she knew not why the consciousness of it should make her so uneasy. There was surely no reproach to her in the fact that their ideas and habits were so different; there was none of her friends with whom she did not differ on points more or less important. The current setting towards her was pure and crystal-clear, yet she drew back from it as from the rush of a dark and turbid torrent.

"Well-met!" cried Woodbury, with a familiar playfulness. "We are both of one mind to-day, and what a day for out-of-doors! I am glad you are able to possess a part of it; your mother is better, I hope?"

"She is much as usual, and I should not have left her, but for the kindness of a friend who comes regularly on this day of the week to take my place for an hour or two."

"Have you this relief but *once* in seven days?"

"Oh, no. Mrs. Styles comes on Tuesdays, and those two days, I find, are sufficient for my needs. Mrs. Waldo would relieve me every afternoon if I would allow her."

"If you are half as little inclined for lonely walks as I am," said Woodbury, "you will not refuse my companionship to-day. I see you are going out the eastern road."

"My favorite walk," she answered, "is in the meadows yonder. It is the wildest and most secluded spot in the neighborhood of the village."

"Ah, I have noticed, from the road, in passing, the beauty of those elms and clumps of alder, and the picturesque curves of the creek. I should like to make a nearer acquaintance with them. Do you feel sufficient confidence in my appreciation of Nature to perform the introduction?"

"Nature is not exclusive," said she, adopting his gay tone, "and if she were, I think she could not exclude you, who have known her in her royal moods, from so simple and unpretending a landscape as this."

"The comparison is good," he answered, walking onward by her side, "but you have drawn the wrong inference. I find that every landscape has an individual character. The royal moods, as you rightly term them, may impose upon us, like human royalty; but the fact that you have been presented at Court does not necessarily cause the humblest man to open his heart to you. What is it to yonder alder thickets that I have looked on the Himalayas? What does East Atauga Creek care for the fact that I have floated on the Ganges? If the scene has a soul at all, it will recognize every one of your footsteps, and turn a cold shoulder to me, if I come with any such pretensions."

Hannah Thurston laughed at the easy adroitness with which he had taken up and applied her words. It was a light, graceful play of intellect to which she was unaccustomed—which, indeed, a year previous, would have struck her as trivial and unworthy an earnest mind. But she had learned something in that time. Her own mind was no longer content to move in its former rigid channels; she acknowledged the cheerful brightness which a sunbeam of fancy can diffuse over the sober coloring of thought.

He let down the movable rails from the panel of fence which gave admittance into the meadow, and put them up again after they had entered. The turf was thick and dry, with a delightful elasticity which lifted the feet where they pressed it. A few paces brought them to the edge of the belt of thickets, or rather islands of lofty shrubbery, between which the cattle had worn paths, and which here and there enclosed little peninsulas of grass and mint, embraced by the swift stream. The tall autumnal flowers, yellow and dusky purple, bloomed on all sides, and bunches of the lovely fringed gentian, blue as a wave of the Mediterranean, were set among the ripe grass like sapphires in gold. The elms which at intervals towered over this picturesque jungle, had grown up since the valley-bottom was cleared, and no neighboring trees had marred the superb symmetry of their limbs.

Threading the winding paths to the brink of the stream, or back again to the open meadow, as the glimpses through the labyrinth enticed them, they slowly wandered away from the road. Woodbury was not ashamed to show his delight in every new fragment of landscape which their exploration disclosed, and Miss Thurston was thus led to make him acquainted with her own selected gallery of pictures, although her exclusive right of possession to them thereby passed away forever.

Across one of the bare, grassy peninsulas between the thicket and the stream lay a huge log which the spring freshet had stolen from some saw-mill far up the valley. Beyond it, the watery windings ceased for a hundred yards or more, opening a space for the hazy hills in the distance to show their purple crests. Otherwise, the spot was wholly secluded: there was not a dwelling in sight, nor even a fence, to recall the vicinity of human life. This was the enticing limit of Hannah Thurston's walks. She had not intended to go so far to-day, but "a spirit in her feet" brought her to the place before she was aware.

"Ah!" cried Woodbury, as they emerged from the tangled paths, "I see that you are recognized here. Nature has intentionally placed this seat for you at the very spot where you have at once the sight of the hills and the sound of the water. How musical it is, just at this point! I know you sing here, sometimes: you cannot help it, with such an accompaniment."

She did not answer, but a flitting smile betrayed her assent. They took their seats on the log, as if by a silent understanding. The liquid gossip of the stream, in which many voices seemed to mingle in shades of tone so delicate that the ear lost, as soon as it caught them, sounded lullingly at their feet. Now and then a golden leaf dropped from the overhanging elm, and quivered slantwise to the ground.

" Ah, that reminds me," said Woodbury, finally breaking the peaceful, entrancing silence—"one of those exquisite songs in 'The Princess' came into my head. Have you read the book? You promised to tell me what impression it made upon you."

" Your judgment is correct, so far," she answered, " that it is poetry, not argument. But it could never have been written by one who believes in the just rights of woman. In the first place, the Princess has a very faulty view of those rights, and in the second place she adopts a plan to secure them which is entirely impracticable. If the book had been written for a serious purpose, I should have been disappointed; but, taking it for what it is, it has given me very great pleasure."

" You say the Princess's plan of educating her sex to independence is impracticable; yet—pardon me if I have misunderstood you—you seem to attribute your subjection to the influence of man—an influence which must continue to exercise the same power it ever has. What plan would you substitute for hers?"

"I do not know," she answered, hesitatingly; "I can only hope and believe that the Truth must finally vindicate itself. I have never aimed at any thing more than to assert it."

" Then you do not place yourself in an attitude hostile to man?" he asked.

Hannah Thurston was embarrassed for a moment, but her frankness conquered. "I fear, indeed, that I have done so," she said. " There have been times when a cruel attack has driven me to resistance. You can scarcely appreciate our position, Mr. Woodbury. We could bear open and honorable hostility, but the conventionalities which protect us against that offer us no defence from sneers and ridicule. The very term applied to us—'strong-minded'—implies that weak minds are our natural and appropriate inheritance. It is in human nature, I think, to forgive honest enmity sooner than covert contempt."

"Would it satisfy you that the sincerity and unselfishness of your aims are honored, though the aims themselves are accounted mistaken."

"It is all we could ask now!" she exclaimed, her eyes growing darker and brighter, and her voice thrilling with its earnest sweetness. "But who would give us that much?"

"*I* would," said Woodbury, quietly. "Will you pardon me for saying that it has seemed to me, until recently, as if you suspected me of an active hostility which I have really never felt. My opinions are the result of my experience of men, and you cannot wonder if they differ from yours. I should be very wrong to arrogate to myself any natural superiority over you. I think there never can be any difficulty in determining the relative rights of the sexes, when they truly understand and respect each other. I can unite with you in desiring reciprocal knowledge and reciprocal honor. If that shall be attained, will you trust to the result?"

"Forgive me: I *did* misunderstand you," she said, not answering his last question.

A pause ensued. The stream gurgled on, and the purple hills smiled through the gaps in the autumnal foliage. "Do you believe that Ida was happier with the Prince, supposing he were faithful to the picture he drew, than if she had remained at the head of her college?" he suddenly asked.

"You will acquit me of hostility to your sex when I say 'Yes.' The Prince promised her equality, not subjection. It is sad that the noble and eloquent close of the poem should be its most imaginative part."

The tone of mournful unbelief in her voice fired Woodbury's blood. His heart protested against her words and demanded to be heard. The deepening intimacy of their talk had brought him to that verge of frankness where the sanctities of feeling, which hide themselves from the gaze of the world, steal up to the light and boldly reveal their features. "No," he said, warmly and earnestly, " the picture is not imaginative. Its counterpart exists in the heart of every true man. There can be no ideal perfection in marriage because there is none in life ; but it can, and should, embody the tenderest affection, the deepest trust, the divinest charity, and the purest faith which human nature is capable of manifesting. I, for one man, found my own dream in the words of the Prince. I have not remained unmarried from a selfish idea of independence or from a want of reverence for woman. Because I hold her so high, because I seek to set her side by side with me in love and duty and confidence, I cannot profane her and myself by an imperfect union. I do not understand love without the most absolute mutual knowledge, and a trust so complete that there can be no question of rights on either side. Where that is given, man will never withhold, nor will woman demand, what she should or should not possess. That is my dream of marriage, and it is not a dream too high for attainment in this life !"

The sight of Hannah Thurston's face compelled him to pause. She was deadly pale, and trembled visibly. The moment he ceased speaking, she rose from her seat, and, after mechanically plucking some twigs of the berried bittersweet, said : " It is time for me to return."

Woodbury had not intended to say so much, and was fearful, at first, that his impassioned manner had suggested the secret he still determined to hide. In that case, she evidently desired to escape its utterance, but he had a presentiment that her agitation was owing to a different cause. Could it be that he had awakened the memory of some experience of love through which she had passed ? After the first jealous doubt which this thought inspired, it presented itself to his mind as a relief. The duty which pressed upon him would be more lightly performed; the test to which he must first subject her would be surer of success.

As they threaded the embowered paths on their homeward way, he said to her, gravely, but cheerfully: "You see, Miss Thurston, your doubt of my sex has forced me to show myself to you as I am, in one respect. But I will not regret the confession, unless you should think it intrusive."

"Believe me," she answered, "I know how to value it. You have made me ashamed of my unbelief."

"And you have confirmed me in my belief. This is a subject which neither man nor woman can rightly interpret, alone. Why should we never speak of that which is most vital in our lives? Here, indeed, we are governed by conventional ideas, springing from a want of truth and purity. But a man is always ennobled by allowing a noble woman to look into his heart. Do you recollect my story about the help Mrs. Blake gave me, under awkward circumstances, before her marriage?"

"Perfectly. It was that story which made me wish to know her. What an admirable woman she is!"

"Admirable, indeed!" Woodbury exclaimed. "That was not the only, nor the best help she gave me. I learned from her that women, when they are capable of friendship—don't misunderstand me, I should say the same thing of men—are the most devoted friends in the world. She is the only consoling figure in an episode of my life which had a great influence upon my fate. The story is long since at an end, but I should like to tell it to you, some time."

"If you are willing to do so, I shall be glad to hear another instance of Mrs. Blake's kindness."

"Not only that," Woodbury continued, "but still another portion of my history. I will not press my confidence upon you, but I shall be glad, very glad, if you will kindly consent to receive it. Some things in my life suggest questions which I have tried to answer, and cannot. I must have a woman's

help. I know you are all truth and candor, and I am willing
to place my doubts in your hands."

He spoke earnestly and eagerly, walking by her side, but
with eyes fixed upon the ground. His words produced in
her a feeling of interest and curiosity, under which lurked a
singular reluctance. She was still unnerved by her former
agitation. "Why should you place such confidence in me?"
she at length faltered. "You have other friends who deserve
it better."

"We cannot always explain our instincts," he answered.
"I *must* tell you, and you alone. If I am to have help in
these doubts, it is you who can give it."

His words seized her and held her powerless. Her Quaker
blood still acknowledged the authority of those mysterious
impulses which are truer than reason, because they come from
a deeper source. He spoke with a conviction from which
there was no appeal, and the words of refusal vanished from
her lips and from her heart.

"Tell me, then," she said. "I will do my best. I hope I
may be able to help you."

He took her hand and held it a moment, with a warm pressure. "God bless you!" was all he said.

They silently returned up the road. On reaching the gate
of the cottage, he took leave of her, saying : "You will have
my story to-morrow." His face was earnest and troubled;
it denoted the presence of a mystery, the character of which
she could not surmise.

On entering the cottage, she first went up-stairs to her own
room. She had a sensation of some strange expression having
come over her face, which must be banished from it before she
could meet her mother. She must have five minutes alone to
think upon what had passed, before she could temporarily put
it away from her mind. But her thoughts were an indistinct
chaos, through which only two palpable sensations crossed each
other as they moved to and fro—one of unreasoning joy, one
of equally unreasoning terror. What either of them portend-

ed she could not guess. She only felt that there was no stable point to which she could cling, but the very base of her being seemed to shift as her thoughts pierced down to it.

Her eyes fell upon the volume of "The Princess," which lay upon the little table beside her bed. She took it up with a sudden desire to read again the closing scene, where the heroine lays her masculine ambition in the hands of love. The book opened of itself, at another page: the first words arrested her eye and she read, involuntarily:

> "Ask me no more: the moon may draw the sea,
> The cloud may stoop from heaven and take the shape,
> With fold on fold, of mountain and of cape,
> But oh, too fond, when have I answered thee?
> Ask me no more
>
> "Ask me no more: what answer could I give?
> I love not hollow cheek and fading eye,
> Yet oh, my friend, I would not have thee die:
> Ask me no more, lest I should bid thee live;
> Ask me no more.
>
> "Ask me no more: thy fate and mine are sealed.
> I strove against the stream, and strove in vain:
> Let the great river bear me to the main!
> No more, dear love, for at a touch I yield—
> Ask me no more."

The weird, uncontrollable power which had taken possession of her reached its climax. She threw down the book and burst into tears.

CHAPTER XXX.

MR. WOODBURY'S CONFESSION.

TOWARDS evening, on Saturday, Bute called at the cottage, and after inquiring concerning the widow's condition, and giving, in return, a most enthusiastic report of Carrie's accomplishments, he produced a package, with the remark:

"Here, Miss Hannah, 's a book that Mr. Max. give me for you. He says you needn't be in a hurry to send any of 'em back. He got a new lot from New York yisterday."

She laid it aside until night. It was late before her mother slept and she could be certain of an hour, alone, and secure from interruption. When at last all was quiet and the fire was burning low on the hearth, and the little clock ticked like a strong pulse of health, in mockery of the fading life in the bosom of the dear invalid in the next room, she took the book in her hands. She turned it over first and examined the paper wrapping, as if that might suggest the nature of the unknown contents; then slowly untied the string and unfolded the paper. When the book appeared, she first looked at the back; it was Ware's "Zenobia"—a work she had long desired to possess. A thick letter slipped out from between the blank ¹eaves and fell on her lap. On the envelope was her name only—"Hannah Thurston"—in a clear, firm, masculine hand. She laid the volume aside, broke the seal and read the letter through from beginning to end:

"DEAR MISS THURSTON:—I know how much I have asked of you in begging permission to write, for your eye, the story which follows. Therefore I have not allowed myself to stand shivering on the brink of a plunge which I have determined to make, or to postpone it, from the fear that the venture of confidence which I now send out will come to shipwreck. Since I have learned to appreciate the truth and nobleness of your nature—since I have dared to hope that you honor me with a friendly regard—most of all, since I find that the feelings which I recognize as the most intimate and sacred portion of myself seek expression in your presence, I am forced to make you a participant in the knowledge of my life. Whether it be that melancholy knowledge which a tender human charity takes under its protecting wing and which thenceforward sleeps calmly in some shadowy corner of memory, or that evil knowledge which torments because it cannot be forgotten, I am not able to foresee. I will say nothing, in advance, to secure a single feeling of sympathy or consideration which your own nature would not spontaneously prompt you to give. I know that in this step I may not be acting the part of a friend ; but, whatever consequences may follow it, I entreat you to believe that there is no trouble which I would not voluntarily take upon myself, rather than inflict upon you a moment's unnecessary pain.

"Have you ever, in some impartial scrutiny of self, discovered to what extent your views of Woman, and your aspirations in her behalf, were drawn from your own nature ? Are you not inclined to listen to your own voice as if it were the collective voice of your sex ? If so, you may to some extent, accept me as an interpretation of Man. I am neither better nor worse than the general average of men. My principal advantages are, that I was most carefully and judiciously educated, and that my opportunities of knowing mankind have been greater than is usual. A conscientious study of human nature ought to be the basis of all theories of reform. I think you will agree with me, thus far; and therefore, however my present confession may change your future relations towards me, I shall have, at least, the partial consolation of knowing that I have added something to your knowledge.

"Let me add only this, before I commence my narrative—
that it treats entirely of the occurrences of my life, which have
brought me near to woman through my emotions. It is my
experience of the sex, so far as that experience has taken a
deeper hold on my heart. You are not so cold and unsympa-
thetic as to repel the subject. The instinct which has led me
to choose you as the recipient of my confidence cannot be
false. That same instinct tells me that I shall neither withhold
nor seek to extenuate whatever directly concerns myself. I
dare not do either.

"My nature was once not so calm and self-subdued as it
may seem to you now. As a youth I was ardent, impetuous,
and easily controlled by my feelings. In the heart of almost
any boy, from seventeen to twenty, there is a train laid, and
waiting for the match. As I approached the latter age, mine
was kindled by a girl two years younger than myself, the
daughter of a friend of my father. I suppose all early passions
have very much the same character: they are intense, absorbing, unreasoning, but generally shallow, not from want of sincerity but from want of development. The mutual attachment
necessarily showed itself, and was tacitly permitted, but without any express engagement. I had never surprised her with
any sudden declaration of love: our relation had gradually
grown into existence, and we were both so happy therein that
we did not need to question and discuss our feelings. In fact,
we were rarely sufficiently alone to have allowed of such confidences; but we sought each other in society or in our respective family circles and created for ourselves a half-privacy
in the presence of others. Nothing seemed more certain to
either of us than that our fates were already united, for we
accepted the tolerance of our attachment as a sanction of its
future seal upon our lives.

"After my father's failure and death, however, I discovered,
with bitterness of heart, that it was not alone my pecuniary
prospects which had changed. Her father, a shrewd, hard
man of business, was one of the very few who prospered in a

season of general ruin—who perhaps foresaw the crash and prepared himself to take advantage of the splendid opportunities which it offered. His wealth was doubled, probably trebled, in a year: he won advantages which compelled the most exclusive circles to receive him, and his family dropped their old associations as fast as they familiarized themselves with the new. I saw this change, at first, without the slightest misgiving: my faith in human nature was warm and fresh, and the satisfied bliss of my affections disposed me to judge all men kindly. I only refrained from asking the father's assistance in my straits, from a feeling of delicacy, not because I had any suspicion that it would not be given. Little by little, however, the conviction forced itself upon my mind that I was no longer a welcome visitor at the house: I was dropped from the list of guests invited to dinners and entertainments, and my reception became cold and constrained. From the sadness and uneasiness on the face of my beloved, I saw that she was suffering for my sake, and on questioning her she did not deny that she had been urged to give me up. She assured me, nevertheless, of her own constancy, and exhorted me to have patience until my prospects should improve.

"It was at this juncture that Miss Remington (Mrs. Blake, you will remember) became a comforting angel to both of us. She had remarked our attachment from its first stage, and with her profound scorn of the pretensions of wealth, she determined to assist the course of true love. We met, as if by accident, at her father's house, and she generally contrived that we should have a few minutes alone. Thus, several months passed away. My position had not advanced, because I had every thing to learn when I first took it, but I began to have more confidence in myself, and remained cheerful and hopeful. I was not disturbed by the fact that my beloved sometimes failed to keep her appointments, but I could not help remarking, now, that when she did appear, she seemed ill at ease and strove to make the interviews as short as possible.

"There was something in Miss Remington's manner, also,

which I could not understand. I missed the frank, hearty
sympathy with faithful and persecuted love, which she had
given me. A restless anxiety, pointing to one thing or
another, but never towards the truth, took possession of me.
One day on making my pre-arranged call, I found Miss Remington alone. Her face was grave and sad. She saw my look
of disappointment: she allowed me to walk impatiently up and
down the room three or four times, then she arose and seized
me by both hands. 'Am I mistaken in you?' she asked:
'Are you yet a man?' 'I am trying to prove it,' I answered.
'Then,' she said, 'prove it to me. If you were to have a
tooth drawn, would you turn back a dozen times from
the dentist's door and bear the ache a day longer, or would
you go in at once and have it out?' I sat down, chilled to
the heart, and said, desperately: 'I am ready for the operation!' She smiled, but there were tears of pity in her eyes.
She told me as kindly and tenderly as possible, all she had
learned: that the girl who possessed my unquestioning faith
was unworthy of the gift: that the splendors of the new circle
into which she had ascended had become indispensable to her:
that her attachment to me was now a simple embarrassment:
that her beauty had attracted wealthy admirers, one of whom,
a shallow-brained egotist, was reported to be especially favored
by her, and that any hope I might have of her constancy
to me must be uprooted as a delusion.

"I tried to reject this revelation, but the evidence was
too clear to be discredited. Nevertheless, I insisted on seeing
the girl once more, and Miss Remington brought about the
interview. I was too deeply disappointed to be indignant:
she showed a restless impatience to be gone, as if some remnant of conscience still spoke in her heart. I told her, sadly,
that I saw she was changed. If her attachment for me had
faded, as I feared, I would not despotically press mine upon
her, but would release her from the mockery of a duty which
her heart no longer acknowledged. I expected a penitent
confession of the truth, in return, and was therefore wholly

unprepared for the angry reproaches she heaped upon me. 'Very fine!' she cried; 'I always thought there was no *suspicion* where there was love! I am to be accused of falsehood, from a jealous whim. It's very easy for you to give up an attachment that died out long ago!' But I will not repeat her expressions further. I should never have comprehended them without Miss Remington's assistance. She was vexed that I should have discovered her want of faith and given her back her freedom: *she* should have been the first to break the bonds. I laughed, in bitterness of heart, at her words; I could give her no other answer.

"The shock my affections received was deeper than I cared to show. It was renewed, when, three months afterwards, the faithless girl married the rich fool whom she had preferred to me. I should have become moody and cynical but for the admirable tact with which Miss Remington, in her perfect friendship, softened the blow. Many persons suppose that a pure and exalted relation of this kind cannot exist between man and woman, without growing into love—in other words, that friendship seeks its fulfilment in the same sex and love in the opposite. I do not agree with this view. The thought of loving Julia Remington never entered my mind, and she would have considered me as wanting in sanity if I had intimated such a thing, but there was a happy and perfect confidence between us, which was my chief support in those days of misery.

"I accepted, eagerly, the proposition to become the Calcutta agent of the mercantile house in which I was employed. The shadow of my disappointment still hung over me, and there were now but few associations of my life in New York to make the parting difficult. I went, and in the excitement of new scenes, in the absorbing duties of my new situation, in the more masculine strength that came with maturity, I gradually forgot the blow which had been struck—or, if I did not forget, the sight of the scar no longer recalled the pain of the wound. Nevertheless, it had made me suspicious and fearful.

17

I questioned every rising inclination of my heart, and suppressed the whispers of incipient affection, determined that no woman should ever again deceive me as the first had done. The years glided away, one by one; I had slowly acquired the habit of self-control, on which I relied as a natural and sufficient guard for my heart, and the longing for woman's partnership in life, which no man can ever wholly suppress, again began to make itself heard. I did not expect a recurrence of the passion of youth. I knew that I had changed, and that love, therefore, must come to me in a different form. I remembered what I heard at home, as a boy, that when the original forest is cleared away, a new forest of different trees is developed from the naked soil. But I still suspected that there must be a family likeness in the growth, and that I should recognize its sprouting germs.

"Between five and six years ago, it was necessary that I should visit Europe, in the interest of the house. I was absent from India nearly a year, and during that time made my first acquaintance with Switzerland, the memory of which is now indissolubly connected, in my mind, with that song which I have heard you sing. But it is not of this that I would speak. I find myself shrinking from the new revelation which must be made. The story is not one of guilt—not even of serious blame, in the eyes of the world. If it were necessary, I could tell it to any *man*, without reluctance for my own sake. Men, in certain respects, have broader and truer views of life than women; they are more tender in their judgment, more guarded in their condemnation. I am not justifying myself, in advance, for I can acquit myself of any intentional wrong. I only feel that the venture, embodied in my confession, is about to be sent forth—either to pitying gales that shall waft it safely back to me, or to storms in which it shall go down. Recollect, dear Miss Thurston, that whatever of strength I may possess you have seen. I am now about to show you, voluntarily, my weakness.

"Among the passengers on board the steamer by which I

returned to India, there was a lady who had been recommended to my care by some mutual acquaintance in England.
She was the wife of a physician in the Company's Service who
was stationed at Benares, and who had sent her home with
her children a year and a half before. The latter were left in
England, while she returned to share the exile of her husband
until he should be entitled to a pension. She was a thoroughly
refined and cultivated woman, of almost my own age, and
shrank from contact with the young cubs of cadets and the os-
tentatious indigo-planters, with their beer-drinking wives, who
were almost the only other passengers. We were thus thrown
continually together, and the isolation of ocean-life contributed
to hasten our intimacy. Little by little that intimacy grew
deep, tender, and powerful. I told her the humiliating story
of my early love which you have just read, and she described
to me, with tearful reluctance, the unhappiness of her married
life. Her husband had gone to England eight years before, on
leave of absence, on purpose to marry. She had been found
to answer his requirements, and ignorant of life as she was at
that time, ignorant of her own heart, had been hurried into
the marriage by her own family. Her father was in moderate
circumstances, and he had many daughters to provide with
husbands; this was too good a chance to let slip, and, as it
was known that she had no other attachment, her hesitation
was peremptorily overruled. She discovered, too late, that
there was not only no point of sympathy between her husband
and herself, but an absolute repulsion. He was bold and
steady-handed as a surgeon, and had performed some daring
operations which had distinguished him in his profession; but
he was hard, selfish, and tyrannical in his domestic relations,
and his unfortunate wife could only look forward with dread
to the continual companionship which was her doom.

"I had been sure of recognizing any symptom of returning
love in my heart—but I was mistaken. It took the form of
pity, and so lulled my suspicions to sleep that my power of
will was drugged before I knew it. Her own heart was not

more merciful towards her. Poor woman! if she had ever dreamed of love the dream had been forgotten. She was ignorant of the fatal spell which had come upon us, and I did not detect my own passion until its reflection was thrown back to me from her innocent face. When I had discovered the truth, it was too late—too late, I mean, for her happiness, not too late for the honor of both our lives. I could not explain to her a danger which she did not suspect, nor could I embitter, by an enforced coldness, her few remaining happy days of our voyage. With a horrible fascination, I saw her drawing nearer and nearer the brink of knowledge, and my lips were sealed, that only could have uttered the warning cry.

"Again I was called upon to suffer, but in a way I had never anticipated. The grief of betrayed love is tame, beside the despair of forbidden love. This new experience showed me how light was the load which I had already borne. On the one side, two hearts that recognized each other and would have been faithful to the end of time; on the other, a monstrous bond, which had only the sanction of human laws. I rebelled, in my very soul, against the mockery of that legal marriage, which is the basis of social virtue, forgetting that Good must voluntarily bind itself in order that Evil may not go free. The boundless tenderness towards her which had suddenly revealed itself must be stifled. I could not even press her hand warmly, lest some unguarded pulse should betray the secret; I scarcely dared look in her eyes, lest mine might stab her with the sharpness of my love and my sorrow in the same glance.

"It was all in vain. Some glance, some word, or touch of hand, on either side, *did* come, and the thin disguise was torn away forever. Then we spoke, for the consolation of speech seemed less guilty than the agony of silence. In the moonless nights of the Indian Ocean we walked the deck with hands secretly clasped, with silent tears on our cheeks, with a pang in our souls only softened by the knowledge that it was mutual. Neither of us, I think, then thought of disputing our fate. But as the voyage drew near its end, I was haunted by wild fancies of escape. I could not subdue my nature to forego a fulfilment that seemed possible. We might find a refuge, I thought, in Java, or Celebes, or some of the Indian Isles, and once beyond the reach of pursuit what was the rest of the world to us? What was wealth, or name, or station? —they were hollow sounds to us now, they were selfish cheats, always. In the perverted logic of passion all was clear and fair.

"This idea so grew upon me that I was base enough to propose it to her—I who should have given reverence to that ignorance of the heart which made her love doubly sacred, strove to turn it into the instrument of her ruin! She heard me, in fear, not in indignation. 'Do not tempt me!' she cried, with a pitiful supplication; 'think of my children, and help me to stand up against my own heart!' Thank God I was not deaf to that cry of weakness; I was armed to meet resistance, but I was powerless against her own despairing fear of surrender. Thank God, I overcame the relentless selfishness of my sex! She took from my lips, that night, the only kiss I ever gave her—the kiss of repentance, not of triumph. It left no stain on the purity of her marriage vow. That was our true parting from each other. There were still two days of our voyage left, but we looked at each other as if through the bars of opposite prisons, with a double wall between. Our renunciation was complete, and any further words would have been an unnecessary pang. We had a melancholy pleasure in still being near each other, in walking side by side, in the formal touch of hands that dared not clasp and be clasped. This poor consolation soon ceased. The husband was waiting for her at Calcutta, and I purposely kept my state-room when we arrived, in order that I might not see him. I was not yet sure of myself.

"She went to Benares, and afterwards to Meerut, and I never saw her again. In a little more than a year I heard she was dead: 'the fever of the country,' they said. I was glad of it—death was better for her than her life had been—now, at least, when that life had become a perpetual infidelity to her heart. Death purified the memory of my passion, and gave me, perhaps, a sweeter resignation than if she had first yielded to my madness. Sad and hopeless as was this episode of my life, it contained an element of comfort, and restored the balance which my first disappointment had destroyed. My grief for her was gentle, tender and consoling, and I never turned aside from its approaches. It has now withdrawn into the past, but its influence still remains, in this—that the desire for that fulfilment of passion, of which life has thus far cheated me, has not grown cold in my heart.

"There are some natures which resemble those plants that die after a single blossoming—natures in which one passion seems to exhaust the capacities for affection. I am not one of them, yet I know that I possess the virtue of fidelity. I know that I still wait for the fortune that shall enable me to manifest it. Do you, as a woman, judge me unworthy to expect that fortune? You are now acquainted with my history; try me by the sacred instincts of your own nature, and according to them, pardon or condemn me. I have revealed to you my dream of the true marriage that is possible—a dream that prevents me from stooping to a union not hallowed by perfect love and faith. Have I forfeited the right to indulge this dream longer? Would I be guilty of treason towards the virgin confidence of some noble woman whom God may yet send me, in offering her a heart which is not fresh in its knowledge, though fresh in its immortal desires? I pray you to answer me these questions? Do not blame your own truth and nobility of nature, which have brought you this task. Blame, if you please, my selfishness in taking advantage of them.

"I have now told you all I meant to confess, and might here close. But one thought occurs to me, suggested by the sudden recollection of the reform to which you have devoted yourself. I fear that all reformers are too much disposed to measure the actions and outward habits of the human race, without examining the hidden causes of those actions. There is some basis in our nature for all general customs, both of body and mind. The mutual relation of man and woman, in Society, is determined not by a conscious exercise of tyranny on the one side, or subjection on the other. Each sex has its peculiar mental and moral laws, the differences between which are perhaps too subtle and indefinable to be distinctly drawn, but they are as palpable in life as the white and red which neighboring roses draw from the self-same soil. When we have differed in regard to Woman, I have meant to speak sincerely and earnestly, out of the knowledge gained by an unfortunate experience, which, nevertheless, has not touched the honor and reverence in which I hold the sex. I ask you to remember this, in case the confidence I have forced upon you should hereafter set a gulf between us.

" I have deprived myself of the right to make any request, but whatever your judgment may be, will you let me hear it from your own lips? Will you allow me to see you once more? I write to you now, not because I should shrink from speaking the same words, but because a history like mine is not always easily or clearly told, and I wish your mind to be uninfluenced by the sympathy which a living voice might inspire.

" On Tuesday next you will be free to take your accustomed walk. May I be your companion again, beside the stream? But, no: do not write: you will find me there if you consent to see me. If you do not come, I shall expect the written evidence, if not of your continued respect, at least of your forgiveness. But, in any case, think of me always as one man who, having known you, will never cease to honor Woman.

" Your friend,

" MAXWELL WOODBURY."

CHAPTER XXXI.

IN WHICH THE STRONG-MINDED WOMAN BECOMES WEAK.

It did not require the sound of a living voice to inspire
Hannah Thurston with sympathy for the story which she had
just read. Never before had any man so freely revealed to
her the sanctities of his experience of women. Completely
absorbed in the recital, she gave herself up to the first strong
impressions of alternate indignation and pity, without reflect-
ing upon the deeper significance of the letter. Woodbury's
second episode of passion at first conflicted harshly with the
pure ideal in her own mind; the shock was perhaps greater
to her than the confession of actual guilt would have been to
a woman better acquainted with the world. Having grown
up in the chaste atmosphere of her sect, and that subdued life
of the emotions which the seclusion of the country creates, it
startled her to contemplate a love forbidden by the world, yet
justifying itself to the heart. Nevertheless, the profound pity
which came upon her as she read took away from her the
power of condemnation. The wrong, she felt, was not so much
in the love which had unsuspectedly mastered both, as in the
impulse to indulge rather than suppress it; but having been
suppressed—passion having been purified by self-abnegation
and by death, she could not withhold a tender human charity
even for this feature of the confession.

Woodbury's questions, however, referred to the future, no
less than to the past. They hinted at the possibility of a new
love visiting his heart. The desire for it, he confessed, had not
grown cold. Deceit and fate had not mastered, in him, the

immortal yearning: was he unworthy to receive it? "Try me," he had written, "by the sacred instincts of your own nature, and according to them pardon or condemn me." She had already pardoned. Perhaps, had she read the same words coming from a stranger, or as an incident of a romance, she would have paused and deliberated; her natural severity would have been slow to relax; but knowing Woodbury as she had latterly learned to know him, in his frankness, his manly firmness and justice, his noble consideration for herself her heart did not delay the answer to his questions. He had put her to shame by voluntarily revealing his weakness, while she had determined that she would never allow him to discover her own.

Little by little, however, after it became clear that her sympathy and her charity were justifiable, the deeper questions which lay hidden beneath the ostensible purpose of his letter crept to the surface. In her ignorance of the coming confession, she had not asked herself, in advance, why it should have been made; she supposed it would be its own explanation. The reason he had given was not in itself sufficient, but presupposed something more important which he had not expressed. No man makes such a confidence from a mere feeling of curiosity. Simultaneously with this question came another—why should he fancy that his act might possibly set a gulf between them? Was it simply the sensitiveness of a nature which would feel itself profaned by having its secrets misunderstood? No; a heart thus sensitive would prefer the security of silence. Was he conscious of a dawning love, and, doubtful of himself, did he ask for a woman's truer interpretation of his capacity to give and keep faith? "It is cruel in him to ask me," she said to herself; "does he think my heart is insensible as marble, that I should probe it with thoughts, every one of which inflicts a wound? Why does he not send his confession at once to *her*? It is she who should hear it, not I! He is already guilty of treason to her, in asking the question of *me!*"

17*

She put the letter suddenly on the table, and half rose from her chair, in the excitement of the thought. Then, as if struck by a stunning blow, she dropped back again. Her face grew cold and deadly pale, and her arms fell nerveless at her sides. Her eyes closed, and her breath came in long, labored sighs. After a few minutes she sat up, placed her elbow on the table and rested her forehead on her hand. "I am growing idiotic," she whispered, with an attempt to smile; "my brain is giving way—it is only a woman's brain."

The fire had long been extinct. The room was cold, and a chill crept over her. She rose, secured the letter and the book, and went to bed. As the balmy warmth stole over her frame, it seemed to soften and thaw the painful constriction of her heart, and she wept herself into a sad quiet. "Oh, if it *should* be so," she said, "I must henceforth be doubly wretched! What shall I do? I *cannot* give up the truths to which I have devoted my life, and they now stand between my heart and the heart of the noblest man I have ever known. Yes: my pride is broken at last, and I will confess to myself how much I honor and esteem him—not *love*—but even there I am no longer secure. We were so far apart—how could I dream of danger? But I recognize it now, too late for him —almost too late for me!"

Then, again, she doubted every thing. The knowledge had come too swiftly and suddenly to be accepted at once. He could not love her; it was preposterous. Until a few days ago he had thought her cold and severe : now, he acknowledged her to be true, and his letter simply appealed to that truth, unsuspicious of the secret slumbering in her heart. He had spoken of the possibility of a pure and exalted friendship between the sexes, such as already existed between himself and Mrs. Blake: perhaps he aimed at nothing more, in this instance. Somehow, the thought was not so consoling as it ought properly to have been, and the next moment the skilful explanation which she had built up tumbled into ruins.

She slept but little, that night, and all the next day went

about her duties as if in a dream. She knew that her mother's eye sometimes rested uneasily on her pale face, and the confession of her trouble more than once rose to her tongue, but she resolutely determined to postpone it until the dreaded crisis was past. She would not agitate the invalid with her confused apprehensions, all of which, moreover, might prove themselves to have been needless. With every fresh conflict in her mind her judgment seemed to become more unsteady. The thought of Woodbury's love, having once revealed itself to her, would not be banished, and every time it returned, it seemed to bring a gentler and tenderer feeling for him into her heart. On the other hand her dreams of a career devoted to the cause of Woman ranged themselves before her mental vision, in an attitude of desperate resistance. "Now is the test!" they seemed to say : "vindicate your sex, or yield to the weakness of your heart, and add to its reproach!"

When Monday came, it brought no cessation of the struggle, but she had recovered something of her usual self-control. She had put aside, temporarily, the consideration of her doubts ; the deeper she penetrated into the labyrinth, the more she became entangled, and she made up her mind to wait, with as much calmness as she could command, for the approaching solution. The forms of terror, of longing, of defence and of submission continually made their presence felt by turns, or chaotically together, but the only distinct sensation she permitted herself to acknowledge was this : that if her forebodings were true, the severest trial of her life awaited her. Her pride forbade her to shrink from the trial, yet every hour that brought her nearer to it increased her dread of the meeting.

Her mother's strength was failing rapidly, and on this day she required Hannah's constant attendance. When, at last, the latter was relieved for the night, her fatigue, combined with the wakeful torment of the two preceding nights, completely overpowered her and she slumbered fast and heavily until morning. Her first waking thought was—"The day is come, and I am not prepared to meet him." The morning was dull and windless, and as she looked upon the valley from her window, a thick blue film enveloped the distant woods, the dark pines and brown oaks mingling with it indistinctly, while the golden and orange tints of the maples shone through. Her physical mood corresponded with the day. The forces of her spirit were sluggish and apathetic, and she felt that the resistance which, in the contingency she dreaded, *must* be made, would be obstinately passive, rather than active and self-contained. A sense of inexpressible weariness stole over her. Oh, she thought, if she only could be spared the trial! Yet, how easily it might be avoided! She needed only to omit her accustomed walk: she could write to him, afterwards, and honor his confidence as it deserved. But an instinct told her that this would only postpone the avowal, not avert it. If she was wrong, she had nothing to fear; if she was right, it would be cowardly, and unjust to him, to delay the answer she must give.

Her mother had slightly rallied, and when Mrs. Styles arrived, as usual, early in the afternoon, the invalid could be safely left in her charge. Nevertheless, Hannah, after having put on her bonnet and shawl, lingered in the room, with a last, anxious hope that something might happen which would give her a pretext to remain.

" Child, isn't thee going ?" the widow finally asked.

" Mother, perhaps I had better stay with thee this afternoon ?" was the hesitating answer.

" Indeed, thee shall not do any such thing! Thee's not been thyself for the last two days, and I know thee always comes back from thy walks fresher and better. Bring me a handful of gentians, won't thee ?"

" Yes, mother." She stooped and kissed the old woman's forehead, and then left the house.

The sky was still heavy and gray, and there was an oppressive warmth in the air. Crickets chirped loud among the dying weeds along the garden-palings, and crows cawed hoarsely from the tops of the elms. The road was deserted, as far as she could see, but the sound of farmers calling to their oxen came distinctly across the valley from the fields on the eastern hill. Nature seemed to lie benumbed, in drowsy half-consciousness of her being, as if under some narcotic influence.

She walked slowly forward, striving to subdue the anxious beating of her heart. At the junction of the highways, she stole a glance down the Anacreon road : nobody was to be seen. Down the other : a farm-wagon was on its way home from Ptolemy—that was all. To the first throb of relief succeeded a feeling of disappointment. The walk through the meadow-thickets would be more lonely than ever, remembering the last time she had seen them. As she looked towards their dark-green mounds, drifted over with the downy tufts of the seeded clematis, a figure suddenly emerged from the nearest path and hastened towards her across the meadow !

He let down the bars for her entrance and stood waiting for her. His brown eyes shone with a still, happy light, and his face brightened as if struck by a wandering sunbeam. He looked so frank and kind—so cheered by her coming—so unembarrassed by the knowledge of the confession he had made, that the wild beating of her heart was partially soothed, and she grew calmer in his presence.

"Thank you !" he said, as he took her hand, both in greeting and to assist her over the fallen rails. When he had put them up, and regained her side, he spoke again : "Shall we not go on to that lovely nook of yours beside the creek ? I have taken a great fancy to the spot ; I have recalled it to my memory a thousand times since then."

"Yes, if you wish it," she answered.

As they threaded the tangled paths, he spoke cheerfully and pleasantly, drawing her into talk of the autumnal plants, of the wayward rapids and eddies of the stream, of all sights and sounds around them. . A balmy quiet, which she mistook for strength, took possession of her heart. She reached the secluded nook, with a feeling of timid expectancy, it is true, but with scarcely a trace of her former overpowering dread. There lay the log, as if awaiting them, and the stream gurgled contentedly around the point, and the hills closed loftily through blue vapor, up the valley, like the entrance to an Alpine gorge.

As soon as they were seated, Woodbury spoke. "Can you answer my questions?"

"You have made that easy for me," she replied, in a low voice. "It seems to me rather a question of character than of experience. A man naturally false and inconstant might have the same history to relate, but I am sure you are true. You should ask those questions of your own heart; where you are sure of giving fidelity, you would commit no treason in bestowing—attachment."

She dared not utter the other word in her mind.

"I was not mistaken in you!" he exclaimed. "You have the one quality which I demand of every man or woman in whom I confide; you distinguish between what is true in human nature and what is conventionally true. I must show myself to you as I am, though the knowledge should give you pain. The absolution of the sinner," he added, smiling, "is already half-pronounced in his confession."

"Why should I be your confessor?" she asked. "The knowledge of yourself which you have confided to me, thus far, does not give me pain. It has not lowered you in my esteem, but I feel, nevertheless, that your confidence is a gift which I have done nothing to deserve, and which I ought not to accept unless—unless I were able to make some return. If I had answered your questions otherwise, I do not think it would have convinced you, against your own feelings. With your integrity of heart, you do not need the aid of a woman whose experience of life is so much more limited than yours."

She spoke very slowly and deliberately, and the sentences seemed to come with an effort. Woodbury saw that her clear vision had pierced through his flimsy stratagem, and guessed that she must necessarily suspect the truth. Still, he drew back from the final venture upon which so much depended. He would first sound the depth of her suspicions.

"No man," he said, gently, "can be independent of woman's judgment, without loss to himself. Her purer nature is a better guide to him than his own clouded instincts. I should not have attributed a different answer to your true self, but to the severe ideas of duty which I imagined you to possess. You were right to suppose that I had already answered for myself, but can you not understand the joy of hearing it thus confirmed? Can you not appreciate the happy knowledge that one's heart has not been opened in vain?"

"I can understand it, though I have had little experience of such knowledge. But I had not supposed that you needed it, Mr. Woodbury—least of all from me. We seem to have had so little in common——"

"Not so!" he interrupted. "Opinions, no matter how powerfully they may operate to shape our lives, are external circumstances, compared with the deep, original springs of character. You and I have only differed on the outside, and hence we first clashed when we came in contact; but now I recognize in you a nature for which I have sought long and wearily. I seek some answering recognition, and in my haste have scarcely given you time to examine whether any features in myself have grown familiar to you. I see now that I was hasty: I should have waited until the first false impression was removed."

The memory of Mrs. Waldo's reproach arose in Hannah Thurston's mind. "Oh no, you mistake me!" she cried. "I am no longer unjust to you. But you surpass me in magnanimity as you have already done in justice. You surprised me by a sacred confidence which is generally accorded only to a tried friend. I had given you no reason to suppose that I was a friend: I had almost made myself an enemy."

"Let the Past be past: I know you now. My confidence was not entirely magnanimous. It was a test."

"And I have stood it?" she faltered.

"Not yet," he answered, and his voice trembled into a sweet and solemn strain, to which every nerve in her body seemed to listen. "Not yet! You must hear it now. I questioned you, after you knew the history of my heart, in order that you might decide for yourself as well as me. Love purifies itself at each return. My unfortunate experience has not prevented me from loving again, and with a purity and intensity deeper than that of my early days, because the passion was doubted and resisted instead of being received in my heart as a coveted guest. I am beyond the delusions of youth, but not beyond the wants of manhood. I described to you, the other day, on this spot, my dream of marriage. It was not an ideal picture. Hannah Thurston, I thought of *you !*"

The crisis had come, and she was not prepared to meet it. As he paused, she pressed one hand upon her heart, as if it might be controlled by physical means, and moved her lips, but no sound came from them.

"I knew you could not have anticipated this," he continued; "I should have allowed you time to test me, in return, but when the knowledge of your womanly purity and gentleness penetrated me, to the overthrow of all antagonism based on shallow impressions, I parted with judgment and will. A power stronger than myself drove me onward to the point I have now reached—the moment of time which must decide your fate and mine."

She turned upon him with a wild, desperate energy in her face and words. "Why did you come," she cried, "to drive me to madness? Was it not enough to undermine the foundations of my faith, to crush me with the cold, destroying knowledge you have gained in the world? My life was fixed, before I knew you; I was sure of myself and satisfied with the work that was before me: but now I am sure of nothing. You have assailed me until you have discovered my weakness, and you cruelly tear down every prop on which I try to lean! If I could hate you I should regain my strength, but I cannot do that—you know I cannot!"

He did not misinterpret her excitement, which yielded more than it assailed. "No, Hannah!" he said tenderly, "I would give you strength, not take it from you—the strength of my love, and sympathy, and encouragement. I know how these aims have taken hold upon you: they are built upon a basis of earnest truth which *I* recognize, and though I differ with you as to the ends to be attained, we may both enlighten each other, and mutual tenderness and mutual respect govern our relations in this as in all else. Do not think that I would make my love a fetter. I can trust to your nature working itself into harmony with mine. If I find, through the dearer knowledge of you, that I have misunderstood Woman, I will atone for the error; and I will ask nothing of you but that which I know you will give—the acknowledgment of the deeper truth that is developed with the progress of life."

She trembled from head to foot. "Say no more," she murmured, in a faint, hollow voice, "I cannot bear it. Oh, what will become of me? You are noble and generous—I was learning to look up to you and to accept your help, and now you torture me!"

He was pitiless. He read her more truly than she read herself, and he saw that the struggle must now be fought out to its end. Her agitation gave him hope—it was the surge and swell of a rising tide of passion which she resisted with the last exercise of a false strength. He must seem more cruel still, though the conflict in her heart moved him to infinite pity. His voice assumed a new power as he spoke again:

"Hannah," he said, "I *must* speak. Remember that I am pleading for all the remaining years of my life—and, it may be, for yours. Here is no question of subjection; I offer you the love that believeth all things, hopeth all things, endureth all things. It is not for me to look irreverently into your maiden heart: but, judging you, as woman, by myself, as man, you must have dreamed of a moment like this. You must have tried to imagine the face of the unknown beloved; you must have prefigured the holy confidence of love which would force you to give your fate into his hands; you must have drawn the blessed life, united with his, the community of interest, of feeling, and of faith, the protecting support on his side, the consoling tenderness on yours——"

She seized his arm with the hand nearest him, and grasped it convulsively. Her head dropped towards her breast and her face was hidden from his view. He gently disengaged the hand and held it in his own. But he would not be silent, in obedience to her dumb signal : he steeled his heart against her pain, and went on :

" You have tried to banish this dream from your heart, but you have tried in vain. You have turned away from the contemplation of the lonely future, and cried aloud for its fulfilment in the silence of your soul. By day and by night it has clung to you, a torment, but too dear and beautiful to be renounced——"

He paused. She did not withdraw her hand from his, but she was sobbing passionately. Still, her head was turned away from him. Her strength was only broken, not subdued.

" Remember," he said, " that nothing in our lives resembles the picture which anticipates its coming. I am not the man of your dreams. Such as I fancy them to be, no man on the earth would be worthy to represent him. But I can give you the tenderness, the faith, the support you have claimed from him, in your heart. Do not reject them while a single voice of your nature tells you that some portion of your ideal union may be possible in us. The fate of two lives depends on your answer : in this hour trust every thing to the true voice of your heart. You say you cannot hate me ?"

She shook her head, without speaking. She was still sobbing violently.

" I do not ask you, in this moment, if you love me. I cannot stake my future on a venture which I feel to be perilous. But I will ask you this : *could* you love me ?"

She made no sign : her hand lay in his, and her face was

bent towards her bosom. He took her other hand, and hold-ing them both, whispered: "Hannah, look at me."

She turned her head slowly, with a helpless submission, and lifted her face. Her cheeks were wet with tears, and her lovely dark-gray eyes, dimmed by the floods that had gushed from them in spite of herself, met his gaze imploringly. The strong soul of manhood met and conquered the woman in that glance. He read his triumph, but veiled his own consciousness of it—curbed his triumphant happiness, lest she should take alarm. Softly and gently, he stole one arm around her waist and drew her to his breast. The violence of her agitation gradually ceased; then, lifting her head, she withdrew from his clasp, and spoke, very softly and falteringly, with her eyes fixed on the ground:

"Yes, Maxwell, it is as I have feared. I will not say that I love you now, for my heart is disturbed. It is powerless to act for me, in your presence. I have felt and struggled against your power, but you have conquered me. If you love me, pity me also, and make a gentle use of your triumph. Do not bind me by any promise at present. Be satisfied with the knowledge that has come to me—that I have been afraid to love you, because I foresaw how easy it would be. Do not ask any thing more of me now. I can bear no more to-day. My strength is gone, and I am weak as a child. Be mag-nanimous."

He drew her once more softly to his breast and kissed her lips. There was no resistance, but a timid answering pressure. He kissed her again, with the passionate clinging sweetness of a heart that seals an eternal claim. She tore herself loose from him and cried with a fiery vehemence: "God will curse you if you deceive me now! You have bound me to think of you, day and night, to recall your looks and words, to—oh, Max-well, to what have you not bound my heart!"

"I would bind you to no more than I give," he answered. "I ask no promise. Let us simply be free to find our way to the full knowledge of each other. When you can trust your life to me, I will take it in tender and reverent keeping. I trust mine to you now."

She did not venture to meet his eyes again, but she took his outstretched hand. He led her to the edge of the peninsula, and they stood thus, side by side, while the liquid, tinkling semitones of the water made a contented accompaniment to the holy silence. In that silence the hearts of both were busy. He felt that though his nature had proved the stronger, she was not yet completely won : she was like a bird bewildered by capture, that sits tamely for a moment, afraid to try its wings. He must complete by gentleness what he had begun by power. She, at the moment, did not think of escape. She only felt how hopeless would be the attempt, either to advance or recede. She had lost the strong position in which she had so long been intrenched, yet could not subdue her mind to the inevitable surrender.

"I know that you are troubled," he said at last, and the considerate tenderness of his voice fell like a balm upon her heart, "but do not think that you alone have yielded to a power which mocks human will. I spoke truly, when I said that the approach of love, this time, had been met with doubt and resistance in myself. I have first yielded, and thus knowledge came to me while you were yet ignorant. From that ignorance the consciousness of love cannot, perhaps, be born at once. But I feel that the instinct which led me to seek you, has not been false. I can now appreciate something of your struggle, which is so much the more powerful than my own as woman's stake in marriage is greater than man's. Let us grant to each other an equally boundless trust, and in that pure air all remaining doubt, or jealousy, or fear of compromised rights, will die. Can you grant me this much, Hannah ? It is all I ask now."

She had no strength to refuse. She trusted his manhood already with her whole heart, though foreseeing what such trust implied. "It is myself only, that I doubt," she answered.

"Be kind to me," she added, after a pause, releasing her hand from his clasp and half turning away: "Consider how I have failed—how I have been deceived in myself. Another woman would have been justly proud and happy in my place, for she would not have had the hopes of years to uproot, nor have had to answer to her heart the accusation of disloyalty to humanity."

"We will let that accusation rest," he soothed her. "Do not think that you have failed: you never seemed so strong to me as now. There can be no question of conflicting power between two equal hearts whom love unites in the same destiny. The time will come when this apparent discord will appear to you as a 'harmony not understood.' But, until then, I shall never say a word to you which shall not be meant to solve doubt, and allay fear, and strengthen confidence."

"Let me go back, now, to my mother," she said. "Heaven pardon me, I had almost forgotten her. She wanted me to bring her some gentians. It is very late and she will be alarmed."

He led her back through the tangled, briery paths. She took his offered hand with a mechanical submission, but the touch thrilled her through and through with a sweetness so new and piercing, that she reproached herself at each return, as if the sensation were forbidden. Woodbury gathered for her a bunch of the lovely fringed gentian, with the short autumn ferns, and the downy, fragrant silver of the life-everlasting. They walked side by side, silently, down the meadow, and slowly up the road to the widow's cottage.

"I will deliver the flowers myself," said he, as they reached the gate, "Besides, is it not best that your mother should know of what has passed?"

She could not deny him. In the next moment they were in the little sitting-room. Mrs. Styles expected company to tea, and took her leave as soon as they appeared.

"Mother, will thee see Mr. Woodbury?" said Hannah,

opening the door into the adjoining room, where the invalid sat, comfortably propped up in her bed.

"Thee knows I am always glad to see him," came the answer, in a faint voice.

They entered together, and Woodbury laid the flowers on her bed. The old woman looked from one to another with a glance which, by a sudden clairvoyance, saw the truth. A new light came over her face. "Maxwell!" she cried; "Hannah!"

"Mother!" answered the daughter, sinking on her knees and burying her face in the bed-clothes.

Tears gushed from the widow's eyes and rolled down her hollow cheeks. "I see how it is," she said; "I prayed that it might happen. The Lord blesses me once more before I die. Come here, Maxwell, and take a mother's blessing. I give my dear daughter freely into thy hands."

Hannah heard the words. She felt that the bond, thus consecrated by the blessing of her dying mother, dared not be broken.

CHAPTER XXXII.

IN WHICH ALL RETREAT IS CUT OFF.

"COME back to-morrow, Maxwell," the Widow Thurston had said, as he took an affectionate leave of her; "come back, and let me hear what thee and Hannah have to say. I am too weak now to talk any more. My life has been so little acquainted with sudden visitations of joy, that this knowledge takes hold of my strength. Thee may leave me too, Hannah; I think I could sleep a little."

The latter carefully smoothed and arranged the pillows, and left the invalid to repose. Woodbury was waiting for her, in the door leading from the sitting-room to the hall. "I am going home now," he said; "can you give me a word of hope and comfort on the way? tell me that you trust me!"

"Oh, I do, I do!" she exclaimed; "Do not mistake either my agitation or my silence. I believe that if I could once be in harmony with myself, what I have heard from your lips to-day would make me happy. I am like my mother," she added, with a melancholy smile, "I am more accustomed to contempt than honor."

He led her into the hall and closed the door behind them. He put one arm protectingly around her, and she felt herself supported against the world. "Hereafter, Hannah," he whispered, "no one can strike at you except through me. Good-by until to-morrow!" He bent his head towards her face, and their eyes met. His beamed with a softened fire, a dewy tenderness and sweetness, before which her soul shivered and tingled in warm throbs of bliss, so quick and sharp as to touch the verge of pain. A wonderful, unknown fascination drew her lips to his. She felt the passionate pressure; her frame trembled; she heard the door open and close as in a dream, and blindly felt her way to the staircase, where she sank upon the lower step and buried her face in her hands.

She neither thought, nor strove to think. The kiss burned on and on, and every throb of her pulses seemed to break in starry radiations of light along her nerves. Dissolving rings of color and splendor formed and faded under her closed lids, and the blood of a new life rustled in her ears, as if the spirits of newly-opened flowers were whispering in the summer wind. She was lapped in a spell too delicious to break—an exquisite drunkenness of her being, beside which all narcotics would have been gross. External sounds appealed no more to her senses; the present, with its unfinished struggles, its torturing doubts, its prophecies of coming sorrow, faded far away, and her soul lay helpless and unresisting in the arms of a single sensation.

All at once, a keen, excited voice, close at hand, called her name. It summoned her to herself with a start which took away her breath.

"My dear girl! Good gracious, what's the matter!" exclaimed Mrs. Waldo, who stood before her. "I saw your mother was asleep, and I've been hunting you all over the house. You were not asleep, too?"

"I believe I was trying to think."

"Bless me, haven't you thought enough yet? I should say, from the look of your face, that you had seen a ghost—no, it must have been an angel! Don't look so, my dear, or I shall be afraid that you are going to die."

"If I were to die, it would make all things clear," Hannah Thurston answered, with a strong effort of self-control; "but I must first learn to live. Do not be alarmed on my account. I am troubled and anxious: I am not my old self."

"I don't wonder at it," rejoined Mrs. Waldo, tenderly. "You must see the loss that is coming, as well as the rest of us."

" Yes, I know that my mother can never recover, and I begin, already, to shrink from the parting, as if it were close at hand."

" Oh, my dear," cried Mrs. Waldo, melting into tears, " don't you see the truth yet ? Don't you see that the parting *is* close at hand ? I was afraid you did not know ; your mother, I was sure, would not tell you ; but, putting myself in your place, I did not think it right that you should be kept in ignorance. She is failing very fast."

Hannah Thurston grew very pale. Her friend led her through the door, and out into the little garden in the rear of the cottage. Some wind, far away to the west, had lifted into a low arch the gray concave of cloud, and through this arch the sinking sun poured an intense, angry, brassy light over the tree-tops and along the hillside fields. They leaned against the paling at the bottom of the garden, and looked silently on the fiery landscape. Hannah was the first to speak.

" You are a good friend to me," she said ; " I thank you for the knowledge. I knew the blow *must* come, but I hoped it might be delayed a little longer. I must bear it with what strength I may."

" God will help you, Hannah," said Mrs. Waldo, wiping away her tears. " He measures the burden for the back that is to bear it."

Woodbury walked home alone, without waiting, as usual, for Bute and the buggy. He threw back his shoulders and inhaled long draughts of the fresher evening air, with the relief of a man who has performed a trying task. He had full confidence in the completeness of his victory, yet he saw how narrowly he had escaped defeat. Had his mind not been previously occupied with this woman—had he not penetrated to the secret of her nature—had he not been bold enough to stake his fortune on the inherent power of his manhood, he must have failed to break down those ramparts of false pride which she had built up around her heart. A man of shallower knowledge would have endeavored to conquer by resistance—would have been stung by her fierce assertion of independence,

18

utterly mistaking the source from whence it sprang. In him it simply aroused a glorious sense of power, which he knew how to curb to the needs of the moment. It thrilled him with admiration, like the magnificent resistance of some wild mare of the steppes, caught in the hunter's lasso. It betrayed an unsuspected capacity for passion which could satisfy the cravings of his heart. This is no tame, insipid, feminine creature, he thought; but a full-blown woman, splendid in her powers, splendid in her faults, and unapproachable in that truth and tenderness which would yet bring her nature into harmony with his own.

A part of the power he had drawn from her seemed to be absorbed into his own being. The rapid flow of his blood lifted his feet and bore him with winged steps down the valley. His heart overleaped the uncertainties yet to be solved, and stood already, deep in the domestic future. After crossing Roaring Brook, he left the road and struck across his own meadows and fields in order to select a site, at once convenient and picturesque, for the cottage which he must build for Bute. Of course there could not be two households at Lakeside.

The next day made good the threat of the brassy sunset It rained in wild and driving gusts, and the sky was filled with the rifled gold of the forests. Woodbury paced his library impatiently, unable to read or write, and finally became so restless that he ordered dinner an hour before his accustomed time, to Mrs. Carrie Wilson's great dismay. Bute was no less astonished when Diamond and the buggy were demanded. "Why, Mr. Max.!" he exclaimed; "you're not goin' out such a day as this? Can't I go for you?"

"I have pressing business, Bute, that nobody can attend to but myself. Don't let your tea wait for me, Mrs. Wilson: I may be late."

Leaving the happy pair—happy in the rain which kept them all day to each other—to their wonder and their anxious surmises, Woodbury drove through the wind, and rain, and splashing mud, to the Widow Thurston's cottage. Hannah met him with an air of touching frankness and reliance, clasping his hand with a tender firmness which atoned for the silence of her lips. She looked pale and exhausted, but a soft, rosy flush passed over her face and faded away.

"I will tell mother you have come," she said. The next moment she reappeared at the door of the sick-room, and beckoned him to enter.

The widow was still in bed, and it was plainly to be seen that she would never leave it again. The bouquet of gentian and life-everlasting stood on a little table near her head. Her prim Quaker cap was uncrumpled by the pillow, and a light fawn-colored shawl enveloped her shoulders. She might have been placed in the gallery of the meeting-house, among her sister Friends, without a single fold being changed. Her thin hands rested weakly on the coverlet, and her voice was scarcely above a whisper, but the strong soul which had sustained her life was yet clear in her eye.

The daughter placed a chair for Woodbury by the bedside. He sat down and took the old woman's hand in both his own. She looked at him with a gentle, affectionate, motherly benignity, which made his eyes dim with the thought of his own scarcely-remembered mother.

"Maxwell," she said at last, "thee sees my days on the earth are not many. Thee will be honest with me, therefore, and answer me out of thy heart. I have not had many opportunities of seeing thee, but thee had my confidence from the first. Thee has had thy struggles with the world; thee is old enough to know thyself, and I will believe that thee hast learned to know Hannah, truly. She is not like other girls: she was always inclined to go her own way, but she has never failed in her duty to me, and I am sure she will not fail in her duty as thy wife."

Hannah, sitting at the foot of the bed, started at these words. She looked imploringly at her mother, but did not speak.

"Yes, Hannah," continued the old woman, "I have no

fears for thee, when thee once comes to understand thy true place as a woman. Thee was always more like thy father than like me. I see that it has not been easy for thee to give up thy ideas of independence, but I am sure that thy husband will be gentle and forbearing, so that thee will hardly feel the yoke. Will thee not, Maxwell?"

"I will," Woodbury replied. "I have told your daughter that I impose no conditions upon our union. It was the purity and truth of her nature which drew me almost against my will, to love her. I have such entire faith in that truth, that I believe we shall gradually come into complete harmony, not only in our feelings and aspirations, but even in our external views of life. I am ready to sacrifice whatever individual convictions may stand in the way of our mutual approach, and I only ask of Hannah that she will allow, not resist, the natural progress of her heart in the knowledge of itself."

"Thee hears what he says?" said the old woman, turning her eyes on her daughter. "Maxwell has answered the question I intended to ask: he loves thee, Hannah, as thee deserves to be loved. The thought of leaving thee alone in the world was a cross which I could not bring my mind to bear. The Lord has been merciful. He has led to thee the only man into whose hands I can deliver thee, with the certainty that he will be thy stay and thy happiness when I am gone. Tell me, my daughter, does thee answer his affection in the same spirit?"

"Mother," sobbed Hannah, "thee knows I would show thee my heart if I could. Maxwell deserves all the honor and gratitude I am capable of giving: he has been most noble and just and tender towards me: I cannot reject him—it is not in my nature—and yet—don't think hard of me, mother—it has all come so suddenly, it is so new and strange——"

Here she paused and covered her face, unable to speak further.

"It seems that I know thee better than I thought," said

the widow, and something like a smile flitted over her wasted features. "Thee needn't say any thing more: my mind is at rest. Come nearer to me, here, and seat thyself at Maxwell's side. I have a serious concern upon me, and you must both bear with me while I tell it."

The daughter came and seated herself at the head of the bed, beside Woodbury. The mother's right hand seemed to feel for hers, and she gave it. The other found its way, she knew not how, into his. The old woman looked at them both, and the expression of peace and resignation left her eyes. They were filled with a tender longing which she hesitated to put into words. In place of the latter came tears, and then her tongue was loosed.

"My children," she whispered, "it is best to be plain with you. From day to day I expect to hear the Master's call. I have done with the things of this life; my work is over, and now the night cometh, when I shall rest. The thought came to me in the silent watches, when I lifted up my soul to the Lord and thanked Him that He had heard my prayer. I thought, then, that nothing more was wanting; and, indeed, it may be unreasonable of me to ask more. But what I ask seems to be included in what has already happened. I know the instability of earthly things, and I should like to see with these eyes, the security of my daughter's fate. Maxwell, I lost the little son who would have been so near thy age had he lived. Will thee give me the right to call *thee* ' son ' in his place? Is thee so sure of thy heart that thee could give Hannah thy name *now?* It is a foolish wish of mine, I know ; but if you love each other, children, you may be glad, in the coming time, that the poor old mother lived to see and to bless your union !"

Woodbury was profoundly moved. He tenderly kissed the wasted hand he held, and said, in a hushed, reverential voice : "I am sure of my own heart. With your daughter's consent, it shall be as you say."

" Mother, mother !" cried Hannah : " I cannot leave thee !"

"Thee shall not, child. I would not ask it of thee. Maxwell knows what I mean: nothing shall be changed while I live, but you will not be parted for long. Nay, perhaps, I am selfish in this thing. Tell me, honestly, my children, would it make your wedding sad, when it should be joyful?"

"It will make it sacred," Woodbury answered.

"I will not ask too much of thee, Hannah," the widow continued. "What I wish would give me a feeling of comfort and security; but I know I ought to be satisfied without it. I have had my own concerns on thy account; I saw a thorny path before thee if thee were obliged to walk through life alone, and I feared thee would never willingly bend thy neck to wear the pleasant yoke of a wife. If I knew that thy lot was fixed, in truth; if I could hear thee speak the words which tell me that I have not lost a daughter but gained a son, the last remaining bitterness would be taken from death, and I would gladly arise and go to my Father!"

All remaining power of resistance was taken away from Hannah Thurston. She had yielded so far that she could no longer retreat with honor. Woodbury had taken, almost even before he claimed it, the first place in her thoughts, and though she still scarcely confessed to herself that she loved him as *her* husband should be loved, yet her whole being was penetrated with the presentiment of coming love. If she still feebly strove to beat back the rising tide, it was not from fear of her inability to return the trust he gave, but rather a mechanical effort to retain the independence which she felt to be gradually slipping from her grasp. Her mother's words showed her that she, also, foreboded this struggle and doubted its solution; she had, alas! given her cause to mistrust the unexpected emotion. Towards men—towards Woodbury, especially—she had showed herself hard and unjust in that mother's eyes. Could she refuse to remove the unspoken doubt by postponing a union, which, she acknowledged to herself, was destined to come? Could she longer hold back her entire faith from Woodbury, with his parting kiss of yesterday still warm upon her lips?

She leaned forward, and bent her head upon the old woman's breast. "Mother," she said, in a scarcely audible voice, "it shall be as thee wishes."

The widow tenderly stroked her dark-brown hair. "If I were not sure it was right, Hannah," she said, "I would give thee back thy consent. Let it be soon, pray, for I see that my sojourn with you is well-nigh its end."

"Let it be to-morrow, Hannah," Woodbury then said. "Every thing shall be afterwards as it was before. I will not take you from your mother's bedside, but you will simply give me the right to offer, and her the right to receive, a son's help and comfort."

It was so arranged. Only the persons most intimately connected with both—Waldos, Merryfields, Bute and Carrie—were to be informed of the circumstances and invited to be present. Mr. Waldo, of course, was to solemnize the union, though the widow asked that the Quaker form of marriage should first be repeated in her presence. She was exhausted by the interview, and Woodbury soon took his leave, to give the necessary announcements.

Hannah accompanied him to the door, and when it closed behind him, murmured to herself:

"I strove against the stream, and strove in vain—
Let the great river bear me to the main!"

The Waldos were alone in their little parlor—alone, but not lonely; for they were one of those fortunate wedded pairs who never tire of their own society. The appearance of Woodbury, out of the wind and rain, was a welcome surprise, and they both greeted him with hearty delight.

"Husband," cried Mrs. Waldo, "do put the poor horse into our stable, beside Dobbin. Mr. Woodbury will not think of going home until after tea."

The clergyman was half-way through the door before the

guest could grasp his arm. "Stay, if you please," he said; "I have something to say, at once, to both of you."

His voice was so grave and earnest, that they turned towards him with a sudden alarm. Something in his face tranquilized while it perplexed them.

"I once promised you, Mrs. Waldo," he continued, "that your husband should perform the marriage ceremony for me. The time has come when I can fulfil my promise. I am to be married to-morrow!"

The clergyman's lips receded so as to exhibit, not only all of his teeth, but also a considerable portion of the gums. His wife's dark eyes expanded, her hands involuntarily came together in a violent clasp, and her breath was suspended.

"I am to be married to-morrow," Woodbury repeated. "to Hannah Thurston."

Mrs. Waldo dropped into the nearest chair. "It's a poor joke," she said, at last, with a feeble attempt to laugh; "and I shouldn't have believed you could make it."

In a very few words he told them the truth. The next moment, Mrs. Waldo sprang upon her feet, threw both arms around him, and kissed him tempestuously. "I can't help it, husband!" she cried, giving way to a mild hysterical fit of laughter and tears: "It's so rarely things happen as they ought, in this world! What a fool I've been, to think you hated each other! I shall never trust my eyes again, no, nor my ears, nor my stupid brains. I'll warrant Mrs. Blake was a deal sharper than I have been; see if she is surprised when you send her word! Oh, you dear people, how happy you have made me—I'd rather it should come so than that husband should get a thousand converts, and build the biggest church in Ptolemy!"

Mr. Waldo also was moved, in his peculiar fashion. He cleared his throat as if about to commence a prayer, walked three times to the door and back, squeezing Woodbury's hand afresh at each return, and finally went to the window and remarked: "It is very stormy to-day."

In proportion as the good people recovered from their happy amazement, Woodbury found it difficult to tear himself away. They stormed him with questions about the rise and progress of his attachment, which his sense of delicacy forbade him to answer. "It is enough," he said, "that we love each other, and that we are to be married to-morrow." As he turned his horse's head towards Ptolemy, a figure wrapped in an old cloak and with a shapeless quilted hood upon the head, appeared on the plank sidewalk hastening in the direction of the widow's cottage. It was Mrs. Waldo.

The Merryfields were also at home when he called. Their life had, of late, been much more quiet and subdued than formerly, and hence they have almost vanished out of this history; but, from the friendly relation which they bore to Hannah Thurston, they could not well be omitted from the morrow's occasion. The news was unexpected, but did not seem to astonish them greatly, as they were both persons of slow perceptions, and had not particularly busied their minds about either of the parties.

"I'm sure I'm very glad, as it were," said Mr. Merryfield. "There are not many girls like Hannah Thurston, and she deserves to be well provided for."

"Yes, it's a good thing for her," remarked his wife, with a little touch of malice, which, however, was all upon the surface; "but Women's Rights will be what they always was, if their advocates give them up."

Darkness was setting down, and the rain fell in torrents, as Woodbury reached Lakeside. Bute, who had been coming to the door every five minutes for the last hour, had heard the rattling of wheels through the storm, and the Irishman was already summoned to take charge of the horse. In the sitting-room it was snug, and bright, and cheerful. A wood-fire blazed on the hearth, and Mrs. Carrie, with a silk handkerchief tied under her chin, was dodging about the tea-table. By the kindly glow in his heart towards these two happy

18*

creatures, Woodbury felt that his cure was complete; their bliss no longer had power to disturb him.

"How pleasant it is here!" he said. "You really make the house home-like, Mrs. Wilson."

Carrie's eyes sparkled and her cheeks reddened with delight. Bute thought: "He's had no unlucky business, after all." But he was discreet enough to ask no questions.

After tea, Woodbury did not go into the library, as usual. He drew a chair towards the fire, and for a while watched Mrs. Wilson's fingers, as they rapidly plied the needles upon a pair of winter socks for Bute. The latter sat on the other side of the fire, reading Dana's "Two Years before the Mast."

"Bute," said Woodbury, suddenly, "do you think we have room for another, in the house?"

To his surprise, Bute blushed up to the temples, and seemed embarrassed how to answer. He looked stealthily at Carrie.

Woodbury smiled, and hastened to release him from his error. "Because," said he, "you brought something to Lakeside more contagious than your fever. I have caught it, and now *I* am going to marry."

"Oh, Mr. Max., you don't mean it! It's not Miss Amelia Smith?"

Woodbury burst into a laugh.

"How can you think of such a thing, Bute?" exclaimed his wife. "There's only one woman in all Ptolemy worthy of Mr. Woodbury, and yet I'm afraid it isn't her."

"Who, Mrs. Wilson?"

"You won't be offended, Sir, will you? I mean Hannah Thurston."

"You have guessed it!"

Carrie gave a little scream and dropped her knitting. Bute tried to laugh, but something caught in his throat, and in his efforts to swallow it the water came into his eyes.

CHAPTER XXXIII.

CONCERNING MARRIAGE, DEATH, GOSSIP, AND GOING HOME.

THE occasion which called the few friends together at the cottage, the next morning, was sad and touching, as well as joyful. At least, each one felt that the usual cheerful sympathy with consummated love would be out of place, in circumstances so unusual and solemn. The widow felt that she was robbing her daughter's marriage of that sunshine which of right belonged to it, but in this, as in all other important decisions of life, she was guided by "the spirit." She perceived, indeed, that Hannah had not yet reached the full consciousness of her love—that the fixed characteristics of her mind fought continually against her heart, and would so fight while any apparent freedom of will remained; and, precisely for this reason, the last exercise of maternal authority was justified to her own soul. In the clairvoyance of approaching death she looked far enough into the future to know that, without this bond, her daughter's happiness was uncertain: with it, she saw the struggling elements resolve themselves into harmony.

Woodbury suspected the mother's doubt, though he did not share it to the same extent. He believed that the fierceness of the struggle was over. The chain was forged, and by careful forbearance and tenderness it might be imperceptibly clasped. There were still questions to be settled, but he had already abdicated the right of control; he had intrusted their solution to the natural operation of time and love. He would neither offer nor accept any express stipulations of rights, for this one promise embraced them all. Her nature could only be soothed to content in its new destiny by the deeper knowledge which that destiny would bring, and therefore, the mother's request was perhaps best for both. It only imposed upon him a more guarded duty, a more watchful self-control, in the newness of their relation to each other.

Mrs. Waldo, unable to sleep all night from the excitement of her honest heart, was with Hannah Thurston early in the morning. It was as well, no doubt, that the latter was allowed no time for solitary reflection, as the hour approached. By ten o'clock the other friends, who had first driven to the Cimmerian Parsonage, made their appearance in the little sitting-room. Woodbury came in company with Mr. Waldo, followed by Bute and Carrie. He was simply dressed in black, without the elaborate waistcoat and cravat of a bridegroom. But for the cut of his coat collar, the Friends themselves would not have found fault with his apparel. His face was calm and serene: whatever emotion he felt did not appear on the surface.

Mrs. Merryfield, in a lavender-colored silk, which made her sallow complexion appear worse than ever, occasionally raised her handkerchief to her eyes, although there were no signs of unusual moisture in them.

The door to the invalid's room was open, and the bed had been moved near it, so that she could both see and converse with the company in the sitting-room. Her spotless book-muslin handkerchief and shawl of white crape-silk were scarcely whiter than her face, but a deep and quiet content dwelt in her eyes and gave its sweetness to her feeble voice. She greeted them all with a grateful and kindly cheerfulness. The solemnity of the hour was scarcely above the earnest level of her life; it was an atmosphere in which her soul moved light and free.

Presently Hannah Thurston came into the room. She was dressed in white muslin, with a very plain lace collar and knot of white satin ribbon. Her soft dark hair, unadorned by a single flower, was brought a little further forward on the temples, giving a gentler feminine outline to her brow. Her face was composed and pale, but for a spot of red on each cheek, and a singularly vague, weary expression in her eyes. When Woodbury took her hand it was icy cold. She received the greetings of the others quietly, and then went forward to the bedside, at the beckon of her mother. The latter had been allowed to direct the ceremony according to her wish, and the time had now arrived.

The bridal pair took their seats in the sitting-room, side by side, and facing the open door where the invalid lay. The guests, on either side of them, formed a half-circle, so arranged that she could see them all. She, indeed, seemed to be the officiating priestess, on whom depended the solemnization of the rite. After a few moments of silence, such as is taken for worship in Quaker meetings, she began to speak. Her voice gathered strength as she proceeded, and assumed the clear, chanting tone with which, in former years, she had been wont to preach from the gallery where she sat among the women-elders of the sect.

"My friends," she said, "I feel moved to say a few words to you all. I feel that you have not come here without a realizing sense of the occasion which has called you together, and that your hearts are prepared to sympathize with those which are now to be joined in the sight of the Lord. I have asked of them that they allow mine eyes, in the short time that is left to me for the things of earth, to look upon their union. When I have seen that, I can make my peace with the world, and, although I have not been in all things a faithful servant, I can hope that the joy of the Lord will not be shut out from my soul. I feel the approach of the peace that passeth understanding, and would not wish that, for my sake, the house of gladness be made the house of mourning. Let your hearts be not disturbed by the thought of me. Rejoice, rather, that the son I lost so long ago is found at the eleventh hour, and that the prop for which I sought, for strength to walk through the Valley of the Shadow, is mercifully placed in my hands. For I say unto you all, the pure affection of the human heart is likest the love of the Heavenly Father, and they who bestow most of the one shall deserve most of the other!"

She ceased speaking, and made a sign with her hand. The hearts of the hearers were thrilled with a solemn, reverential awe, as if something more than a human presence overshadowed them. Woodbury and Hannah arose, in obedience to her signal, and moved a step towards her. The former had learned the simple formula of the Friends, and was ready to perform his part. Taking Hannah's right hand in his own, he spoke in a clear, low, earnest voice: "In the presence of the Lord, and these, our friends, I take Hannah Thurston by the hand, promising, through Divine assistance, to be unto her a loving and faithful husband, until Death shall separate us."

It was now the woman's turn. Perhaps Woodbury may have felt a pulse fluttering in the hand he held, but no one saw a tremor of weakness in her frame or heard it in the firm, perfect sweetness of her voice. She looked in his eyes as she pronounced the words, as if her look should carry to his heart the significance of the vow. When she had spoken, Mr. Waldo rose, and performed the scarcely less simple ceremonial of the Cimmerian Church. After he had pronounced them man and wife, with his hands resting on theirs linked in each other, he made a benedictory prayer. He spoke manfully to the end, though his eyes overflowed, and his practised voice threatened at every moment to break. His hearers had melted long before: only the Widow Thurston and the newly-wedded pair preserved their composure. They were beyond the reach of sentiment, no matter how tender. None of the others suspected what a battle had been fought, nor what deeper issues were involved in the victory.

The two then moved to the bedside, and the old woman kissed them both. "Mother," said Woodbury, "let me be a son to you in truth as in name."

"Richard!" she cried, "my dear boy! Thee is welcomer than Richard, for Hannah's sake. Children, have faith in each other—bear each other's burdens. Hannah, is there peace in thy heart now?"

"Mother, I have promised," she answered; "I have given my life into Maxwell's hands: peace will come to me."

"The Lord give it to thee, as He hath given it to me!" She closed her eyes, utterly exhausted, but happy.

The marriage certificate was then produced and signed by those present, after which they took their leave. Woodbury remained until evening, assisting his wife in her attendance on the invalid, or keeping her company in the sitting-room, when the latter slept. He said nothing of his love, or his new claim upon her. Rightly judging that her nature needed rest, after the severe tension of the past week, he sought to engage her in talk that would call her thoughts away from herself. He was so successful in this that the hours fled fast, and when he left with the falling night, to return to Lakeside, she felt as if a stay had been withdrawn from her.

The next morning he was back again at an early hour, taking his place as one of the household, as quietly and unobtrusively as if he had long been accustomed to it. Another atmosphere came into the cottage with him—a sense of strength and reliance, and tender, protecting care, which was exceedingly grateful to Hannah. The chaos of her emotions was already beginning to subside, or, rather, to set towards her husband in a current that grew swifter day after day. The knowledge that her fate was already determined silenced at once what would otherwise have been her severest conflict; her chief remaining task was to reconcile the cherished aims of her mind with the new sphere of duties which encompassed her life. At present, however, even this task must be postponed. She dared think of nothing but her mother, and Woodbury's share in the cares and duties of the moment became more and more welcome and grateful. It thrilled her with a sweet sense of the kinship of their hearts, when she heard him address the old woman as "mother"—when his arm, as tender as strong, lifted that mother from the bed to the rocking-chair, and back again—when she saw the wasted face brighten at his coming, and heard the voice of wandering memory call him, in the wakeful watches of the night. She, too, counted the minutes of the morning until he appeared, and felt the twilight drop more darkly before the cottage-windows after he had gone.

But, as the widow had promised, she did not part them long. On the fifth day after the marriage she sank peacefully to rest, towards sunset, with a gradual, painless fading out of life, which touched the hearts of the watchers only with the solemn beauty and mystery of death, not with its terror. Her external consciousness had ceased, some hours before, but she foresaw the coming of the inevitable hour, and there was a glad resignation in her farewell to her daughter and her newly-found son. " Love one another !" were her last, faintly-whispered words, as her eyes closed on both.

Hannah shrank from leaving the cottage before the last rites had been performed, and Miss Sophia Stevenson, as well as Mrs. Waldo, offered to remain with her. Woodbury took charge of the arrangements for the funeral, which were simple and unostentatious, as became the habit of her sect.

A vague impression of what had happened was floating through Ptolemy, but was generally received with an incredulity far from consistent with the avidity of village gossip. The death of the Widow Thurston had been anticipated, but the previous marriage of her daughter was an event so astounding—so completely unheralded by the usual prognostications, and so far beyond the reach of any supposable cause— that the mind of Ptolemy was slow to receive it as truth. By the day of the funeral, however, the evidences had accumulated to an extent that challenged further doubt. But doubters and believers alike determined to profit by the occasion to gratify their curiosity under the Christian pretext of showing respect to the departed. The rumor had even reached Atauga City by the evening stage, and the Misses Smith, having recently supplied themselves with lilac dresses, which, as a half-mourning color, would not be inappropriate, resolved also to attend the funeral services.

As the hour drew nigh, the road in front of the little cottage was crowded with vehicles. It was a mild, sunny October afternoon, and as the room in which the corpse lay would not contain a tenth part of the guests, they filled the yard and garden and even the side-walk in front, entering the house as they arrived, to take that silent look at the dead which is suggested, let us believe, more by human sympathy than by human curiosity. And, indeed, a solemn loveliness of repose rested on the thin, composed features of the corpse. All shadow of pain had passed away, and an aspect of ineffable peace and comfort had settled in its place. Her hands were laid, one over the other, upon her breast—not with the stony pressure of death, but as if in the light unconsciousness of sleep. Upon the coffin-lid lay a wreath of life-everlasting, its gray, silvery leaves and rich, enduring odor, harmonizing well with the subdued tastes and the quiet integrity of the sect to which the old widow had belonged. Even the Rev. Lemuel Styles, to whom the term "Quaker" implied a milder form of infidelity, stood for a long time beside the coffin, absorbed in the beauty of the calm, dead face, and murmured as he turned away: "She hath found Peace."

Two old Friends from Tiberius, with their wives, were also in attendance, and the latter devoted themselves to Hannah, as if it were a special duty imposed upon them. Before the coffin-lid was screwed down, they sat for some time beside the corpse, with their handkerchiefs pressed tightly over their mouths. Their husbands, with Mr. Waldo and Merryfield, bore the coffin to the hearse. The guests gathered around and in front of the house now began to open their eyes and prick their ears. The daughter must presently appear, as first of the mourners, and in company with her husband, if she were really married. They had not long to wait. Hannah, leaning on Woodbury's arm, issued from the front door of the cottage, and slowly passed down the gravel walk to the carriage in waiting. Her unveiled face was pale and profoundly sad; her eyes were cast down, and none of the company caught their full glance. Woodbury's countenance indicated the grave and tender sympathy which filled his heart. He saw the spectators, without seeming to notice them, and the keenest curiosity was baffled by his thorough self-possession. Both were surrounded by an atmosphere of sorrow and resignation, in which all expression of their new nuptial relation was lost. They might have been married for years, so far as any thing could be guessed from their manner.

The other carriages gradually received their occupants and followed, in the order of their nearness to the deceased, whether in the bonds of sect or those of friendship. Among these the Waldos claimed a prominent place and the Merryfields were close behind them. The procession was unusually large; it seemed, indeed, as if all Ptolemy were present. On reaching the Cimmerian churchyard, Bute and the farmers whose lands adjoined Lakeside were on hand to assist the mourners and their friends in alighting from the carriages, and to take care of the horses. The grave was dug at a little distance from those of the Cimmerians, in a plot of soft, unbroken turf. Supports were laid across its open mouth, and when the coffin had been deposited thereon, preparatory to being lowered, and the crowd had gathered in a silent ring, enclosing the mourners and their immediate friends, one of the Friends took off his broad-brimmed hat and in simple, eloquent words, bore testimony to the truth and uprightness, to the Christian trust and Christian patience of the departed. The two women again pressed their handkerchiefs violently upon their mouths, while he spoke. Woodbury took off his hat and reverently bent his head, though the other Friend stood bolt upright and remained covered.

Mr. Waldo then followed, with an earnest, heart-felt prayer. He was scarcely aware how much he risked in thus consecrating the burial of a Quaker woman, and it was fortunate that no laxity of doctrine could be discovered in the brief sentences he uttered. It was not Doctrine, but Religion, which inspired his words, and the most intolerant of his hearers felt their power while secretly censuring the act. He, too, referred to the widow's life as an example of pious resignation, and prayed that the same Christian virtue might come to dwell in the hearts of all present.

When the coffin had been lowered, and the first spadeful of earth, though softly let down into the grave, dropped upon the lid with a muffled, hollow roll, Hannah started as if in pain, and clung with both hands to her husband's arm. He bent his head to her face and whispered a word; what it was, no other ear than hers succeeded in hearing. The dull, rumbling sounds continued, until the crumbling whisper of the particles of earth denoted that the coffin was forever covered from sight. Then they turned away, leaving the mild Autumn sun to shine on the new mound, and the thrush to pipe his broken song over the silence of the dead.

The moment the churchyard gate was passed, Ptolemy returned to its gossip. The incredulous fact was admitted, but the mystery surrounding it was not yet explained. In the few families who considered themselves "the upper circle," and were blessed with many daughters, to none of whom the rich owner of Lakeside had been indifferent, there was great and natural exasperation.

"I consider it flying in the face of Providence," said Mrs. Hamilton Bue to her husband, as they drove homewards; "for a man like him, who knows what society is, and ought to help to purfect it from fanaticism, to marry a strong-minded woman like she is. And after all he said against their doctrines! I should call it hypocritical, _I_ should!"

"Martha," her husband answered, "If I were you, I wouldn't say much about it, for a while yet. He's only insured in the Saratoga Mutual for a year, to try it."

Mrs. Styles consoled her sister, Miss Legrand, who at one time allowed herself dim hopes of interesting Woodbury in her behalf. "I always feared that he was not entirely firm in the faith ; he never seemed inclined to talk with Mr. Styles about it She, you know, is quite an Infidel, and, of course, he could not have been ignorant of it. It's very sad to see a man so misled—'the lust of the eye,' Harriet."

"I should say it was witchcraft," Harriet remarked, with a snappish tone ; "she's a very plain-looking girl—like an owl with her big gray eyes and straight hair." Miss Legrand wore hers in ropy ringlets of great length.

"I shouldn't have believed it if I hadn't seen it with my own eyes !" exclaimed Miss Celia Smith to her sister, Miss Amelia. "I always thought they were dead set against each other." Miss Celia was more inclined to be emphatic than choice in her expressions.

"They made believe they were," her sister replied. "She must have been afraid he'd back out, after all, or they wouldn't have been married so, right off the reel. It was her last chance: she's on the wrong side of thirty-five, I should say." Miss Amelia was thirty-three, herself, although she only confessed to twenty-five. The memory of a certain sleigh-ride the winter before, during which her incessant fears of an overturn obliged Woodbury to steady her with his arm, was fresh in her mind, with all its mingled sweet and bitter. Several virgin hearts shared the same thought, as the carriages went homeward—that it was a shame, so it was, that this strong-minded woman, whom nobody imagined ever could be a rival, should sneak into the fold by night and carry off the pick of the masculine flock !

Meanwhile, the objects of all this gossip returned to the desolate cottage. When they entered the little sitting-room, Hannah's composure gave way, under the overwhelming sense of her loss which rushed upon her, as she saw that every thing was restored to its usual place, and the new life, without her mother, had commenced. Her tears flowed without restraint, and her husband allowed the emotion to exhaust itself before he attempted consolation. But at last he took her, still sobbing, to his breast, and silently upheld her.

"Hannah," he said, "my dear wife, how can I leave you here alone, to these sad associations? This can no longer be your home. Come to me with your burden, and let me help you to bear it."

"Oh, Maxwell," she answered, "you are my help and my comfort. No one else has the same right to share my sorrow. My place is beside you: I will try to fill it as I ought: but— Maxwell—can I, dare I enter your home as a bride, coming thus directly from the grave of my mother?"

"You will bring her blessing in the freshness of its sanctity," he said. "Understand me, Hannah. In the reverence for your sorrow, my love is patient. Enter my home, now, as the guest of my heart, giving me only the right to soothe and comfort, until you can hear, without reproach, the voice of love."

His noble consideration for her grief and her loneliness melted Hannah's heart. Through all the dreary sense of her loss penetrated the gratitude of love. She lifted her arms and clasped them about his neck. "Take me, my dear husband," she whispered, "take me, rebellious as I have been, unworthy as I am, and teach me to deserve your magnanimity."

He took her home that evening, under the light of the rising moon, down the silence of the valley, through the gathering mists of the meadows, and under the falling of the golden leaves. The light of Lakeside twinkled, a ruddy star, to greet them, and with its brightening ray stole into her heart the first presentiment of Woman's Home.

CHAPTER XXXIV.

CONCERNING THE NEW HOUSEHOLD OF LAKESIDE.

IN a day or two all the familiar articles of furniture which Hannah desired to retain, were transferred to Lakeside with her personal effects, and the cottage was closed until a new tenant could be found. In the first combined shock of grief and change, the secluded beauty of her new home was especially grateful. The influences of Nature, no less than the tender attentions of her husband, and the quiet, reverent respect of Bute and Carrie, gradually soothed and consoled her. Day after day the balmy southwest wind blew, hardly stirring the smoky purple of the air, through which glimmered the floating drifts of gossamer or the star-like tufts of wandering down. The dead flowers saw their future resurrection in these winged, emigrating seeds; the trees let fall the loosened splendor of their foliage, knowing that other summers were sheathed in the buds left behind; even the sweet grass of the meadows bowed its dry crest submissively over the green heart of its perennial life. Every object expressed the infinite patience of Nature with her yearly recurring doom. The sun himself seemed to veil his beams in noonday haze, lest he should smite with too severe a lustre the nakedness of the landscape, as it slowly put off its garment of life.

For years past, she had been deprived of the opportunity so to breathe the enchantment of the heavenly season. As soon as the chill of the morning dew had left the earth, she went forth to the garden and orchard, and along the sunny margin of the whispering pine-wood behind the house, striving to comprehend the change that had come over her, and fit her views of life to harmony with it. In the afternoons she went, at Woodbury's side, to a knoll overhanging the lake, whence the landscape was broader and grander, opening northward beyond the point, where now and then a sail flashed dimly along the blue water. Here, sitting on the grassy brink, he told her of the wonderful life of the tropics, of his early hopes and struggles, of the cheating illusions he had cherished, the sadder knowledge he had wrested from experience, and that immortal philosophy of the heart in which all things are reconciled. He did not directly advert to his passion for herself, but she felt it continually as the basis from which his confidences grew. He was a tender, trustful friend, presenting to her, leaf by leaf, the book of his life. She, too, gave him much of hers in return. She found a melancholy pleasure in speaking of the Past to one who had a right to know it, and to whom its most trifling feature was not indifferent. Her childhood, her opening girlhood, her education, her desire for all possible forms of cultivation, her undeveloped artistic sympathies and their conflict with the associations which surrounded her—all these returned, little by little, and her husband rejoiced to find in them fresh confirmations of the instinctive judgment, on the strength of which he had ventured his love.

In the evenings they generally sat in the library, where he read to her from his choice stores of literature, and from the reading grew earnest mutual talk which calmed and refreshed her mind. The leisure of his long years in India had not been thrown away: he had developed and matured his natural taste for literature by the careful study of the English and French classics, and was familiar with the principal German and Italian authors, so far as they could be known through translations. He had also revived, to some extent, his musty knowledge of the Greek and Latin poets, and his taste had thus become pure and healthy in proportion to the variety of his

acquiremeuts.   Hannah had, now and then, perhaps (though
this is doubtful, in the circumscribed community of Ptolemy),
encountered men of equal culture, but none who had spoken
to her as an equal, from the recognition of like capacities in
her own mind. She saw, in this intercourse with her husband,
the commencement of a new and inexhaustible intellectual
enjoyment.   That clamor of her nature for the supposed rights
denied to her sex was, in part, the result of a baffled mental
passion, which now saw the coveted satisfaction secured to
it ; and thus the voice of her torment grew weaker day by
day.

Day by day, also, with scarce a spoken word of love, the
relations between the two became more fond and intimate.
Woodbury's admirable judgment taught him patience. He
saw the color gradually coming back to the pale leaves of the
flower, and foresaw the day when he might wear it on his·
bosom.   The wind-tossed lake smoothed its surface more and
more, and gleams of his own image were reflected back to him
from the subsiding waves.   The bride glided into the wife by
a gentle, natural transition. She assumed her place as head
of the household, and Carrie, who was always nervously
anxious under the weight of the responsibility, transferred it
gladly to her hands. The sense of her ownership in the treasures of Lakeside, which had at first seemed incredible, grew
real by degrees, as she came to exercise her proper authority,
and as her husband consulted with her in regard to the proposed changes in the garden and grounds. All these things
inspired her with a new and delightful interest. The sky of
her life brightened as the horizon grew wider. Her individual sphere of action had formerly been limited on every side ;
her tastes had been necessarily suppressed ; and the hard,
utilitarian spirit, from which she shrank, in the associations of
her sect, seemed to meet her equally wherever she turned.
Her instinct of beauty was now liberated ; for Woodbury,
possessing it himself, not only appreciated, but encouraged its
vitality in her nature.   The rooms took the impression of her

taste, at first in minor details and then in general arrangements, and this external reflection of herself in the features of her home reacted upon her feelings, separating her by a constantly widening gulf from her maiden life.

The gold of the forests corroded, the misty violet bloom of the Indian Summer was washed away by sharp winds and cold rains, and when winter set in, the fire on the domestic hearth burned with a warm, steady flame. Immediately after the marriage, Woodbury had not only picked out a very pretty site for the cottage which he must now build in earnest for Bute's occupancy, but had immediately engaged masons and carpenters to commence the work. It was on a low knob or spur of the elevation upon which stood his own house, but nearer the Anacreon road. Bute and Carrie were in ecstasies with the design, which was selected from "Downing's Landscape Gardening." It was a story and a half high, with overhanging balconies, in the Swiss style, and promised to be a picturesque object in the view from Lakeside, especially as it would just hide the only ragged and unlovely spot in the landscape, to the left of Roaring Brook. By great exertion on Bute's part, it was gotten under roof, and then left for a winter's seasoning, before completion in the spring. This house and every thing connected with it took entire possession of the mind of Mrs. Carrie Wilson, and not a day passed without her consulting Hannah in regard to some internal or external arrangement. She would have flowered chintz curtains to the windows of the "best room"—blue, with small pink roses: the stuff would be cheap and of course she would make them herself: would it be better to have them ruffled with the same, or an edging of the coarse cotton lace which she had learned to knit? Bute had promised her a carpet, and they could furnish the room little by little, so that the expense would not be felt. "We must economize," she invariably added, at the close: "we are going to lay something by every year, and I want to show Bute that I can manage to have every thing nice and tasty, without spending much."

19

The little woman still retained her admiration for Hannah, perhaps in an increased degree, now that Woodbury (for whom Carrie had conceived such a profound respect) had chosen her to be his wife. She confided to the latter all her wonderful plans for the future, utterly forgetful how they differed from the confidences which she had been accustomed to bestow. Hannah could not help remarking her present unconsciousness of that ambition which she had once pitied as mistaken, though she had not the heart to check it. A similar change seemed to be taking place in herself. " Is it always so ?" she reflected. " Is the fulfilment of our special destiny as women really the end of that lofty part which we resolved to take in the forward struggle of the race? Was my desire to vindicate the just claims of my sex only the blind result of the relinquishment of earlier dreams ? It cannot be : but this much is true—that the restless mind is easily cradled to sleep on the beatings of a happy heart."

The strict seclusion of her life was rarely broken. The Waldos and Merryfields came once or twice for a brief call, but Woodbury, though he went occasionally to Ptolemy, did not urge her to accompany him. Sometimes, on mild days, he drove with her over the hills, re-exploring for her the picturesque little nooks of the upland which he had discovered. Hannah was contented with this ; she knew that Society awaited her, after a time, but it could not now deny her that grateful repose, in which she gathered strength, and hope, and harmony with herself. Indeed, the life of Ptolemy flowed more quietly than usual, this season. The Great Sewing-Union was not reorganized, because the Cimmerians had decided on a " Donation Party" for Mr. Waldo's benefit, instead of a Fair ; the Abolitionists had not sufficient cohesive power without the assistance of Hannah and Mrs. Merryfield, and prepared their contributions separately at home ; and thus only the Mission Fund remained. The latter, however, was stimulated to fresh activity by the arrival of a package of letters, early in December, from Mrs. Jehiel Preeks (formerly Miss Eliza

Clancy), dated from Cuddapah, in the Telugu Country. She had passed a week at Jutnapore, and was shocked to find that her brown namesake, for whom she had made the mousseline-de-laine frock with tucks, had been married a year, although not yet fourteen, and exhibited to her a spiritual grand-baby, on her arrival. She forwarded to Miss Ruhaney Goodwin a letter in the Telugu language from her son Elisha, which the spinster had framed and hung up beside her looking-glass. "It's more like bird-tracks than any thing else," she whispered, confidentially, "but the sight of it gives me a deal of comfort."

Thus, the labors for the Mission Fund were resumed, but the young men who attended looked back to the days of the Great Sewing-Union with regret. The mixed composition of the latter had been its great charm, and even the ladies of the Fund missed the extended comparison of stuffs and patterns, and the wider range of mantua-making gossip which they had enjoyed during the previous winter. The curiosity in regard to the Woodburys still continued to be rife; but Mrs. Waldo, who was continually appealed to, as their nearest friend, for an explanation of the mystery, knew no more than any of the others what had passed between the two before their marriage. The first sharpness of public comment on the occurrence soon gave place to a more just and reasonable feeling. Both were popular, in a different way, in Ptolemy. A moderate amount of good-luck would not have been grudged to either, but that they should find it in each other was the thought which astounded the community. The strangest things, however, soon grow common-place, and all that had been said or thought, in the first period of wonderment, was gradually forgotten. Both Mrs. Styles and Mrs. Hamilton Bue called at Lakeside, and went home well pleased with the kindly courtesy and hospitality which they received. They saw that the husband and wife evidently understood each other and were happy in the knowledge: any thing further than this the keenest scrutiny failed to discover. Woodbury had the coolness of a thorough man of the world in turning aside impertinent questions, such as many good persons, with their unformed American ideas of propriety, see no harm in asking. It is true that he sometimes gave offence in this way, but his apparent unconsciousness of the fact healed the wound, while it prevented a repetition of the impertinence.

Hannah admired the self-possession of her husband, as a power, the attainment of which was beyond her own reach. The characteristic which had most repelled her, on their first acquaintance, was now that which threw around her a comforting sense of protection and defence. It was not a callous condition of his finer sensibilities, she saw; it was a part of his matured balance and repose of character, yet the latter still sometimes impressed her almost like coldness, in comparison with her own warmth of sentiment. For this reason, perhaps, as her love to him deepened and strengthened—as his being became more and more a blissful necessity—his composed, unchanging tenderness often failed to satisfy, in full measure, the yearnings of her heart. While she was growing in the richness of her affections, he seemed to be standing still.

With all Woodbury's experience of woman, he had yet much to learn. No course could have been better chosen than the delicate and generous consideration which he exhibited towards his wife, up to a certain point. His mistake was, that he continued it long after the necessity had ceased, and when, to her changed nature, it suggested a conscientious sense of justice rather than the watchfulness of love. He was waiting for her heart to reach the knowledge which already filled it to overflowing, betraying itself daily by a subtle language which he did not understand. The experiences through which he had passed had familiarized him with the presence of passion in himself: his heart did not throb less powerfully, but it throbbed beneath a mask of calmness which had been sternly enforced upon him. He did not reflect that his wife, with all the pervading passion of the ripened woman, still possessed, in this her first love, the timidity of a girl, and could not ask for that independent speech of the heart which he withheld.

Even with regard to the questions which had so nearly kept them asunder, she would have preferred frank discussion to silence. Here, however, he had promised her full liberty of action, and she could not refer to them without a seeming doubt of his word. Once or twice, indeed she timidly approached the subject, but he had avoided it with a gentleness and kindness which she could not resist. She suffered no reproach to rest upon him, in her inmost thought; she reproached herself for having invoked the promise—for having obliged him to raise the thin, impalpable screen which still interposed itself between their hearts. Mrs. Styles, in reporting her visit, had said: "they look as if they had already been married ten years," and she had said truly. That calm, which was so grateful in the first tumult of the wife's feelings, which enabled her to pass through the transition of her nature in peace, now sometimes became oppressive in the rush of happy emotions that sought but knew not how to find expression.

The knowledge that Woodbury had modified his personal habits so as to avoid offending her prejudices, also gave her pain. She learned, from Carrie, that he had been in the habit of drinking a glass or two of claret at dinner, and of smoking in the library after meals, or as he read in the evenings. Now, the wine had disappeared from the table, and he took his cigar in the garden, or in the veranda. Both the habits were still repugnant to her sense of right, but love was beginning to teach her tolerance. He was, perhaps, partly weaned from them, she thought, and in that case it would be wrong in her to lead him back to his old subjection; yet, on the other hand, what sacrifice had he not made for her? and what had she made for him?

Towards the end of winter, she found that her mind was becoming singularly confused and uncertain. The reconciliation with her destiny, the harmony of heart and brain, which she seemed to be on the point of attaining, slid back again into something which appeared to be a disturbance of temperament rather than of intellect. Things, trifling in themselves, exalted or depressed her without any apparent reason; unreasonable desires presented themselves to her mind, and in this perpetual wavering of the balance of her nature, nothing seemed steady except her love for her husband. She longed, at times, to throw herself upon his breast and weep the confession she did not dare to speak; but her moments of strength perversely came when he was absent, and her moments of cowardice when he was present. Through all the uncertain, shifting range of her sensations, ran, nevertheless, a dazzling thread of some vague, foreboded bliss, the features of which she could not distinguish. She often repeated to herself the song of Clärchen, in Goethe's " Egmont," which was among the works her husband had read with her:

> " Blessèd,
> Depressèd,
> Pensively brooding amain;
> Trembling,
> Dissembling,
> Hovering in fear and in pain:
> Sorrowing to death, or exulting the angels above,
> Blessed alone is the heart in its love!"

One afternoon she was seized with such an intense longing for the smell of tobacco-smoke, that she could scarcely wait until Woodbury, who had ridden into Ptolemy, returned home. As soon as he had taken off his great-coat and kissed her, as was his wont, she drew him into the library.

"Maxwell," she said, "I have a favor to ask of you."

"Have you? I shall be delighted to grant it."

"You will think it strange," she continued, blushing: " I wish you would light a cigar; I think I should find the smoke agreeable."

"That is not asking a favor, Hannah; it is granting one to me. I'll take one of my best, and you shall have a fair trial."

He laughed pleasantly at what he considered a benevolent effort on her part to endure his favorite indulgence. He placed easy-chairs for them, on opposite sides of the fire, lest her experiment might fail from being overdone, and lighted one of his choicest Cabañas. The rich, delicate, sedative odor soon pervaded the air, but she held her ground. He took down Sir Thomas Browne, one of his favorites, and read aloud the pleasant passages. The snowy ashes lengthened in the cigar, the flavor of the book grew more choice and ripe, and after an hour he tossed the diminutive remaining end into the grate, saying:

"Well, what is the result?"

"I quite forgot the cigar, Maxwell," she answered, "in my enjoyment of Sir Thomas. But the odor at first—you will laugh at me—was delightful. I am so sorry that you have been so long deprived of what must be to you an agreeable habit, on my account."

"I have only been acting up to my principles," he said, "that we have a right to exercise our individual freedom in such matters, when they do not interfere directly with the comfort of others. But here, I am afraid, Sir Thomas helped to neutralize your repugnance. Shall we go on with him, a chapter and a cigar at a time? Afterwards I can take Burton and Montaigne, if you are not fully acclimated."

He spoke gayly, with a dancing light in his eyes, but the plan was seriously carried out. Hannah was surprised to find in Montaigne a reference to the modern doctrine (as she supposed it to be) of "Women's Rights." It was not a pleasant reflection that the cause had made so little progress in three centuries. The reading of this passage brought up the subject in a natural way, and she could not help remarking:

"Discussions on the subject will never come to an end, until we have some practical application of the theory, which will be an actual and satisfactory test of its truth."

"I, for one, would not object to that," Woodbury answered, "provided it could be tried without disturbing too much the established order of Society. If a large class of women should at any time demand these rights, a refusal to let the experiment be tested would imply a fear of its success. Now, I do not believe that any system can be successful which does not contain a large proportion of absolute truth, and while I cannot think, as you know, that woman is fitted for the same career as man, I am not afraid to see her make the trial. I will pledge myself to abide by the result."

"If all men were as just, Maxwell, we should have no cause to complain. After all, it is the right *to try*, rather than the right *to be*, which we ask. The refusal to grant us that does not seem either like the magnanimity of the stronger, or even an assured faith in his strength."

"Men do not seriously consider the subject," said he. "The simple instinct of sex dictates their opposition. They attribute to a distorted, unfeminine ambition, what is often— in *you*, Hannah, I know it—a pure and unselfish aspiration. The basis of instinct is generally correct, but it does not absolve us from respect for the sincerity of that which assails it."

"I will try to be as just to you, in return !" she exclaimed. "I feel that my knowledge has been limited—that I have been self-boastful of the light granted to my mind, when it was only groping in twilight, towards the dawn. My heart drew back from you, because it feared a clashing of opinions which could never harmonize.

She was on the verge of a tenderer confession, but he did not perceive it. His words, unwittingly, interrupted the current of her feelings. His voice was unintentionally grave and his brow earnest, as he said: "I trust, more than ever, to the true woman's nature in you, Hannah. Let me say one thing to set your mind at rest forever. It was my profound appreciation of those very elements in your character which led you to take up these claims of Woman and make them your own, that opened the way for you to my heart. I reverence the qualities without accepting all the conclusions born of them. I thank God that I was superior to shallow prejudice, which would have hindered me from approaching you, and thus have lost me the blessing of my life !"

He rose and laid away the book. Every word he had said was just and noble, but it was not the fervid, impassioned utterance which her heart craved to hear. There were tears in her eyes, but he misinterpreted them.

Ah, the "true woman's nature!" Did he trust to it? Did he know it, in its timidity, in its exacting fondness, in its pride of devotion and its joy of sacrifice?

Not yet.

19*

CHAPTER XXXV.

IN WHICH WE ATTEND ANOTHER MEETING IN FAVOR OF "WOMEN'S RIGHTS."

EARLY in April, Mr. Isaiah Bemis again made his appearance in Ptolemy. He had adopted REFORM as his profession, and in the course of fifteen years' practice had become a Jack-of-all-trades in philanthropy and morals. He was ready, at the shortest notice, to give an address on Total Abstinence, Vegetarianism (or "Vegetality," as he termed it, with a desire to be original), Slavery, Women's Rights, or Non-Resistance, according to the particular need of the community he visited.

He also preached, occasionally, before those independent religious bodies which spring up now and then in a spasmodic protest against church organization, and which are the natural complement of the Perfectionists in Government and Society, who believe that the race is better off without either. In regard to Spiritualism he was still undecided: it was not yet ingrafted upon the trunk of the other Reforms as an accepted branch of the same mighty tree, and a premature adherence to it might loosen his hold on those boughs from which he sucked sustenance, fame, and authority.

By slender contributions from the Executive Committees of the various Societies, and the free hospitality of the proselytes of one or the other, all through the country, Mr. Bemis was in the possession of a tolerable income, which came to him through the simple gratification of his natural tendencies. To harangue the public was a necessity rather than a fatigue. He was well stored with superficial logic wherewith to overwhelm ordinary disputants, while with his hosts, from whom no opposition was to be expected, he assumed an air of arrogant superiority. This was principally their own fault. A man who hears himself habitually called an Apostle and a Martyr, very soon learns to put on his robes of saintship. None of his subjects was bold enough to dispute the intellectual and moral autocracy which he assumed. Thus, for fifteen years, a Moral Gypsy, he had led a roving life through the country, from Maine to Indiana, interrupted only by a trip to England, in 1841, as a "delegate at large" to the "World's Anti-Slavery Convention." During all this time his wife had supported herself by keeping a boarding-house in a small town in New Jersey. He was accustomed to visit her once a year, and at such times scrupulously paid his board during the few weeks of his stay—which circumstance was exploited as an illustration of his strict sense of justice and his constancy to the doctrine of Women's Rights.

Central New York was a favorite field for Mr. Bemis, and he ranged its productive surface annually. His meetings being announced in advance in the *Annihilator*, his friends were accustomed to have all the arrangements made on his arrival. On reaching Ptolemy, however, two or three days still intervened before the meeting could be held, on account of Tumblety Hall having been previously engaged by the "Mozart Ethiopian Opera," and the "Apalachicolan Singers." Mr. Bemis, as a matter of course, claimed the hospitality of the Merryfields in the interval. He was not received with the expected *empressement*, nor were his Orphic utterances listened to with the reverence to which he was used. The other friends of the cause—foremost among them Seth Wattles—nevertheless paid their court as soon as his arrival became known, and (spiritually) on bended knees kissed the hand of the master.

The arrangements for the coming meeting were first to be discussed. Attention had been drawn away from the reform during the previous summer by the renewed agitation in favor of Temperance, and it was desirable to renovate the faded impression. The Rev. Amelia Parkes had been invited, but was unable to leave her congregation; and Bessie Stryker was more profitably engaged in lecturing before various literary associations, at one hundred dollars a night (payable only in gold). Mr. Chubbuck, of Miranda, could be depended upon, but he was only a star of the second magnitude, and something more was absolutely required.

"We must get Miss Thurston—I mean Mrs. Woodbury—again. There is nothing else to be done," remarked Mr. Bemis, drawing down his brows. He had not forgotten that the people of Ptolemy had freely given to her the applause which they had withheld from his more vigorous oratory.

"I rather doubt, as it were," said Mr. Merryfield, "whether Hannah will be willing to speak."

"Why not?" thundered Bemis.

"She's lived very quietly since her marriage, and I shouldn't wonder if she'd changed her notions somewhat."

"*I* shouldn't wonder," said Seth, drawing up his thick nostrils, "if her husband had forbidden her ever to speak again. If he could bully her into marrying him, he could do that, too."

"You're mistaken, Seth," exclaimed Mr. Merryfield, coloring with a mild indignation, "there's nothing of the bully about Woodbury. And if they two don't love each other sincerely, why, Sarah and me don't!"

"We can easily find out all about it," said Mr. Bemis, rising and buttoning his coat over his broad chest. "Mr. Wattles, will you come with me? We will constitute ourselves a Committee of Invitation."

Seth, nothing loath, put on his hat, and the two started on their errand. It was but a short walk to Lakeside, which they reached soon after Woodbury had taken his customary place in the library, with a cigar in his mouth and a volume of Pepys' Diary in his hand. Hannah sat near him, quiet and happy: she was not only reconciled to her husband's habit, but enjoyed the book and talk which accompanied it more than any other part of the day. On this occasion they were interrupted by Bute, who announced the visitors in the following style:

"Miss' Woodbury, here's Seth Wattles and another man has come to see you."

Hannah rose with a look of disappointment, and turned towards her husband, hesitatingly.

"Shall I go, also?" he asked.

"I would prefer it, Maxwell; I have no private business with any one."

Bute had ushered the visitors into the tea-room. The door to the library was closed, but a faint Cuban perfume was perceptible. Seth turned towards Mr. Bemis with elevated eyebrows, and gave a loud sniff, as much as to say: "Do you notice that?" The latter gentleman scowled and shook his head, but said nothing.

Presently the door opened and Hannah made her appearance, followed by her husband. She concealed whatever embarrassment she may have felt at the sight of Mr. Bemis, frankly gave him her hand, and introduced him to her husband.

"Be seated, gentlemen," said the latter, courteously. "I would ask you into the library, but I have been smoking there, and the room may not be agreeable to you."

"Hem! we are not—exactly—accustomed to such an atmosphere," said Mr. Bemis, taking a chair.

Woodbury began talking upon general topics, to allow his guests time to recover from a slight awkwardness which was evident in their manner. It was not long, however, before Mr. Bemis broached the purpose of his visit. "Mrs. Woodbury," said he, "you have heard that we are to have a meeting on Wednesday evening?"

"Yes."

"We have been disappointed in getting the Rev. Amelia Parkes, and the advocacy of The Cause is incomplete unless a woman takes part in it. I have therefore come to ask your assistance. We wish, this time, to create an impression."

It was not a welcome message. She knew that such a test

must come, some time; but of late she had been unable to apply her mind steadily to any subject, and had postponed, by an agreement with herself, the consideration of all disturbing questions. She looked at her husband, but his calm face expressed no counsel. He was determined that she should act independently, and he would allow no word or glance to influence her decision.

"It is long since I have spoken," she said at last; "I am not sure that I should be of service." She wished to gain time by an undecided answer, still hoping that Woodbury would come to her assistance.

"*We* are the best judges of that," said Mr. Bemis, with something of his old dictatorial tone. "I trust you will not fail us, now when we have such need. The interest in The Cause has very much fallen off, in this neighborhood, and if you desert us, to whom shall we look for help?"

"Yes, Hannah," chimed in Seth, "you know we have always looked upon you as one of the Pillars of Progress."

It grated rather harshly upon Woodbury's feelings to hear his wife addressed so familiarly by the ambitious tailor; but she was accustomed to it, from the practice of her sect to bear testimony against what they call "compliments."

"I have not lost my interest in the cause," Hannah answered, after another vain attempt to read Woodbury's face; "but I have freely uttered my thoughts on the subject, and I could say nothing that has not been already heard."

"Nothing else is wanted," said Mr. Bemis, eagerly. "The Truth only gains by repetition; it still remains eternally new. How many thousand times have the same Bible texts been preached from, and yet their meaning is not exhausted—it is not even fully comprehended. How much of the speaker's discourse do you suppose the hearers carry home with them? Not a tenth part—and even that tenth part must be repeated ten times before it penetrates beneath the surface of their natures. Truth is a nail that you cannot drive into ordinary comprehensions with one blow of the hammer: you must pile stroke upon stroke, before it enters far enough to be clinched fast. It is not the time for you to draw back now, in a season of faint-heartedness and discouragement. If you fail, it will be said that your views have changed with the change in your life, and you will thus neutralize all your labors heretofore."

"That cannot be said of me!" exclaimed Hannah, thoroughly aroused and indignant. "My husband has been too just—too generous, differing with me as he does—to impose any restrictions upon my action!" She turned towards him. He answered her glance with a frank, kindly smile, which thanked her for her words, but said no more. "Well, then!" she continued; "I will come, if only to save him from an unjust suspicion. I will not promise to say much. You overestimate my value as an advocate of the reform."

"It is not for me," said Mr. Bemis, with affected humility, "to speak of what *I* have done; but I consider myself competent to judge of the services of others. Your influence will be vastly increased when your consistency to The Cause shall be known and appreciated. I now have great hopes that we shall inaugurate an earnest moral awakening."

Little more was said upon the subject, and in a short time the two reformers took their leave. After Woodbury had returned from the door, whither he had politely accompanied them, he said, in his usual cheerful tone: "Well, Hannah, shall we return to Old Pepys?"

Her momentary excitement had already died away. She appeared perplexed and restless, but she mechanically rose and followed him into the library. As he took up the book, she interrupted him: "Tell me, Maxwell, have I done right?"

"You should know, Hannah," he answered. "I wish you to act entirely as your own nature shall prompt, without reference to me. I saw that you had not much desire to accept the invitation, but, having accepted it, I suppose you must fulfil your promise."

"Yes, I suppose so," she said; but her tone was weary and

disappointed. How gladly would she have yielded to his slightest wish, if he would only speak it! What a sweet comfort it would have been to her heart, to know that she had sacrificed something belonging to herself, even were it that higher duty which had almost become a portion of her conscience, for his sake! The independence which he, with an over-considerate love, had assured to her, seemed to isolate her nature when it should draw nearer to his. His perfect justice crushed her with a cold, unyielding weight of—not obligation, for that cannot coexist with love—but something almost as oppressive. She had secured her freedom from man's dictation—that freedom which once had seemed so rare and so beautiful—and now her heart cried aloud for one word of authority. It would be so easy to yield, so blissful to be able to say: "Maxwell, I do this willingly, for your sake!"—but he cruelly hid the very shadow of his wish from her sight and denied her the sacrifice! He forced her independence back upon her when she would have laid it down, trusting all she was and all she might be to the proved nobility of his nature! Self-abnegation, she now felt, is the heart of love; but the rising flood of her being was stayed by the barriers which she had herself raised.

All the next day her uneasiness increased. It was not only her instinctive fear of thwarting her husband's hidden desire which tormented her, but a singular dread of again making her appearance before the public. She was not conscious of any change in her views on the question of Woman, but they failed to give her strength and courage. A terrible sinking of the heart assailed her as often as she tried to collect her thoughts and arrange the expected discourse in her mind. Every thing seemed to shift and slide before the phantasm of her inexplicable fear. Woodbury could not help noticing her agitation, but he understood neither its origin nor its nature. He was tender as ever, and strove to soothe her without adverting to the coming task. It was the only unhappy day she had known since she had come to Lakeside.

The next morning dawned—the morning of Wednesday—and noon came swiftly as a flash, since she dreaded its approach. The dinner had been ordered earlier than usual, for the meeting was to commence at two o'clock; and as soon as it was over, Woodbury said to her: "It is time you were ready, Hannah. I will take you to Ptolemy, of course, and will attend the meeting, or not, as you desire."

She drew him into the library. "Oh, Maxwell!" she cried; "will you not tell me what you wish me to do?"

"My dear wife," he said, "do not torment yourself on my account. I have tried to fulfil to the utmost my promise to you: have I said or done any thing to make you suspect my sincerity?"

"Oh, nothing, nothing! You have kept it only too well. But, Maxwell, my heart fails me: I cannot go! the very thought of standing where I once stood makes me grow faint. I have no courage to do it again."

"Then do not," he answered; "I will make a suitable apology for your failure. Or, if that is not enough, shall I take your place? I will not promise," he added, smiling, "to go quite so far as you might have done, but I will at least say a few earnest words which can do no harm. Who has so good a right to be your substitute as your husband?"

"Maxwell," she sobbed, "how you put me to shame!" It was all she could say. He took her in his arms, kissed her tenderly, and then drove into Ptolemy.

Tumblety Hall was crowded. The few advocates of the cause had taken good care to spread the news that Mrs. Woodbury was to be one of the speakers, and there was a general, though indefinite curiosity to hear her again, now that she was married. Mr. Bemis rubbed his hands as he saw how rapidly the benches were filling, and observed to Seth Wattles: "The iron is hot, and we have only to strike hard." After the audience had assembled, the latter was chosen Chairman of the meeting, Mr. Merryfield declining, on account of his having so frequently filled that office, "as it were."

Seth called the meeting to order with a pompous, satisfied air. His phrases were especially grandiloquent; for, like many semi-intelligent persons, he supposed that the power of oratory depended on the sound of the words. If the latter were not always exactly in the right place, it made little difference. "Be ye convinced, my brethren," he concluded, "that absoloot Right will conquer, in spite of the concatenations and the hostile discrepancies of Urrur (Error)! Our opponents have attempted to shut up every door, every vein and artery, and every ramification of our reform, but the angel of Progress bursts the prison-doors of Paul and Silas, and when the morning dawns, the volcano is extinct!"

Mr. Bemis followed, in what he called his "sledge-hammer style," which really suggested a large hammer, so far as voice and gesture were concerned, but the blows did not seem to make much impression. He had, however, procured a few new anecdotes, both of the wrongs and the capacities of woman, and these prevented his harangue from being tedious to the audience. They were stepping-stones, upon which the latter could wade through the rushing and turbid flood of his discourse.

It had been arranged that Hannah should follow him, and Mr. Chubbuck, of Miranda, close the performance. When, therefore, Mr. Bemis sat down, he looked around for his successor, and the audience began to stir and buzz, in eager expectation. She was not upon the platform, but Woodbury was seen, pressing down the crowded side-aisle, apparently endeavoring to make his way to the steps. He finally reached them and mounted upon the platform, where a whispered consultation took place between himself and Mr. Bemis. The countenance of the latter gentleman grew dark, and he in turn whispered to Seth, who, after some hesitation, arose and addressed the meeting:

"We have again an illustration," he said, "of the vanity of human wishes. We expected to present to you the illustrious prototype of her sex, to whose cerulean accents you have often listened and applauded, but disappointment has chilled the genial current of our souls. She has sent a subsidy in her place, and he is prepared to await your pleasure, if you will hear the spontaneous vindication."

A movement of surprise ran through the audience, but their disappointment at once gave place to a new curiosity, and a noise of stamping arose, in token of satisfaction. Woodbury, whose demeanor was perfectly serious and collected, in spite of a strong tendency to laugh at Seth, stepped forward to the front of the platform, and, as soon as silence returned, began to speak. His manner was easy and natural, and his voice unusually clear and distinct, though the correctness of his pronunciation struck his hearers, at first, like affectation.

"I appear voluntarily before you, my friends," he said, "as a substitute for one whom you know. She had promised to speak to you on a subject to which she has given much earnest thought, not so much for her own sake as for that of her sex. Being unable to fulfil that promise, I have offered to take her place,—not as the representative of her views, or of the views of any particular association of persons, but as a man who reveres woman, and who owes her respect in all cases, though he may not always agree with her assertion of right. ('Good!' cried some one in the audience.) I stand between both parties; between you who denounce the tyranny of man (turning to Mr. Bemis), and you who meet with contempt and abuse (turning back towards the audience) all earnest appeals of woman for a freer exercise of her natural faculties. No true reform grows out of reciprocal denunciation. When your angry thunders have been launched, and the opposing clouds dissolve from the exhaustion of their supply, the sunshine of tolerance and charity shines between, and the lowering fragments fuse gently together in the golden gleam of the twilight. Let me speak to you from the neutral ground of universal humanity; let me tell you of some wrongs of woman which none of you need go far to see—some rights which each man of you, to whom God has given a help-meet, may grant beside his own hearth-stone and the cradle of his children! We Americans boast of our superior civilization; we look down with a superb commiseration not only upon the political, but the social and domestic life of other lands. Let us not forget that the position which woman holds in the State—always supposing that it does not transcend the destiny of her sex—is the unerring index on the dial of civilization. It behooves us, therefore, in order to make good our boast, to examine her condition among us. We are famed, and perhaps justly, for the chivalrous respect which we exhibit towards her in public; do we grant her an equal consideration in our domestic life? Do we seek to understand her finer nature, her more delicate sensibilities, her self-sacrificing desire to share our burdens by being permitted to understand them?"

The attention of the audience was profoundly enlisted by these words. The calm, dispassionate, yet earnest tone of the speaker was something new. It was an agreeable variation from the anathemas with which they not only did not sympathize, but which they were too indifferent to resent. Mr. Bemis, it is true, fidgeted uneasily in his arm-chair, but he was now quite a secondary person. Woodbury went on to advocate a private as well as public respect for woman; he painted, in strong colors, those moral qualities in which she is superior to man; urged her claim to a completer trust, a more generous confidence on his part; and, while pronouncing no word that could indicate an actual sympathy with the peculiar rights which were the object of the meeting, demanded that they should receive, at least, a respectful consideration. He repeated the same manly views which we have already heard in his conversations with his wife, expressing his faith in the impossibility of any permanent development not in accordance with nature, and his confidence that the sex, under whatever conditions of liberty, would instinctively find its true place.

His address, which lasted nearly an hour, was received with hearty satisfaction by his auditors. To the advocates of the reform it was a mixture of honey and gall. He had started, apparently, from nearly the same point; his path, for a while, had run parallel with theirs, and then, without any sensible divergence, had reached a widely different goal. Somehow, he had taken, in advance, all the strength out of Mr. Chubbuck's oration; for, although the latter commenced with an attack on Woodbury's neutral attitude, declaring that "we cannot serve two masters," the effort was too sophistical to deceive anybody. His speech, at least, had the effect to restore Mr. Bemis to good humor. Miss Silsbee, a maiden lady from Atauga City, was then persuaded to say a few words. She recommended the audience to "preserve their individuality: when that is gone, all is gone," said she. "Be not like the foolish virgins, that left their lamps untrimmed. O trim your wicks before the eleventh hour comes, and the Master finds you sleeping!"

There seemed to be but a very remote connection between these expressions and the doctrine of Women's Rights, and the audience, much enlivened by the fact, dispersed, after adopting the customary resolutions by an overwhelming majority. "We have sowed the field afresh," cried Mr. Bemis, rubbing his hands, as he turned to his friends on the platform, "in spite of the tares of the Enemy." This was a figurative allusion to Woodbury.

The latter resisted an invitation to take tea with the Waldos, in order to hurry home to his wife. Mrs. Waldo had been one of his most delighted hearers, and her parting words were: "Remember, if you don't tell Hannah every thing you said, I shall do it, myself!"

On reaching Lakeside, Hannah came to the door to meet him. Her troubled expression had passed away, and a deep, wonderful light of happiness was on her face. Her eyes trembled in their soft splendor, like stars through the veil of falling dew, and some new, inexpressible grace clung around her form. She caught his hands eagerly, and her voice came low and vibrant with its own sweetness.

"Did you take my place, Maxwell?" she asked.

He laughed cheerfully. "Of course I did. I made the longest speech of my life. It did not satisfy Bemis, I am sure, but the audience took it kindly, and you, Hannah, if you had been there, would have accepted the most of it."

"I know I should!" she exclaimed. "You must tell me all—but not now. Now you must have your reward—oh, Maxwell, I think I can reward you!"

"Give me another kiss, then."

He stooped and took it. She laid her arms around his neck, and drew his ear to her lips. Then she whispered a few fluttering words. When he lifted his face he saw upon it the light and beauty of unspeakable joy.

CHAPTER XXXVI.

IN WHICH THE MAN AND WOMAN COME TO AN UNDERSTANDING.

WOODBURY, without having intended it, very much increased his popularity in Ptolemy by the part he had taken in the meeting. His address was marked by a delicate tact which enabled him to speak for Woman, on behalf of his wife, while preserving his own independence of her peculiar views. The men suspected that her opinions had been modified by his stronger mind, and that this was the secret of her non-appearance : they were proud that he had conquered the championess. The women, without exception, were delighted with his defence of their domestic rights ; most of them had had more or less experience of that misapprehension of their nature which he portrayed, and the kindness, the considerate justice which dictated his words came very gratefully to their ears. Even Mrs. Hamilton Bue remarked to a neighbor, at the close of his speech : "Well, if he's learned all that from *her*, she's done *some* good, after all!"

Thus it happened that the marriage came to be regarded with favor. Ptolemy not only submitted with a good grace to what was irrevocable, but readily invented a sufficient justification for it. Hannah found a friendly disposition towards her, as she began to mingle a little more with the society of the place : the women, now that they recognized her as one of themselves, approached her more genially and naturally than hitherto, and the men treated her with a respect, under which no reserved hostility was concealed. The phenomenon was adopted, as is always the case, into the ordinary processes of nature.

But a new life had commenced at Lakeside, and this and all other changes in the temper of the community passed unnoticed. The spring advanced with a lovelier mystery in every sprouting germ, in every unfolding bud. In those long, sunny days when the trodden leaves of the last year stir and rustle under the upward pressure of the shooting grass, when new violets and buttercups open from hour to hour, and the shimmering, gauzy tints of the woodlands deepen visibly between dawn and sunset, the husband and wife saw but the external expression of the rich ripening of their own lives. The season could not impart its wonted tender yearnings, for they slept in the bliss of the possession they had only prefigured before, but it brought, in place of them, a holier and more wonderful promise. Here, the wife's nature at last found a point of repose : around this secret, shining consciousness, the struggling elements ranged themselves in harmonious forms. A power not her own, yet inseparable from both, and as welcome as it was unforeboded, had usurped her life, and the remembrance of the most hardly-won triumphs which her mind had ever achieved grew colorless and vain.

By the end of May the cottage for Bute was completed. It was all that Downing had promised from the design, except in regard to the expense, which was nearly double his estimate. However, it formed a very picturesque feature in the foreground of the landscape from Lakeside, and was conveniently situated for the needs of the farm. It was a day of jubilee for Bute and Carrie when they took possession of it. Mrs. Waldo must needs be present at the migration, and assist with her advice in the arrangement of the furniture. Fortunately, the little "best room" had but two windows, and Mrs. Wilson's dream of the chintz curtains was realized. Bute had bought a brownish ingrain carpet, somewhat worn, at an auction sale in Ptolemy, for a very trifling sum ; and in addition to the portraits of General and Lady Washington, which Mrs. Babb had inherited from Jason, and bequeathed to him in turn, Woodbury had given him a splendidly-colored lithograph of an

"American Homestead," with any quantity of cattle and poultry. It is impossible to describe the pride of Mrs. Wilson in this room. One window commanded a cheerful view of the valley towards Ptolemy, while the white front of Lakeside looked in at the other. Bute had surrounded the looking-glass and picture-frames with wreaths of winter-green, which reminded Woodbury of his impromptu ball-room in the Bowery, and in the fireplace stood a huge pitcher filled with asparagus, blossoming lilacs, and snow-balls. It was Mrs. Wilson's ambition to consecrate the house by inviting them all to tea, and a very pleasant party they were.

When the guests had left, and the happy tenants found themselves alone, the little wife exclaimed: "Oh, Bute, to think that we should have a house of our own!"

"Yes," said he, "*'t is* our'n, jist as much as though we owned it, as long as we *think* so. Property's pretty much in *thinkin'*, onless you've got to raise money on it. I know when I'm well off, and if you'll hitch teams with me in savin', Carrie, we can leastways put back all the interest, and it'll roll up as fast as we want it."

"You'll see, Bute," his wife answered, with a cheerful determination; "it's a life that will suit me *so* much better than sewing around from house to house. I'll raise chickens and turkeys, and we can sell what we don't want; and then there's the garden; and the cow; and we won't spend much for clothes. I wish you'd let me make *yours*, Bute; I'm sure I could do it as well as Seth Wattles."

The grin on Bute's face broadened, as he listened to the lively little creature, and when she stopped speaking, he took her around the waist by both arms and lifted her into the air. She was not alarmed at this proceeding, for she knew she would come down gently, getting a square, downright kiss on the way. Never were two persons better satisfied with each other.

At Lakeside there were also changes and improvements. The garden was remodelled, the grounds were extended, and

fresh consignments of trees and plants continually arrived from
the Rochester nurseries.   Both Woodbury and his wife
delighted in the out-door occupation which these changes gave,
and the spring deepened into summer before they were aware.
To a thoroughly cultivated man, there is no life compared to
that of the country, with its independence, its healthy enjoyments, its grateful repose—provided that he is so situated that
his intellectual needs can be satisfied.   Woodbury's life in
Calcutta had accustomed him to seek this satisfaction in himself, or, at best, to be content with few friends.   In Hannah,
he had now the eager, sympathetic companion of his mind, no
less than the partner of his affections.   The newest literature
came to him regularly from New York and Boston, and there
was no delight greater than to perceive how rapidly her tastes
and her intellectual perceptions matured with the increase of
her opportunities of culture.

    The tender secret which bound them so closely soothed her
heart for the time, without relieving its need of the expression
and the answer which still failed.   His watchful fondness was
always around her, folding her more closely and warmly, day
by day; but he still seemed to assert, in her name, that freedom which her love no longer demanded—nay, which stood
between her and the fulfilment of her ideal union with him.
She craved that uncalculating passion which is as ready to
ask as to give—the joy of mutual demand and mutual surrender.   The calm, deep, and untroubled trust which filled his
nature was not enough.   Perhaps love, she thought, in the
self-poised, self-controlled being of man, takes this form; perhaps it lies secure and steadfast below the tender agitations,
the passionate impulses, the voiceful yearnings which stir the
soul of woman.   If so, she must be content; but one thing
she must yet do, to satisfy the conscience of love.   She must
disabuse his mind of the necessity of granting her that independence which she had ignorantly claimed; she must confess
to him the truer consciousness of her woman's nature; and—
if her timid heart would allow—she must once, though only

once, put in words all the passionate devotion of her heart for him.

The days went by, the fresh splendor of the foliage darkened, the chasing billows of golden grain drifted away and left a strand of tawny stubble behind, and the emerald bunches on the trellises at Lakeside began to gather an amethystine bloom. And the joy, and the fear, and the mystery increased, and the shadow of a coming fate, bright with the freshest radiance of Heaven, or dark with unimagined desolation—but which, no one could guess—lay upon the household. Woodbury had picked up in the county paper, published at Tiberius, a little poem by Stoddard, of which these lines clung to his memory and would not be banished:

> " The laden summer will give me
> What it never gave before,
> Or take from me what a thousand
> Summers can give no more!"

Thus, as the approach of Death is not an unmingled sorrow, the approach of Life is not an unmingled joy. But, as we rarely breathe, even to those we best love, the fear that at such times haunts our hearts, chased away as soon as recognized, so to her he was always calm and joyfully confident.

September came, and fiery touches of change were seen on the woods. The tuberoses she had planted in the spring poured from their creamy cups an intoxicating dream of the isles of nutmeg-orchards and cinnamon-groves; the strong, ripe blooms of autumn lined the garden walks, and the breath of the imprisoned wine dimmed the purple crystal of the grapes. Then, one morning, there was a hushed gliding to and fro in the mansion of Lakeside; there was anxious waiting in the shaded rooms; there were heart-wrung prayers, as the shadows of the different fates sank lower upon the house, and fitfully shifted, like the rapid, alternate variations of cloud and sunshine in a broken sky. Death stood by to dispute the consummation of life; but, as the evening drew on, a faint, wailing cry of victory was heard, and Life had triumphed.

Woodbury's strong nature was shaken to its centre, both by the horrible weight of the fears which had been growing upon him throughout the day, and the lightning-flash of over-whelming gladness which dispersed them. As he took the helpless, scarcely human creature in his arms, and bent his face over it, his tears fell fast. He knelt beside the bed, and held it before the half-closed eyes of the mother, who lay silent, pale, as if flung back, broken, from the deeps of Death. The unfeeling authority which reigned in the chamber drove him away. The utmost caution, the most profound repose, was indispensable, the physician said. All night long he watched in the next room, slowly gathering hope from the whispered bulletins of the nurse. In the morning, he left his post for a little while, but soon returned to it. But a single interview was granted that day, and he was forbidden to speak. He could only take his wife's hand, and look upon the white, saintly beauty of her face. She smiled faintly, with a look of ineffable love, which he could not bear unmoved, and he was forbidden to agitate her.

Gradually the severity of the orders was relaxed, and he was allowed to enter the room occasionally, in a quiet way, and look upon the unformed features of his son. The mother was slowly gaining strength, and the mere sight of her hus-band was so evident a comfort to her that it could not now be denied. In the silent looks they interchanged there was a profounder language than they had yet spoken. In him, the strong agitation of the man's heart made itself felt through the mask of his habitual calm; in her, the woman's all-yielding love confessed its existence, and pleaded for recognition. Wood-bury, too grateful for the fact that the crisis of imminent danger was slowly passing away, contented himself with these voiceless interviews, and forcibly shut for a while within his heart the words of blessing and of cheer which he longed to utter.

On the fifth day the physician said to him: "She is now safe, with the ordinary precautions. I have perhaps been a little over-despotic, because I know the value of the life at stake. You have been patient and obedient, and you shall have your reward. You may see her as often as you like, and I will allow you to talk, on condition that you break off on the least appearance of fatigue."

After his departure, Woodbury, glad at heart, hastened to his wife's chamber. She lay perfectly still, and the curtains were drawn to shield her face from the light. "She is asleep," said the nurse.

"Leave me a while here, if you please," said he, "I will watch until she wakes."

The nurse left the room. He knelt beside the cradle, and bent over the sleeping babe, giving way, undisturbed by a watching eye, to the blissful pride of a father's heart. Presently his eyes overflowed with happy tears, and he whispered to the unconscious child: "Richard! my son, my darling!"

The babe stirred and gave out a broken wail of waking. He moved the cradle gently, still murmuring: "Richard, my darling! God make me worthy to possess thee!"

But he was not unseen; he was not unheard. Hannah's light slumber had been dissolved by the magnetism of his presence, but so gently that her consciousness of things, returning before the awaking of the will, impressed her like a more distinct dream. As in a dream, through her partially-closed lids, she saw her husband kneel beside the cradle. She saw the dim sparkle of his tears, as they fell upon the child; she heard his soliloquy of love and gratitude—heard him call that child by her father's name! Her mother's words flashed across her mind with a meaning which she had never thought of applying to her own case. *Her* father, too, had wept over his first-born; in his heart passion had smouldered with intensest heat under a deceitful calm; and her mother had only learned to know him when the knowledge came too late. To

herself, that knowledge had come now: she had caught one
glimpse of her husband's heart, when he supposed that only
God's ear had heard him. In return for that sacred, though
involuntary confession, she would voluntarily make one as
sacred. The duty of a woman gave her strength; the dignity
of a mother gave her courage.

When the babe was again lulled into quiet, she gently
called: "Maxwell!"

He rose, came to the bed, softly put his arms around her,
and laid his lips to hers. "My dear wife," he said.

"Maxwell, I have seen your heart," she whispered; "would
you see mine? Do you recollect what you asked me that
afternoon, in the meadows—not whether I loved, but whether
I *could* love? You have never repeated the other question
since."

"There was no need to ask," said he; "I saw it answered."

"My dear husband, do you not know that feeling, in a
woman, must be born through speech, and become a living
joy, instead of lying as a happy, yet anxious weight beneath
the heart? Maxwell, the truth has been on my tongue a
thousand times, waiting for some sign of encouragement from
you; but you have been so careful to keep the promise which
I accepted—nay, almost exacted, I fear—that you could not
see what a burden it had become to me. You have been too
just to me; your motive was generous and noble: I complain
of myself only in having made it necessary. You did right to
trust to the natural development of my nature through my
better knowledge of life; but, oh, can you not see that the
development is reached? Can you not feel that you are
released from a duty towards me which is inconsistent with
love?"

"Do you release me willingly, my wife?" he cried, an eager
light coming into his eyes. "I have always felt that you were
carried to me by a current against which you struggled. I
could not resist the last wish of your mother, though I should
never, alone, have dared to hasten our union. I would have

waited—would have given you time to know your heart—time to feel that the only true freedom for man or woman is reached through the willing submission of love."

"Ignorant as I was," she answered, "I might never have come to that knowledge. I should have misunderstood the submission, and fought against it to the last. Mother was right. She knew me better than I knew myself. Maxwell, will you take back your promise of independence? Will you cease to allow that cold spectre of justice to come between our hearts?"

"Tell me why you ask it?" said he.

"Because I love you! Because the dream whose hopelessness made my heart sick has taken your features, and is no more a dream, but a blessed, blessed truth! Ask yourself what that means, and you will understand me. If you but knew how I have pined to discover your wish, in order that I might follow it! You have denied me the holiest joy of love—the joy of sacrifice. As you have done it for my sake, so for my sake abandon the unfair obligation. Think what you would most desire to receive from the woman you love, and demand that of me!"

"My darling, I have waited for this hour, but I could not seem to prematurely hasten it. I have held back my arms when they would have clasped you; I have turned away my eyes, lest they might confuse you by some involuntary attraction; I have been content with silence, lest the voice of my love might have seemed to urge the surrender which your heart must first suggest. Do you forgive me, now, for the pitiless passion with which I stormed you?"

"There is your forgiveness," she murmured, through her tears, pointing to the cradle.

He tenderly lifted the sleeping babe, and laid it upon her bosom. Then he knelt down at the bed, and bent his face upon the pillow, beside her own. "Darling," he whispered, "I accept all that you give: I take the full measure of your love, in its sacred integrity. If any question of our mutual rights remain, I lay it in these precious little hands, warm with the new life in which our beings have become one."

"And they will forever lead me back to the true path, if I should sometimes wander from it," was her answer.

THE END.

COMPLETION

OF THE

LIFE AND LETTERS

OF

Washington Irving.

BY PIERRE M. IRVING.

IN FOUR VOLUMES.

The Publisher has the satisfaction of announcing that the 4th volume of this delightful and attractive work is completed. It includes a COPIOUS INDEX TO THE FOUR VOLUMES, prepared by S. Austin Allibone, LL.D., author of the "Dictionary of Authors."

⁎ This work is not a bald biographical account of an individual, but chiefly consists in a series of sprightly and charming LETTERS, written in various parts of Europe and t e United States, and graphically describing notable events, national characteristics, and distinguished statesmen and literary men, whose names are "familiar in our mouths as household words"—the whole extending over a period of more than SIXTY YEARS, and including the times of the First Napoleon, the times of Jefferson, and Madison, and Aaron Burr;—associations and correspondence with Scott, Lockhart, Moore, Rogers, Leslie, James, Dickens, and a host of others in England, France, and Spain: while the literary and political incidents and characteristics of the whole of the present century, at nome and abroad, are recalled by the vivid biographical touches of these familiar letters. The genial humor, and the magnetic characteristics of the writer, are especially drawn out of the domestic and family letters, which form a large part of the volumes. No epistolary or biographical collection in the English language, or perhaps in any other, is comparable with this in the variety, scope, and interest of the topics, and the characters introduced. It may be described as "the Autobiography of Washington Irving, as [unconsciously] related in several hundred familiar letters to friends; with pen-pictures of the times in which he lived."

The materials for this work, if more freely used, would have filled six or eight volumes. The editor, who received from his distinguished relative these materials, with the request that he should use them as he thought best, has selected and compressed into four volumes, the matter most essential to the narrative, and most illustrative of the author's characteristics. It was at first hoped that this might be done in three volumes, but this was found to be impracticable, and many intelligent readers have earnestly asked for as many more.

A new impression of the four volumes is now ready, at

$1.50 per Volume.

The prices in the Publisher's Catalogue are therefore to be corrected as follows:

Irving's Life, 4 vols., cloth, extra.................................$ 6.00
" " " half calf, extra........................... 10.00
" " " half calf, antique......................... 10.00

40,000 sets will be wanted to accompany the revised editions of Irving's Works already printed and sold.